TreeHouse
Blues

Memories of Big Family Life
On the Move in the 1950s

By Cathay L. Gunn

Copyright

KIERAN PUBLISHING
WWW.KIERANPUBLISHING.COM
FACEBOOK: KIERANPUBLISHING
P.O. BOX 3683 SANTA BARBARA, CA 93130
KIERANPUBLISHING@GMAIL.COM

COVER DESIGN BY CATHAY GUNN
LAYOUT BY ANNA LAFFERTY

ALL PHOTOS COURTESY OF CATHAY GUNN AND WALTER GUNN

ISBN: 978-0-9966015-1-1

NOTE: *This is a work of nonfiction. Names, characters and
incidents are taken directly from the author's childhood
memories. Some names have been altered for privacy.*

Dedication

For my mother, Bonnie Moreaux,
who left this earth February 26, 2017.
She taught me the importance of family.
"No matter where we move next, or what happens,
we always have each other."
She was my inspiration and my rock.

.

And for my dad, Walt Gunn,
who taught me that life is an Adventure,
and we are The Adventurers.

Table of Contents

v

Preface

...In which we get a Child's Eye View...

To become a child again is to refresh oneself with eyes that see the newness of the world, in all its beauty, its terror, and its immense joy. Take a dip in that pool. You will find that the wonder of the world is never very far away.

That is the state of mind in which I wrote this memoir.
                                                    Cathay L. Gunn

Prologue

Bonnie Moreaux and Walter Gunn
June 21, 1949

Fourteen months later, my now pregnant mother moves back in with her parents in North Hollywood while my dad is away attending his first year of medical school at Stanford University in Palo Alto, California. Throwing us all off-guard, I surprise everyone by being born six weeks premature.

Everything's rosy,
We're all in a whirl
And here is the reason—
Our new baby girl!
I love you, dearest.

Bonnie

Her name is Cathay Laurel
Born 6 a.m. December 3, 1950
Weighed 4 lb. 0 oz.
Parents Bonnie & Walt Gunn

11825 Cantara St.
No. Hollywood
California

Mr. Walter G. Gunn
746 Santa Ynez St.
Stanford, California

Bonnie does not want to disturb Walt's studies
and does not call. Instead, she sends him a birth
announcement. Walt finishes his finals and rushes
home before Christmas. He finally meets his tiny
new daughter in the incubator at the hospital for
the first time at Christmas.

SAN FRANCISCO
1953–1954

"THE SUNNYDALE PROJECTS"

At age one and a half, during my dad's final year of medical school, I move with my parents into the City of San Francisco Housing Project known as 'Sunnydale.' Rent for a two-bedroom apartment is $17/month. At this time medical students are eligible as well as other disadvantaged populations. During the 1950s the Stanford University Hospital is located in San Francisco on Webster and Sacramento Streets. Stanford's teaching facility, Lane Hospital, is located across the street.

First Memory – Laps

Tick tock. Tick tock.

I sit on Nana's lap – great, soft, pillow Nana. Sitting on the big, square, overstuffed chair. Nana so round. I pat her great arm. She laughs. I roll my head back and forth against her pillow bosom. So soft. She smoothes my hair.

"Your Mama has a surprise for you."

I watch the door beside the chair. Where is Mommy? Suddenly the door swings open. In walks Mommy. A big, white bundle lies in her arms.

What is it? I lean on Nana's arm, hoisting myself higher. I see a tiny face, all wrapped…

I see a *baby*! And it is wrapped in MY BLANKET! My blanket. *Mine*. Not for baby. Mine. I reach up and pull on it.

"Mine!"

Mommy pulls back.

Mommy sets me on the big, square, overstuffed chair. The back is itchy. I bounce my head on it. My feet dangle just over the edge of the big, square cushion.

"Are you ready, Cathay?"

I reach up. Mommy leans over me, blocking out the room. The Bundle comes closer. She lays it on my lap, fixing my small arms firmly around it. It weighs heavy against my legs! Warm. I stare into that tiny face. It moves! (Not like my dolly.) My hand squeezes that bundle. Something jumps inside! I watch the little face… tiny, tiny movements.

"Cathay – this is your brother Michael."

Mine.

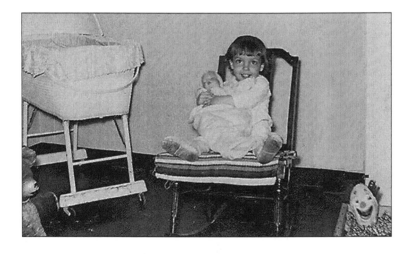

The Protector

*C*old.

My eyes flash open. Gray fuzz stretches all around me.
I fling my arm out. Bed is too big. *Not my bed. Too dark.*
Where's my nightlight? Something bumpy pokes under
my leg and side…a coat? A window looms up above my
head. *Where am I?* I don't know this room.

HONNNKK! So loud it bursts through the window
and zings right through me. A big, big black train! I know
it! A monster train! So scary outside!

Suddenly a strange, high tinggg pings inside my ears
– *a bell in my head?! What is that?!* I burrow my face into
the bed. So quiet in the room – so loud a ringing in my
ears! Scar-ry!

"MAMAAA!"

I sit up on the big bed. My skin tingles. *I want…out…*
of…here! I peer over the edge – down, down it seems –

4

so far! I cannot see the floor in the dark. With a twist, I heave my body over on my tummy and scoot past wooly lumps of more bunched up coats. Down, down I slide my legs over the edge, till I touch bottom and tumble backwards, off-balance, onto a rug. My chest tight, my breath comes in spurts. I wobble to the lighted crack in the wall. Muffled sounds emerge from behind it. I slap the door up high till my hand settles on its prize. With a pounding within me, on tiptoe I twist the knob, pull the door back and step, blinking, into the dazzle of light.

The noise races towards me: a blended cacophony of tinkles, rumbles and guffaws. A forest of tree-trunk legs blocks the way. I freeze. I gaze wildly about, my head tilted upward, reeling from side to side, while I search in vain for my Protector. My heart thumps harder; my body jiggles as tears fling off my cheeks. I gaze up, up at faces so close together – too many in a single space. None of them glance down at me. Glasses swivel in their hands. Heads toss backward with wild laughter. Grotesque they are, shining in the garish light, like clowns out-of-place, away from the circus.

I feel myself in a bubble, invisible and utterly alone.

All of a sudden, She appears. *Mommy!* Warmness and light. She wraps her arms around me, blocking out the dark sight of ominous cartoons. Murmurings in my ear overwhelm the harsh onslaught of voices beyond. Back in The Room we tread.

It is dark. She sets me back on the bed. *No!* I do not want to be alone with the Big Black Train and the Ringing inside my head! I cling to her; her hands pry my fingers from her dress. Softly, then, she rocks me on the edge, my body curled against the curves of her arms.

> "Twinkle, twinkle little star,
> How I wonder what you are,
> Up above the world so high,

5

Like a diamond in the sky,
Twinkle, twinkle little star,
How I wonder what you are."

She lays me against the bed and drapes a heavy coat over me, the silk lining cool against my arms and feet. I stiffen. *Don't leave me!*

"Mamaa!"

She stays. A familiar hand caresses my back, stroking in rhythmical circles. A new melody wafts over me. The incessant drone of guests' voices continues to filter through. Gradually, they dissolve into a distant murmur, like a babbling brook, lulling, lulling... My body sinks heavier and heavier, melding with the coats and the bed, becoming one, as I slowly drift off...into nothingness... so pure...so sweet...so mine.

"Lullaby, and goodnight..."

Seeing Double

My hands pressed against the glass, I peer between them through the giant hospital window. Daddy's strong hands under my arms hold me up so I can see better.

...Babies, babies, babies! All in tiny beds. Some squirm like little kittens. Others lie perfectly still. Some are crying...such a funny hiccup cry. Not very loud... *not like Mikey at home.* Some are red! *Very* red. I hope we don't get one of those. A lady in white bustles between them. She wears a white mask on her face!

"What do you think, Cathay?" Daddy nudges me with his chin.

"So many!"

Daddy chuckles.

Hmm… Is this a baby store?! But no… Mommy's baby was in her tummy… I know it… So how did it get in here?

"Lookie, Cathay," points Daddy. "There's Patrick."

I stare. *Patrick…he's not red…he's not even crying. Patrick…* "A boy Patrick…and a girl…" *Oh!*

"But where's…" I begin, searching the window.

"Oh ho! Let's go see Mommy!" urges Daddy. He sets me down and grabs my hand. I give one last backward glance at the window before he pulls me away.

"Wait!" *Isn't the girl there, too?*

Down the big corridor we march; Daddy's huge strides and my quick hip-hopping steps beside him to keep up. I skim over the gray polished floor of the long, white tunnel as we fly past door after door. Suddenly he stops.

There, through the open doorway I see Mommy. She stands facing us, her hand upon the bed, wearing her blue chenille robe. I race in.

"Mommy!"

Arms wide, she beams her giant smile at me. But something more important drags my gaze down to her tummy. With one hand I yank back her robe and study her body, still full beneath the white nightgown. But not so much. I pat her tummy.

"Mommy, is Julie still in there?" *(She wasn't in the window!)*

Mommy scrunches up her face and looks over my head at Daddy. "We have a boy, Sweetie. Didn't Daddy show you?"

"I know! I know!" I cry. "I saw the boy! Patrick! But where's the girl? Where's Julie?" I *know* she must still be in there…

Suddenly Daddy guffaws, and Mommy joins him

with a twitter.

"No, sweetness," she smiles. "We said if it was a *girl,* we'd name her 'Julie.' But it's a *boy.* So we named him 'Patrick.'"

Oh.

"Only one baby?"

"Only one baby."

Little did I know that a year later, Julie would, indeed, arrive. But not yet.

Cathay, Mike, Pat

TreeHouse Blues

HOLLYWOOD
1954–1955

After Dad's completion of medical school we
all move back down to Hollywood, California.
Dad begins his Medical Internship at Los Angeles
County Hospital. Our family of five squeezes into
Dad's mother's house on La Mirada Street.

Red Terror

Sun beats down as I crawl across the lawn to the big palm tree. Mommy said: *"No leaving the yard. Don't go past the tree."* The grass tickling my hands is warm. I sit up under the shade now and pat the grass here. *Nice and coool…* I scoot backwards towards the trunk.

Hot…cold. I reach my face waay out from under the palm, eyes closed. *Mmm. Warm.* Back under the tree – *All gone!*

Uh oh. Where's Annie? I twist 'round under the tree, no longer on the grass. Floppy baby Annie lies, face down, in the dirt.

"No!" I scold. "You sit right here!" I press my sundress into my lap, making a little seat. In she goes.

"There!"

I gather my white metal cups and plates closer to me. Tiny red flowers snake along the edges. "Let's have chocolate milk, Annie! Bosco time!" I scoop up a cupful of dirt with one hand and pour it into the other teacup, watching it fall. *So smooth.*

"Bosco, Bosco, tastes so great," I sing. "For you and me, oh I can't wait." I set the cup on the ground. "Let's put some sugar in it."

Then I pinch up a smidgen of dirt and sprinkle it, rubbing my fingers back and forth over the cup. "Drink it down!"

I raise the teacup to baby Annie's mouth and…

Ow! Something hot on my leg. *Owie! Owie!!* Other leg… Suddenly, stings race all over my legs and bottom. I glance down – red ants!! Swarming out of a tiny hole right next to me – in a little mountain of dirt – marching in a line…up my legs and all over them! They're *everywhere!*

"Mamaa!" I roll over onto my feet, tear up the porch steps and through the front door, shrieking all the while.

"Mommy! Mommy! I'm burning! I'm burning!" My legs are on fire. *Owie Owie! Hurting, hurting!*

Mommy's eyes grow big as apples as she stands stock-still. Quickly, then, she grabs me by the arms, pinning them to my sides, and whisks me into the bathroom. Like a whirlwind, she kicks the rug away with one foot and slams the door with the other. She plops me down. Leaning over the tub, she plugs it with one hand while the other twists the faucet. Mad splashing fills the tub as I hop up and down.

"Stop the burning, Mommy! Stop the burning!"

She tears at my clothes, crying, "Help me, Cathay! Take them off!"

With one swift motion she hoists me up in the air – the wall rushes up – and down - *Splash!* – into the cold, cold water. Yow!

Suddenly, tiny red bodies float all around me – drowned! No longer biting, no longer moving…floating, floating. Mommy drowned the ants!

And put out their fire.

13

I watch as tiny crumples of red rush forward, swirl together in a circle, now faster, faster – then – GONE – down the hole.

Shivering on the mat, I wait for her in my towel, still itching, still sore. White powder shakes from an orange box in Mommy's hand – onto my legs, my bottom. Her cool hand smoothes it over. Heaving a great sigh, my clean dress on, I follow Mommy into the kitchen. At last...

Now it's time for Bosco!

Hollywood Cereal

"It's Howdy Doo–dy Time! It's Howdy Doo-dy Time! Da da da DA, da-da! Da da da DA, da-da! Dee dee dee DEE, de-dee! Dee dee dee DEE, de-dee!" *Slurrp... Mmm...*

Come on, little o's...get on that spoon! YA! Hop! Hop! One! Two! Three! I got you! Ummm... Go down the tunnel...swish, swish! Slurp! Open. Ahhh-HH... Just like the doctor... mmm... I got you! You can't come out. Mmm... Just like hide-and-go-seek! You hide – but I feel you in there! Goodbye, o's! Ha, ha, ha! You can't play hide-and-go-seek with me; I always know you're there! Just like Buzzy next-door...

Buzzy can't hide. He always runs out so I can see him. Maybe he doesn't know how to play. He's still three. Not four, like me. – Slurp – His mommy, Mrs. Sheppod, found him, though – time for his bath! Ha, ha! And he ran away the wrong way! Right into his Mommy! Ha, ha! He got mad. And she chased him inside. Smack, slurp.

Mommy said Mr. Sheppod is really Lassie's father. No, not Lassie! That's silly! He's not a dog! Ha, ha! He would look funny! Timmy's father, not Lassie's father. But how can he be Timmy's father? Timmy doesn't live next-door. Buzzy and Lindy do. And their Mommy looks different. Not like on TV. And where's Lassie? I never see her there. So how is he Timmy's father on "Lassie?" Slurp.

Mommy said he was. Hmm. Maybe she's wrong. But she said, 'ye-es, ye-es!' And it does look like him…but different, too. But…but…he talks different to Buzzy than to Timmy. And next-door they have a little dog. Not like Lassie at all. Pudge. He doesn't never try to save anybody! Smack, sma-

And…AND…I saw Buzzy hurt him! He kicked him! Why? Why did he kick his own dog? Poor Pudge! Mommy said he really wanted to kick Lindy, but he couldn't, so he kicked Pudge, who wouldn't tell on him. Why did he want to kick Lindy? She's nice to me. She's bigger than him. Why did he want to kick someone bigger than him? Mommy said because she gets all the attention…

Attention… Wasn't that what you did when you said the Pledge of Aleashums? Like on TV. 'Stand at attention.' Huh? Attention. When people look at you. People look at Lindy, and not Buzzy? She has a ponytail. I like ponytails. She doesn't play with me, though. She's five. More than five. Buzzy does, sometimes. But he likes his dog better. Why did he kick his dog? His daddy found out. He heard Pudge yelping and ran outside. He was really mad! His face got big and red. Timmy's father never yells like that! Maybe he's NOT really Timmy's father.

Slurp. Buzzy doesn't really play with me. He pinches sometimes. Mommy says 'cause he really wants to pinch Lindy. Why? Why does he want to pinch Lindy? I don't like pinching. It hurts. Lindy wouldn't like it, either. Slurp.

What's Mikey doing? Banging his head again. On the toilet

seat. Why does he do that? Mommy says because he gets so
mad. He's too noisy. Grandmamma calls him 'Steamboat.' He
makes a long, long whistle sound. Not a whistle. A singing
sound – long, long, and all the same sound…ooooooooo…
Like a steamboat 'whistle,' she says. But it's not a whistle. A
whistle is like a bird. It's what Daddy does. Smack, smack…

Mommy can't do it. She tries. Everybody laughs. So she
hums instead. I can hum. I can't whistle, but I can hum. Birds
can sort of whistle. I can pretend to be a bird – but it doesn't
sound like a whistle. So I'm a different kind of bird. Not a
whistling kind. Maybe when I'm five I can whistle! Or maybe
not. Mommy can't whistle. But we can both hum. I wish
we could be on TV and hum and sing Mommy's songs, and
everyone would clap! Like on Pinkie Lee. All the children up
high in their seats…

We walked down there…hip-hop, hip-hop… Mommy said
we could see him. But the studio was 'closed.' Why? My nose
squished on the glass… Cold and hard. All dark inside. No
Pinkie Lee in there. Nobody. Mommy was wrong.

…'Twenty Froggies.' 'Playmate.' I can sing those. Slurrrp.

"Mommy! I'm finished! Can I go outside and pway?"

The Visit

The screen door slammed behind me. Grandmamma's big Hoover roared on inside, slightly muted. Outside on the cool porch of our stucco house I stopped. I cocked my head at the wavering fronds of the palm tree. Just barely they waved at me. *How do they do that? It's not windy. ...Because it's alive.* Mommy told me that it was. I stared back and waved my fingers up and down.

Grasping the rail, I twisted backward – "Mommy! I'm going for a visit to Mrs. Bwady" – then began my descent.

I waddled from side to side, stiff-legged, savoring the pavement jolt.

"One – two, buckle my shoe,
Three – four, shut the door!"

La Mirada Street stretched on and on before me. Like a huge rolling sea of tar and concrete – except it wasn't moving. Red tile-roofed houses with colorful window boxes dotted each side. I glanced down at my feet. *Are the diamonds out today?* Sure enough, shimmering like specks of fairy dust the sidewalk spoke to me of my riches. *My diamonds!* So many I couldn't count them – but I knew my feet sparkled on the bottom with all those diamonds underneath them. I stared hard at each jeweled square as my feet squished down, spilling them out on either side.

"Hey, Cathay! Slow-poke today!" Six-year-old Lacie with the ruffled dresses and black wavy hair streaked by. Skipping as always, she smiled smugly back at me before sailing ahead.

I studied her from behind as she bounced UP and down after each step. *How does she do that?* I lunged forward, leaping with all my might, but I knew it wasn't a "skip." Faster I pushed, slapping my side now as I galloped.

"Giddyup!" I whispered. "Giddyup!" I was a horse! Flying across the plain, my tail streaming behind me, my legs blurred in the wind! My nose darted upward as I rattled my head. "Neigh-eigh-eigh!"

I stopped. Mrs. Brady's house. She was always asking me to come visit. I say nothing. Instead I stare at her purse, straps over one arm, clutched tightly against her dress with the other. Shiny brown with gold studs edging the top. *What's inside?* She leans over me with her bright red lips. *I'd like to see that lipstick. Maybe it's inside that purse.* Grandmamma carries a pretty gold-handled mirror inside hers. "See the monkey?" she says. Try as I might, I never find the monkey in the mirror. Only me. Maybe only Grandmamma can see it. I like the mirror, though. *I wonder what special treasures are inside Mrs. Brady's purse?*

I tripped up the pansy-lined path to the porch. Without warning the screen door flew open.

"Why hello there!" A stranger in a stiff white cap and

shirtdress smiled at me. *Uh...*

"Were you looking for Mrs. Brady?" She bent down, hands on her knees. A voice from behind her screeched out, "Let her in, Miss Marie."

I entered the darkened chamber. All the blinds were shut in the living room. Books lined the windowsills and floor. Lots and lots of books. Not the kind with pictures, though. Just pictures on the cover. And there, smack in the middle of the room was a bed! Mrs. Brady lay sprawled across it, the bedding rumpled about her.

"Why, you've come at last!" she beamed at me. "Miss Marie – this is 'Cath –uh' – from down the street. How are you today, Cath-uh?"

"Umm..." *Why doesn't she say my name right?*

"Would you like some lemonade?"

I nodded, staring at the legs of her bed.

"Marie – get her a glass, will you?" Mrs. Brady propped herself up on her elbow – then abruptly collapsed with a groan. *Lacie said she had a broken hip. I craned my neck, trying to see where it was broken. Maybe they already glued it, and now she has to wait for it to dry.*

"Don't ever get old," she rasped. "It'll eat you like a spider." I stumbled backward and bumped into a little table. Two figurines toppled over, but luckily, didn't break. I set them right, longing to play with them (a white poodle and a calico cat) but I didn't dare.

Miss Marie reappeared with a tall glass of lemonade. Before I could accept it from her outstretched hand, Mrs. Brady snapped, "Take it back – dump some out. She's a child, Marie – you want her to spill it?" Miss Marie retreated, soon to reappear with the half-filled glass. Secretly I was glad.

Sipping the ice-cold drink, I stared up at Mrs. Brady over the rounded rim.

"How's your grandma?"

"Fine," I gurgled.

"And your Mother and Dad?"

"Fine."

"How many babies does she have?"

I held up two fingers, carefully relinquishing one hand from the glass.

"And how old are *you*?"

I held up four fingers, rather crookedly. Mrs. Brady studied me a moment. "You shouldn't be so shy, child. Cat got your tongue?"

Instinctively I stuck out the doubted member as proof – then slapped my hand over it, in case she thought me rude. I shook my head, eyes wide. She threw back hers and laughed a big bellowing blast. But she stopped short with a cry, rubbing her side.

"Marie!" she yelled. "Bring me the bedpan!"

I stared as Miss Marie threw back the covers, lifted Mrs. Brady's bottom and stuck it right inside a huge silver dish! Quickly she tucked the sheet around her again. *What is she doing?* Mrs. Brady paid no attention to me, but stared straight ahead. *Why is she sitting in a dish?* I waited a moment, then gazed all around the book-lined room, searching for that special purse. Not in sight.

"Marie! Don't leave it here!"

Miss Marie hurried back into the living room, threw up the covers once more, and retrieved the silver bowl.

Slowly this time, she carried it past me on her way down the hall. Standing on tiptoe, I glimpsed inside just before it disappeared. Water in there... *No! Ohh! She went to the potty in the silver bowl!* My mouth fell open. She cocked her head and grimaced.

"Like I said, Cath-uh. Never get old."

I nodded, the mysterious brown purse long forgotten. I set my glass on the little table, next to the dog and cat, and gazed at the door.

"You want to leave so soon?"

I turned back. "Um. Yes," I whispered.

Mrs. Brady shook her head a moment, her eyes to the ceiling.

"Marie! Get the door, will ya? Our guest wants to leave!"

Cringing *(her voice is so loud!)* I tried to smile; then dropped my eyes to the floor. Miss Marie silently held the screen door open for me.

"You come back and see me now, you hear?" Mrs. Brady called out from behind.

Down the path I flew, once more in the sunshine day.

"Mrs. Bwa-dy is a la-dy,

Mrs. Bwa-dy is a la-dy.

Hop, hop, hop."

Up the driveway and around the back of our house I marched, singing my new song. Suddenly I stopped. There, peeking out of the open garage, something silver glinted in the sun. Leaning on its side against the washer was Mommy's old silver pie tin. I yanked it up and rubbed my hand around the inside of it, feeling its smooth, warmed surface. Then I gazed around the garage till I spied a wooden crate in the corner. Grunting, I dragged that crate over to the washer and set it on its end. Then, one hand on the rounded top of the washer, another clutching my precious find, I scrambled up onto the crate and heaved myself, stomach first, on top of the washer. *Whoa!* It was slippery! I finally jockeyed myself upright, legs straddling the curved surface of the white enamel throne. With a cry of triumph I raised my body ever so slightly and sat down hard – on my silver prize. Mrs. Brady's bedpan!

I glanced down at the ground – far below. I was higher than everyone else!

"Miss Marie!" I mimicked. "I am finished! You get in here and get...my...silver... BOWL!" I began rocking back and forth, holding onto the sides of the pie pan.

"Miss Marie! You come here right now!" I raised myself up so she could see I meant business. "I mean it -"

All of a sudden the garage tilted sideways as I slipped, in slow motion, down the cool surface of the washer, my bedpan flinging up in the air and over my head. The cement floor raced up and slammed into me. *Smash!* I stared up at the blue sky just outside the garage, my bottom aching, my arm and shoulder bruised and throbbing.

"MAMAAA!"

The screen door slammed, feet running... arms surrounding me as Mommy hoisted me up onto her shoulder.

"What happened? What happened, darling?" she cooed.

"I –I fell off the washing machine..."

Grandmamma peered at me from behind her.

"Landsakes, child. Whatever were you doing up there?!"

"I was pw-pwaying Mrs. Bwady."

"Good Gracious! I never saw Mrs. Brady climb on a washer!" Grandmamma wrinkled her forehead, hands on her hips. "But I tell you what. Come on inside, and you can help me make a lemon pie."

I clapped my mouth shut, frozen in mid-sob, and stared back into those piercing green eyes. Mommy set me down with a kiss. Then she took my hand, and the two of us followed Grandmamma down the driveway, up the tall back steps and into the kitchen.

TreeHouse Blues

COLORADO SPRINGS
1955-1956

Pat, Mike, Cathay

Dad chose Penrose Cancer Hospital in Colorado Springs, Colorado for his Medical Residency – for the first year, that is. He earns $200/month – the highest-paid Resident on staff. At last we have our own (rented) home.

Yet some insecurity starts to build.

The Angel

Ooh, what a pretty purple scarf! Billowing high above my head, a filmy lavender veil drifts down and blocks out all other view. Closer now it comes. Ominous dark spots appear on the fabric; they grow uglier and larger as the scarf envelops me. Now taut, it pulls against my skin and cinches around my legs. I can't move! I'm falling! Headlong I tilt into the darkness. I feel the sack hoisted up and bounced - bumpity-bump - along the ground. Voices growl. Men. Mean, angry sounds. Loud guffaws. "I've got one!" A car motor turns. Hmmm-mmm. Chugga chugga. Where are we going? It's hot. The scarf sucks into my mouth. I can't breathe! MAMAAA!

With a start, my hand lashes free and slaps down on the soft, wooly bedclothes. A clock ticks. It's dark – but I'm in my own little room. I gaze into nothingness and feel boot steps creeping inside my head. My heart pounds. My face is wet. I can just make out the outline of the door opposite. Suddenly it swings open. There, framed against the darkness, floats a glowing white angel. Arms extended, her gown flows all around her. She glides towards me – the most beautiful creature I have ever seen! She shimmers into view. It's Mommy! Without a sound she leans down over my bed and enfolds me in her arms. A warmth of peace flows through me. A moment. She rises.

"I'll be back," she whispers.

The cold draft returns. The shadows leer closer. I shiver.

All of a sudden the apparition reappears, bearing a wondrous gift in her outstretched hand. Now beside the bed, its glimmer is unmistakable. She offers me a round, puffy glazed doughnut! It is huge! I stare, as it glistens and beckons.

"For me?!" I whisper.

"For you, little darling," she smiles through the shadows.

But where did it come from?! We never have doughnuts. Mommy NEVER buys them for us. It's a mystery! It just appeared! I can hardly eat it, it's so strange and wondrous. But with one tentative nibble, I quickly lose all fear and memory of that bad dream. The sweet dough melts in my mouth as I savor each tendril of icing.

Down under the covers I snuggle with a satisfied sigh, Mommy's kisses and elixir washing over me.

Bring on the night.

Pussy Willow

With day two of Kindergarten under my belt, I tromped down the steps after my classmates at the clanging of the bell. Today I would ride home with the Holland's! I scurried to catch up with Caroline and Susannah. Right out the schoolyard gate they sauntered, and on down the receding sidewalk.

"Are you sure this is the right way?" I faltered. Kindergartner Caroline glanced back at me.

"Of course!" she snorted. "Susannah knows the way!"

I relaxed. Susannah, a big third grader, knew everything. She was our fearless leader.

"Wait for me!" I crowed. I skimmed ahead of Caroline so I could get behind her big sister. I studied her purposeful stride as I stretched my legs to plant each shoe into her just-vacated footsteps. I felt bigger already.

Soon we rounded a curve that disappeared into a tangle of brush. Moments later we emerged into another world. My eyes traveled miles and miles in three directions. Tan. Everything tan. Way off in the distance the Cheyenne Mountains poked the sky. A giant sun-filled bowl seemed to surround us. Driving through it in the car was one thing. Now, it looked HUGE.

Susannah halted where another road dead-ended against our path. "Here's our waiting place. We live down that way," she pointed. "Mama said she'd meet us here."

A steep, grassy bank rose up behind us. I tucked myself against it and gazed sideways up the embankment. A whisper of gray caught my eye.

"What's this?"

"Oh," replied Susannah. "Pussy willows."

Like little kitties sleeping in the sun! I reached up and rubbed the plump nub between my thumb and forefinger. *So soft and furry! Mmm...*

Meanwhile, Caroline and Susannah chattered behind me about their new TV. *I wish I could take these home...*

"Do you have a television set?" Caroline was asking me.

"Huh? Oh...no..." I murmured, glancing back. A big box with moving pictures, I knew that. Like a movie in your home. Black and white pictures.

"My Grandmother has one, at our old house," I offered. "But that's in California." I went back to petting my little pussy willows.

"Wasn't that scary, Susannah?" trilled Caroline. "About the bad men?"

I dropped the pussy willow and peered over my shoulder. "What bad men?"

"It looked just like *this*." Caroline's voice sank to a whisper, her hand sweeping the horizon. "Didn't it, Susannah? Where they were riding their horses."

"What do you mean?" I persisted.

Susannah turned to face me. "They kidnapped a girl, Lucy Grey."

"Did they catch them?"

"No. No one knows where they went. But they're out there somewhere."

"Yes!" Caroline jumped up and down, her eyes huge. "They found Lucy Grey, and she was DEAD!"

"No she wasn't!" Susannah retorted.

"Well, she *looked* like it!"

My throat tightened. I wanted to ask how old Lucy Grey was, but I didn't dare.

"Why didn't they find the bad men?" I croaked.

Susannah shook her head. "They're too 'foxy,' Mama

29

said. They know just how to hide."

"But maybe they'll catch them *next* week," Caroline chirped hopefully.

I stared out at the expanse of Tan. It stretched wide open before me, becoming stranger and meaner all the way to the mountains. No houses. No buildings. Only an occasional bush. Nothing moved. I studied each bush. Especially the close ones. *Maybe they're hiding right there…just waiting to jump out and grab someone else!* The dry breeze tickled my cheek with an angry snarl.

"Wh-when's your Mommy coming?" I quavered.

"Well – *soon*, I think," shrugged Susannah.

I fought the urge to flee, shrieking, back towards the school. But the road there disappeared into those bushes… I eyed the roadway I knew led towards my house. I saw myself frantically racing in that direction, deserting my friends. *But then I would be all alone…*

I turned around and peered into the pussy willows, getting as close to them as I could, so that they blocked out all view of the behemoth landscape. Gradually at first, and then with a rush, I felt a cold chill of vast space against my back. *Uhh!* I wheeled right around, my eyes zigzagging back and forth through the Tan. Only a slight ruffle of grasses moved. No bushes. Nothing else.

I glanced out the corner of my eye at Susannah and Caroline. They bubbled and laughed over something about a cat, and a mouse with a bell. They seemed to have forgotten all about the bad men. About where we were…all alone…

At last Mrs. Holland rumbled up to our meeting place, and saved us. I could not tell her that, though. Susannah and Caroline didn't, either. I don't think they remembered. *Maybe Mrs. Holland would laugh…*

I burst through the front door.

"Mommy, Mommy!" I cried. "I can't go back to

school! Please let me stay with you and Mike and baby Patrick!"

"Don't you *like* school, sweetheart?" Mommy bent towards me, her big belly thrust between us.

"I – I...yes-s..." I stammered. "But...there's bad men..." I trailed off, no words flying to my aid.

Bad men?!" Mommy's eyes widened. "What do you mean?" How could I tell her about the huge, angry expanse of Tan, the prickly bushes full of eyes, harboring evil bad men lying in wait?

"I – there's bad men out there," I blubbered. "Please, Mommy, please! I can't go home with Mrs. Holland! You come get me!"

Mommy couldn't get me. Only on Thursdays now would she have the car. Daddy needed it very early for work.

Luckily, the next day was Thursday.

On the way home from school I pointed out the pussy willows. I leaned up against the seatback.

"See?!" I whispered into her hair. "That's where we wait for Mrs. Holland! This is where the bad men are!"

"She picks you up from *here?*"

"Yes! Yes!"

"Well, the Holland's live just down this road, where we're taking Susannah and Caroline now. That's why she wants you to wait here."

I glanced sidelong at my backseat companions. "I don't want to!" I whimpered. "What about the bad men?!"

I waited in the car with Mike and Pat while Mommy ushered Susannah and Caroline into their house. When she returned, she eased behind the steering wheel and smiled down at me.

"Mrs. Holland will pick you up from the schoolyard from now on."

Next day, Susannah joined Caroline and me as we emerged from kindergarten, and led us to the waiting car just outside the gate. I sank back into the vinyl and breathed a sigh of relief…

That afternoon Mommy met me at the front door. "Guess what, sweetheart? We have a new carpool!"

I stared in wondrous confusion. "A swimming pool in our car?"

"No, no," she laughed. "We will be *sharing* the drive to school with a new little girl and her mother. I met them today. From now on Mrs. Rankin will take you to and from school on Mondays and Wednesdays, and we will take Betty on Thursdays."

I frowned. "From the *schoolyard*?"

"Yes!" she promised. "I made *sure* of that."

No more scary times by the pussy willows. From now on, I got home safely – direct from the schoolyard to my corner. (I was a big enough girl to walk half a block home past other *houses*!)

October ushered in a chill in the air. Leaves whirled and swirled in the early morn. I eyed them in wonder out Betty's car window. The station wagon lurched to a halt.

"Well?" Mrs. Rankin startled me out of my reverie. "Time's a-wasting! Out the door, girls!" I heaved against the door handle and sidled out onto the curb and into the school.

Clang clang! Clang clang!!

At noon Miss Kay swung the big brass bell for the kindergartners' dismissal. I skipped down the steps and out the door into the lunchtime droves of older children.

I wonder if I get to go home for lunch, like Susannah, when I'm a big girl… I gazed out at the older children munching on sandwiches, giggling and gurgling together on the lunchtime benches. Hmm...maybe it would be more fun to stay here and eat... I stood still, weighing the deliciously different scenarios.

With a start, I scanned through the throngs for Betty and Caroline. They should've been right nearby... *Didn't they come outside yet?* I scrutinized the stragglers. And where is Susannah? I peered around at the older girls; then hastened towards the perimeter of the yard. *Sometimes she joins us at the gate...*

No one there. *Maybe they're all already in the car...* I glanced beyond the brick pillars to the curb. No brown station wagon. *Is Mrs. Rankin not here yet?* I turned back to the yard, searching through the clumps of students. Shrill cries jarred the air. I swallowed. Where did they go? Frantically I scanned the schoolyard...

Slowly now I dragged my feet through the chaos of colors and sounds. Fewer and fewer kindergartners did I see. The children seemed bigger, and older, than ever before. *Betty and Caroline surely should be here by now...* I tried to quell the gnawing fear that had seized my stomach and threatened to explode upward. Mrs. Rankin's voice echoed back to me. *'Anyone who's not out there after school will be left behind.'* ...*Left behind...left behind...*

I gazed downward and studied the fine, dark crevices separating the cracked blacktop. The pavement blurred, and slowly undulated. I took a big breath and raised my eyes. Fewer and fewer children roamed the yard. Lunch eaten, several girls joined the jump-rope queue, while boys zoomed past, chasing balls.

I gravitated once again towards the gate. Gripping the edge of the brick wall, I peered out. Just around the bend of those bushes, I knew, lay the barren wastelands of Tan. The brush sharpened and beckoned. I drew back, my heart thudding. *Ba-bump, ba-bump, ba-bump…*

Once more I faced the milling children, carefree and happy, as they squealed and scampered. Aimlessly I stumbled through them: an obstacle course of whirling wind-up toys. No longer could I see them clearly; my face wet, my body seized by spastic waves.

The sky grew upward – it was HUGE – the sea of blue expanding higher and wider. I did not know anymore where I was in the yard. I stopped, lost and surrounded by an alien race of happy beings. Nobody came. Nobody was coming.

Clang clang! Clang clang!

Bells jangled the end of lunch like alarms vibrating through my body. Simultaneous cries erupted from the masses in one final snatch at freedom. When the silence at last took over, only one voice emerged: my high-pitched warble that enclosed and locked me against the vast world beyond…

Dimly through my watery vision I spied a small parade trudging down the sidewalk. I held my breath and strained for clarity. Was it - ? *Yes!* The rescue party!

Shimmering in sunlight, a small carriage led the way. Baby Patrick kicked up his leg from the stroller; Mommy, rigid arms extended from the handle, her ballooned belly fairly bursting, broke into a trot. Mike toddled behind, one fat fist gripping her flying skirt.

In moments the entourage had veered crazily through the schoolyard, dodging the last retreating students right up to me.

"Mommommom…" I babbled. Mommy's eyes flashed like fire before all sight blotted out as she enveloped me in her quivering arms. I clung to her, my face pressed into her roundedness.

"Where's Mrs. Rankin?" I sobbed. "She didn't get me! She didn't get me!"

"I don't know why, sweetheart," murmured Mommy. "I finally called her, and she said you weren't here." … *will be left behind…will be left behind…*

I drew back. "I was here! I am here!"

"I know you were, sweetness," Mommy's eyes burned into mine. "And she will never take you home again."

Then, without a word, I unhooked myself from her form. One hand firmly attached to the stroller beside Mommy's, with Mike riding the floor bar, Patrick gurgling up ahead, I joined the parade.

All together we pushed our way past the bushes and into the Tan. For a moment, tiny sparks rushed towards me and pricked my skin. I squeezed my eyes tight; we stopped.

"How about some pussy willows for your room?" Mommy's voice caressed my ear.

I opened my eyes and latched onto her smile. I nodded. She bent them towards me while I twisted the tough branches until they snapped. *One…two…three… four.* I got them! Then we set out again through the vast wasteland.

Ever so slowly, I took a breath.

I edged closer to her, secure in the knowledge that together, we were a force to be reckoned with.

Daddy, Cathay, Patrick, Mommy

Homecoming

"Mommy's at the hospital," I confided. "Having a baby." Sitting cross-legged on my bed, I bounced Buh-tricia Doll up and down on my lap. (She was almost five – like me.)

"I don't know *when* she's coming back."

I sat very still. Slowly I rocked Buh-tricia, then squeezed her tight.

"Don't worry," I whispered. "She's coming back."

"Soup's on!" Down the hall Daddy's deep voice boomed. I flipped over and shimmied off the bed. Then I set Buh-tricia on my pillow and tucked my sweater up under her chin.

I scurried down the hall towards the kitchen. *It smells like a barbecue!* The kitchen window was wide open; gray swirls muddied up my view of the room.

"Hamburgers – hot off the griddle!" grinned Daddy, white apron across his chest, spatula in hand. He sat down at the table. "Let's eat!"

I glanced around the kitchen. "Where's Mike and Pat?"

"Go get them," he said. I turned and padded into their room.

Nineteen-month-old Patrick sat on the rug, sucking his thumb. Mike, two and a half, zoomed his cars around him, buzzing his lips.

"Dinner, Mike!"

Without a word, he dropped his car and trundled into the kitchen. Patrick toddled after him.

Daddy helped Mike up to the table and heaved Pat into his high chair. I picked up my fork and stabbed my charcoal pellet. A few more stabs and it crumbled open. I stared. *It's pink inside!* Black on the outside, and bright pink hiding within.

"Daddy!" I wailed. "*Pink* hamburgers?!" He scrunched his forehead and pursed his lips. Then sunshine broke out on his face.

"We have hot cocoa!" he beamed. Shuffling over from the stove, he ladled steaming hot chocolate milk into my cup.

"Ooh!" shrilled Mike.

I sipped my special drink while eyeing that pink quivering meat on my fork. *At least it isn't cold.*

"Bedtime, everybody!" warbled Daddy.

"What about a bath?" I asked.

"Mm…maybe tomorrow night. Jammy time, folks!" Daddy stood at the sink, water running. "Go, go, go!" he shooed.

I stood there. Mike scrambled down from his chair and wandered down the hall. Patrick slapped his hand against his high chair. I turned and eyed Daddy.

"What about Paddy?"

"What? Oho!" Daddy ambled over to the high chair and lifted Patrick up – and down. Then he returned to the sink, whistling.

Pat sat on the floor and sucked his thumb.

"What about Paddy's *jammies?*" I persisted.

Daddy cocked his head; then laughed. Scooping Paddy up, he set him on his shoulders and lumbered down the hall.

"Don't forget his diaper," I called after him.

Under the covers I burrowed my knees up close to me and clutched my dolly to my chest. "I dunno, Buh-tricia," I whispered in her ear. I listened to the stillness. The room was filled with it. "I don't think Daddy knows how to be a Mommy."

Next morning I woke with a start. Buh-tricia was still a sleepyhead, so I left her facedown on the pillow and crawled out of bed.

"Daddy! Daddy!" I cried. "Can we go see baby Julie?"

Stumbling into the kitchen, I stopped short. Not Daddy, but a strange woman with gray hair stood at the stove.

"Bonjour, ma petite!" she cooed. "Your Dad-dee went to work. I yam stay-ing weet you today." She served Mike, Pat and me steaming bowls of cream of wheat. Slowly I approached the table and sat.

At least she knows how to cook.

Two days later I leaned against the living room

window and stared at the tiny white crystals floating in the air. Before me it was *very* quiet; behind me I could hear Mike and Pat splashing in the bath with Madame Renée. The glass chilled my nose. I wanted to stay that way forever, and not turn around.

With a dull *thunk* I heard the front door close. I stood still as a mouse. No footsteps. No soft voice called out. I waited.

A hand squeezed each shoulder. I looked up. Daddy smiled and squatted behind me.

"Ho, ho!" he chuckled. "You've discovered the first snow!"

I nodded, staring straight ahead.

"Where's Mommy?"

"She's at the hospital, getting ready to feed baby Julie."

"Why isn't she home?"

"Why, she's coming home tomorrow! With a new little sister for you!"

I pressed up against the glass and tapped it with my forehead…*one, two, three, four…*

"Say…do you know," Daddy exclaimed, "Mommy and I were just standing at her window, watching the new snow begin to fall?" I eyed him out of the corner of my eye.

"We were talking about you. Why, I bet she's still standing there right this minute, watching the same snowflakes as you!"

I twisted my head. "Really?"

"Yup."

I scooted a step backward and squatted against his knee. His arm encircled me. I felt his warmth all around me. We both gazed at the tiny white crystals. They swirled faster now.

"Daddy," I whispered. "Is it really and truly *snow?*"

Saturday.

"Mommy's coming home!" I crooned to Buh-tricia. But the day crawled by...

Naptime. I played instead.

"Cathay," Daddy rumbled. He leaned against my doorframe, curling his finger at me. Oh! I jumped up from the rug, dangling Buh-tricia, and prepared to dash for my bed.

"I have a secret for you." Daddy squatted down. "Now don't tell Mike and Pat."

I puffed up my chest. "Ok, Daddy. What, what?!"

He whispered in my ear. "Follow me."

I tiptoed after him as he sauntered into the living room; then stopped and glanced towards the boys' room down the hall. They were napping. I nodded solemnly at Daddy. We were a team. With a twinkle in his eye, he tilted his head towards the coffee table, now pushed up near the wall. I followed his gaze. There sat a giant, glassy square. I could make out our dim silhouettes in it.

"Is that a TV?!"

"Yup."

"A *real* one?"

He nodded. "It's a surprise gift for Mommy's birthday – and baby Julie's, too."

Just like Susannah and Caroline's!

"Now, remember – it's OUR secret."

After nap I pranced back and forth outside Mike and Pat's room, guarding the 'treasure.' I knew Daddy was counting on me.

At last, it was time. Into the car we hopped. Daddy winked at me and I twisted my imaginary key across my mouth and flung it away. I was good as gold.

Outside the hospital Mike, Pat and I stared out of the parked car at the lacy white curtain wafting all around us. We scrambled from one window to another. *It doesn't make a single sound!* Paddy slapped the cold glass and gurgled.

I squinted. Through the gauzy veil I spied two huddled figures hurrying towards us.

"Here comes Mommy!" I shrieked. But *where's the baby?*

The car door opened and Mommy slid inside. All three of us vied for a hug. I flung my arms around her wet neck over the seat back. Her familiar flower smell engulfed me.

"Mommy, Mommy, Mommy!" the chorus twittered.

Mike thrust his shoulder against my arm and lunged forward. "There's something new for you, Mommy, and it's on the coffee table!" he blurted.

I jerked back and stared. *How did he know?!*

"Be quiet!" I hissed. "Dad-dee!"

"Ho, now!" chortled Daddy. "Let's get home, shall we?"

Just then I heard a whimper. Mommy tugged open her big coat. Tucked inside I saw a tiny red face curling and uncurling, its eyes closed.

"Here's your baby sister!" Mommy smiled. We all stopped and stared.

In the driveway Mike and I raced to be first into the living room. "You weren't supposed to know!" I cried. Once inside I flung out my arms to hold him at bay.

"Mommy," I ventured. "Let's *everybody* go into the living room and *visit.*"

"Yes! Yes!" Mike hopped up and down.

"Mommy *first,*" I insisted. We crept s-l-o-w-l-y behind her – till Mike darted forward. I grabbed Mommy's arm and urged her on. Daddy rubbed his hands in glee, "Ho, ho, ho!" Mike and I stopped in our tracks and stared down that silent box of glass. Patrick grabbed at Mommy's skirt. We waited.

"What? What is it? Where am I supposed to look?" Mommy's head swiveled from side to side. I felt like

I'd been holding my breath, and my chest was about to explode! *Why doesn't she see it?!*

"There! There!" Mike burst out, wildly waving his arm.

"Oh! Oh my goodness!" Mommy's eyes popped like olives. She crumpled backwards onto the couch; Daddy caught her.

"It's a tela-bishon!" Mike shrieked. This time I didn't care.

Suddenly, we were all on the couch; Patrick crawling into Mommy's lap next to baby Julie, Mike and I on either side of Mommy, nuzzling close. Daddy slumped next to me. I rubbed my cheek against her wet wool coat, inhaling her. She looked up at Daddy.

"It's good to be home."

Mike, Pat, Cathay

Epiphany

The snow-capped peaks towered, majestic and unnoticed in the winter light, behind Cheyenne Mountain Elementary School. Magpies, vying for vocal dominance, eyed the schoolyard din below.

"I'm making a cake!" With glee I flung the shovel of sand upside down. I patted the concoction into the pail. Helen, absorbed in her own culinary vision, hummed happily beside me. Without warning, jarring voices smashed through our idyllic world.

"Kindergarten babies! Born in the gravy!"

Glancing up I spied a freckle-faced boy smirking down at us from the fenced off play area above. Others soon took up the chant.

"Don't listen to them!" whispered Helen. With a flounce, we wheeled about and turned our backs on them.

"I hate that song!" I muttered.

"Me, too," agreed Helen. "But *next* year *we'll* be able to sing it." I wasn't so sure I really wanted to sing it.

Clang, clang! Clang, clang! The big brass bell flew up and down in Miss Kay's outstretched hand. Gradually, the chatter subsided as we assembled in our class formations. Recess was over.

We all filed through the double doors and down the long corridor to the auditorium. With a tussle, Helen dashed in line ahead of me.

"Frontsies!" she grinned, craning back.

With excitement we fanned out into the large hall, festooned with evergreens. Miss Kay directed our class up near the stage.

"Kindergartners," she called. "I want you to all sit on your jackets on the floor in front of the folding chairs."

"Huh?" I plopped down beside Helen, who squirmed on the hardwood floor.

"I guess next year we get to sit on the seats. But why not now?" she complained. The din reverberated around us as children rushed about to sit with their friends. Again Miss Kay flipped the bell.

"Boys and girls!" she exclaimed. "Silence!"

A lull soon descended upon the crowd. Into the air sprang sharp, bright notes as the upright piano leaped into play. The lights dimmed.

Helen leaned over and whispered, "I'd *never* get up in front of everybody like those big kids! Would you?"

Before I could reply, the red velvet curtains tugged noisily to each side. Lights faded around us while brilliant rays from above found their marks on the stage. Little arms and legs marched stiffly in time to the music as miniature toy soldiers sprang to life. Pretty-frocked dollies twirled to meet them in "Santa's workshop." Music, colors, sequins, flailing limbs all washed into one great swirl of magic as I soaked up the scene.

All too soon, the room swiveled into clarity once more as lights blared forth overhead and hands clapped all around me. Children giggled and shoved as Miss Kay prodded the kindergartners up to their feet.

"All students whose parents have come for the performance may stay here to meet them," she announced.

In a blur boys and girls flowed by me as I froze in my tracks and waited.

"There you are!" rang a merry voice from behind. Mommy, with the new baby snug against her shoulder, stooped down and planted a kiss on the top of my head. "Wait here just a moment. I want to have a word with Miss Kay." With that, she headed towards the back of the room, with Mike and Pat in tow.

I glanced about the swiftly emptying auditorium. Only a few stragglers tarried, as mothers bundled them down the aisle to the rear doors. I turned towards the stage once more and saw my chance. With a deep breath, I clambered up the three short stairs on the side. Slowly, then, I trod across the gigantic wooden apron that gleamed before me.

I stopped; then gazed out at the room full of empty chairs, all facing me so expectantly. Suddenly they seemed to glow. The spaces in the seats became alive as I felt their electricity feeding into me. The sparkling vapor buoyed me up and held me fast. Bit by bit I raised my arms and reached for the walls. Larger and larger I grew, filling the stage. I was *huge!* Never before did I feel so full and happy.

"Ready to go?"

Pop! The bubble burst; the colors dulled, as, reluctantly, I opened my eyes to the space behind me. There stood Mommy. She cocked her head and raised her eyebrows. Then she smiled and seized my hand.

"Time to go home now!"

The moment had passed; but a seed was planted.

Pat, Cherie, Cathay, Mike

The Apple Tree

*B*ang!

I bolted out the back door, letting it slam behind
me. Into a spring wonderland I twirled, my pink frock
billowing about. Miniature daisies dotted the back lawn
before me.

The Apple Tree waits! I dashed up to its massive trunk
and patted it tenderly, then wrapped my arms around
it in a giant hug. The bark scratched against my cheek
as I nuzzled it. Daddy had finally hung the hand-made
swing on its high, sloping bough. I coiled my fingers
around the coarse cords; then caressed the huge wooden
seat with satisfaction. *No one else has a swing like this!*
With a flounce I landed on the target, leaned back and
pushed off.

Up, up in the sky I fly; now higher, now faster! I let my
head fall back on my shoulders and gazed up into the

47

dappled green canopy rushing towards me. Streaks of sunlight darted here and there like dancing icicles as I swung back and forth under them. A single patch of blue winked at me every few beats right in the middle of my lacey umbrella. *I'm flying!* Into the sky I sailed, with a rush of wind streaming by, my hair floating behind. Ah, the thrill of it! I sniffed the air and smiled at the new green apples peeking out at me. Now two, now three – no, four! *I'm too dizzy to count.*

Gradually I let my foot drag the load down to a halt. *Where is Cherie? I'm ready for The Game...* I hunched my shoulders in delicious anticipation. This time I've got her. *She'll never be able to get it today....*

We had been playing a guessing game: "What Color Underwear Am I Wearing?" Each day we took turns. But I noticed she'd been guessing too easily. Most of mine were white, so she figured it out pretty quickly. *Not today, though.*

"Cathay! Are you ready for The Game?!" Cherie's pink-cheeked face popped over the side fence.

With a whoop, I invited her up on the swing in my place.

"You go first," I offered.

"O.K."

Swaying back and forth she chanted, "What color underwear do I have on today?"

"White," I guessed.

"No...."

"Yellow?"

She slid to a halt. "Hey! You got it!" Quickly she wrapped her legs high up around the ropes as she heaved her body upside down, allowing her dress to fall over her face. Yellow they were!

"O.K, my turn!" I cried.

Swiftly we switched positions. Licking my lips with a

smug air I swung out and sang: "What color underwear am I wearing today?"

"White!" declared Cherie.

"No...."

"Pink!"

"No...."

"Blue?"

"No!... You'll never guess!" I crowed.

The swing rapidly accelerated. Cherie grimaced in frustration.

"Purple?"

I shook my head. "Unh, unh uhhh!"

"Oh – yellow – like me!"

"Nope. Give up?"

Mystified, she nodded.

Without a word I flipped myself upside down and clung to the ropes, dress cascading down to reveal my stark naked bottom. Tossing my skirt aside with my

Apple tree in winter

49

nose, I could see Cherie's topsy-turvy mouth gape open. I giggled.

She gasped, "That's not fair!"

Just then I heard a sharp rap on the window beyond. My eyes twisted in their sockets to see Mommy shake her head and wag her finger at me. Guiltily I swung my legs down, surprised. Through the kitchen window she crooked her finger back and forth.

O.K. The fun is over.

I skipped over the soft grass to the back door; then stopped for a momentary smirk at Cherie.

This time I had outsmarted her.

Cathay, Patrick, Mike

The Inner Room

A peal of laughter rang out.

"Oh, Bonnie, you're too much!"

I glanced up from my play, startled, in time to see Alice Parker neatly sidestep Mommy's proffered dollar bill.

"Your sweet brood napped the entire time I was here," she protested.

"Oh, come on, Alice," wheedled Mommy. "You gave Julie a bottle – and anyway, you gave up your time to come over here!"

Mommy stuffed the crumpled bill into our neighbor's pocket. With a chuckle Mrs. Parker scurried around the arm of the couch and out of Mommy's reach. I settled my new baby doll, Tiny Tears, on the rug just as the rumpled money sailed over the back of that sofa.

"Bye, Bonnie!" Mrs. P. sang out as she scooted off through the front door.

Mommy sighed; then shook her head at me with a wry smile.

"We did sleep!" I clamored.

"I know you did, Sweetie."

After dinner, with Mike and Pat tucked in, I helped Mommy sing lullabies to baby Julie.

"When's Daddy coming home?" He'd been gone three days for a BIG MEETING in Chicago.

"Tomorrow night," she whispered.

We tiptoed out before Julie could stir. After she tucked me into my own bed, Mommy turned back at the door.

"I'll be gone just a minute," she said lightly. "I'm just going to run across the street and give Mrs. Parker that money. She deserves a little something for helping me out today, and I'm not taking "No" for an answer!" She smiled. "Nighty-night. Sleep tight. Don't let the bedbugs bite!"

"I won't," I quavered.

"Don't fall out of bed," she teased.

I nodded.

With a click, the room descended into darkness. Only a small glow emanated from the nightlight on the dresser top. I listened as Mommy's footsteps faded. Thud! The front door clunked. Silence. I stared into the shadows.

No one was home. No grownup was home. *I am five years old, and I am the oldest one in this house. It's nighttime, and I'm "in charge."*

I rotated my head from side to side. The walls seemed to move gradually in, then out, pulsating. I could feel the long hallway beyond my door. Mike and Pat slept down there, little 'Paddy' in his crib, and Mike in his trundle bed. They didn't know we were alone. Baby Julie… *What if she wakes up? I can't pick her up by myself. No one is home…*

The room began to shine with an eerie glow. A ringing sound shrieked a warning – from right inside my ears! My breathing pumped faster. My chest tightened. Cotton filled up my mouth. Water began rushing inside my head. Shakily I reached out and pulled up the blanket.

A sudden cold chill raced down my spine. *What if there's a fire?* I screwed my eyes shut. *No, no! Don't let that come in!* I opened my eyes. Slyly, a finger of red eased around my brain and undulated, menacing. *It's hot in here.* I could see shadows of red knocking at my door, now sliding snakily under the crack and along the walls. *No, no! You can't come in! How would I get Mike and Pat and baby Julie?! Nobody would know if the house caught on fire and we were all alone! Mommy is across the street, laughing, Daddy is gone and we will be burning up and no one would know!*

My legs were giant logs. I couldn't move. *I'm only five, and the BIG FIRE could be everywhere!* With one supreme effort I wrenched my body around under the covers, seized my pillow, and screamed into its muffling softness. Red grew Large and impervious all around me, a flickering monster of doom. Slowly Red faded to black…. Exhausted, I slipped into a cloud of dreamless sleep.

"Good morning, Merry Sunshine, how did you wake so soon? You shied away the little stars, and scared away the moon!"

I opened my eyes to a beaming face as Mommy swished back the curtains to allow the sun rays in.

"You were fast asleep when I peeked in at you last night," she smiled. "Mrs. Parker wasn't home, so I just slipped the money into her mailbox."

I stared, dumbfounded.

"I was back quicker that the shake of a lamb's tail," she added.

"Ready for breakfast?"

SAN ANTONIO
1956 (June – December)

Cathay, Mommy, Julie, Mike

Dad has enlisted in the U.S. Army to help pay the bills for his burgeoning family. Our family of six now heads toward hot, humid, bug-infested Texas for his six months of basic training.

Deja Vu

"Oh, Susannah! Oh, don't you cry for me! For I've come from Alabama with my banjo on my knee!"

Daddy warbled from the front seat of the old green Pontiac. Mommy joined in, rocking baby Julie next to him. Mike, Pat and I fidgeted in the back seat. Two long days on the road from Colorado, following the trail of the moving van, had taken its toll.

"Are we ever gonna get there?" I grumped.

At last across the border of Texas, Daddy surprised us. We would pay an unexpected visit to his old patient, Mrs. Sewell.

"Here we are!" announced Daddy. We rumbled to a stop before a ranch house behind a rough-hewn fence.

"We'll wait here while Daddy sees if anyone is home," Mommy suggested. I squinted out the window. Daddy opened the gate and sauntered through the large front yard to the screen door. Moments later a plump, aproned woman burst out.

"Why, sake's alive, I shore dint 'spect to see you out these here parts!" she exclaimed. "Come on in, Dr. Gunn!"

Daddy turned around and waved us up from the car. We trundled out and Mike and I raced through the gate with Patrick toddling to catch up.

"Walk!" Mommy called in her sharpest voice, pulling us up short.

Slowly, then, I crossed the threshold and scrutinized the surroundings. Red and brown plaid curtains, a copper hurricane lamp, and copious animal knickknacks festooned the living room. A peaked-roof coo-coo clock with chickens and pigs caught my eye. I stared, hoping it would strike.

From the shadows a large, round man, overflowing his suspendered blue jeans, nodded affably. "You remember my husband Locke, Dr. Gunn," drawled Mrs. Sewell. "Locke, how's about fixin' our guests some nice cool lemonade." *Mmmmm...I grinned up her.*

"Now, Locke here had a hankerin' for a late breakfast this mornin'," she continued. "So will that do for you all?"

"Oh, you needn't put yourselves out," murmured Mommy.

"Nonsense!" Mrs. Sewell replied. "I'm jes' sorry you dint git here an hour or two sooner. I'd 'a' had these young'uns give me a hand in the henhouse!"

Farmers! Real farmers! I watched Mr. and Mrs. Sewell with renewed interest. Mr. Sewell nodded a lot and shuffled his feet, but didn't say much. I followed Mrs. Sewell into the kitchen.

Yellow gingham curtains fluttered over the open windows; pots and pans hung from hooks above the biggest stove I had ever seen. Up onto a high stool I scrambled for my front row seat.

Her immense arms pounded and tossed a stretchy white glob from a bowl. She stamped it with rings before shoving the spongy discs into the oven. Then, lickety-split, Mrs. Sewell pulled down pans and worked up a sizzle and a scrumptious aroma in no time.

I studied her as she whirled her large frame around the kitchen. *Funny...she doesn't look sick...doesn't act sick...*I knew most of Daddy's patients got *very* sick. *Maybe she's all better...*

"Soup's on!" called Mrs. Sewell. Mike, Pat and I clambered up onto folding chairs around a card table on the patio. *We get to eat outside without the grownups, and we're having BREAKFAST for lunch which they call 'supper!'*

My eyes jumped at the strange pink meat on my plate.
"That's not bacon!" I blurted.

"Oh, yes it is, honey," laughed Mrs. Sewell at
the screen door. "Canadian bacon – from the Texas
panhandle!" I stared, not sure what to believe. One bite,
though, and I knew we'd come to a magical place!

Corralled back in the house, we fidgeted. Daddy
stepped in. "Time to hit the road!" Mommy changed
diapers on the sofa while Mike and I fought over the
bathroom. I won first dibs. When I ventured back out,
something felt different.

My ears perked up to a hushed drone of voices in
a corner of the living room. Daddy and Mrs. Sewell.
Daddy reached down and picked up his black doctor's
bag. The two of them rose from the sofa and quietly
headed down the hallway. Daddy jerked his head at
Mommy who set Julie in her infant seat and silently
followed. *Where are they going?*

I waited till I spied the three of them slip into another
room; then tiptoed after. The door swung closed – but
not quite. I pressed my face against the frame and
peered through the narrow opening.

Mrs. Sewell lay prone across a large bed – her bottom
bare! Mommy sat on her right side, her hand against her
back. Daddy crouched over on her left, a huge needle
poised above her! A sudden intake of breath sounded
loud in my ears. Mine. I stared at that needle as it
shimmered to life and flashed at me before disappearing
into Mrs. Sewell's flesh.

"Ow-ow-OW!" she yelped. I swallowed. Mommy's
hand began sweeping in slow circles on her back.

"There, there, it's all right," she soothed. "It'll soon be

over." *Just like Mommy talks to US!*

"Dab nab it!" yelled Mrs. Sewell. "What's taking so long?!" Daddy's hand held steady in a fist on top of her, his thumb slowly moving…

My eyes clouded over. I swayed. A thin veil of mist beaded up before me – then evaporated. No longer did I see three…only two on the bed. A baby sat in a high chair – but it was 'baby' Mike, not Julie. Down a long time tunnel I gazed…

…Now Daddy lies across the bed, his pants rumpled down just below his bottom. Mommy sits on his left, a huge needle gleaming in her hand. She hunches over him; then jerks back up.

"I can't!" she cries.

Daddy groans. "Yes you can! Just DO it!"

Mommy's hand shakes as she lowers it closer and closer… The needle grazes his bottom. She pushes it s-l-o-w-l-y into his skin, her face pinched and furrowed.

"Not like that!" thunders Daddy. Stop!"

She pulls back up. "It won't go in!" she wails. Mommy is shaking; my own body is heaving.

Daddy's face turns on the bed towards her. "You've got to do it fast! *Jab it in, damn it!" he roars. "Just SLAM it in!"*

Mommy whimpers; catches her breath. Her arm rises up. Suddenly she is tall; she grows taller still. Her arm quivers in the sunlight; then like lightning her hand slams into Daddy's flesh.

"Ooff!" His body jumps in a responding tremor against the bed – then lays still.

"Not…quite…so…hard," he moans.

Daddy shrinks smaller and smaller. Mommy crumples next to him, smaller still. Everything in the room grows bigger and bigger around them. They are lifeless midgets on the gigantic bed…

The tunnel between us closed in, tighter, tighter – BLACK.

I blinked. The room brightened into view through the

crack in the door. Mrs. Sewell struggled to her feet.

"Well!" she harrumphed. "I'm certainly glad that's over with!"

I scarcely had time to flatten myself against the wall before she yanked the door wide open. Head held high, Mrs. Sewell stormed down the hall and out of sight. Once more, she had regained her crown as Mrs. Farmer. Mommy and Daddy slowly followed.

I stared after them; then peered back into the now vacated bedroom. Sunlight streamed through the window. The bed was empty; the needle gone. No high chair. No baby Mike.

Back on the road, we waved our last to Mr. and Mrs. Sewell. Mike and Pat nodded sleepily next to me. I sat very still. Straight ahead, Daddy's arm lay across the seat back, resting on Mommy's shoulder. Baby Julie sucked noisily in her lap on her bottle. Under the weight, Mommy shifted and settled. She turned. My eyes slowly traced the curve of her cheek, her lips...

Mommy crooned,

"Hush, little baby, don't say a word,
Daddy's gonna buy you a mocking bird..."

With a sigh, I turned to my window and gazed as the blur of tall, dried grass blazed by.

Cathay, Mike and Pat

San Antonio Blues

Slam! The screen door banged behind me as I felt myself unceremoniously ushered onto the front porch.

"Out, Out, Out!" Grandmamma charged. "It's a beautiful day! Get into it!"

With a backward scowl, I flounced across the wooden boards and flopped onto the big porch swing. It was my solace in time of need. I sighed. Three-year-old Mike didn't have to go outside. *Why me?* I shoved off, stretching my bare toes to reach the floor.

Creakk...creakk... The rhythm of the pendulum coddled me into complacency. The afternoon sun warmed my legs as I rocked in and out of dappled shadow. Bit by bit, my lids weighed down over my eyes. Soon the sun pressed insistently against my skin, little beads of moisture popping out on the back of my neck.

Sticky. Texas is sticky. I jiggled the white chain. My eyes fluttered open. Something big and strange popped into view.

With a start, I jerked up. There smack underneath the roving swing a huge brown spider lay in wait. As big as a pancake it was! Medium brown – the color of peanut brittle. Not like your average dark brown Colorado house spider. It looked like Daddy's hand, fingers all spread out. I froze. We eyed each other in silence. *How do I get down over that gigantic beast?!* I waited. Glancing at the house, I knew no one would hear me inside. I had no choice. Gathering up all my courage, I clambered up onto the seat of the swing, took a breath, and leaped heroically onto the porch, inches beyond the repellant culprit.

"Grandmamma!" I shrieked as I threw open the screen door and tumbled inside.

Mike and Grandmamma came running.

"There's a – there's a – HUGE spider under the swing!" I wailed.

Grandmamma glared suspiciously at me. "Are you sure you're not tricking me to come back inside?"

"Yes, yes!" I pumped her arm and we all piled out onto the porch.

"Where?!" she demanded.

Dumbfounded, I stared at the empty expanse that had once held the dreaded arachnid.

"Why – it – it was here just a minute ago!" I stammered.

"Well, it's gone now," Grandmamma remarked dryly.

Little Mike howled. "Where's the spider? Where's the spider? There's no spider!"

I lunged at him. Grandmamma scooped him up and

out of harm's way.

"You go on and play," she ordered.

I'm not staying out HERE!" I envisioned the hairy creature leaping out at me from its secret hiding place.

"All right," agreed Grandmamma. Back in the house we trooped. "But you behave. Little Patrick and baby Julie are still asleep."

I made a beeline for my bedroom and shut the door. Even inside here the sun's rays had worked their way through the window. My pillow was red-hot.

Soon absorbed with Tiny Tears and her bottle, I cooed softly to my dolly so no one would hear. Suddenly the door burst open.

"What you doing?" chirped Mike.

"Go 'way!" I grumbled, irritated at the interruption.

All at once, Mike leaped up on my bed and bounced up and down.

"Spider! Spider! Spider!" he taunted.

"Stop it!"

With a quick thrust Mike grabbed Tiny Tears and threw her on the floor. Outraged, I seized his shoulders between my hands, feeling my entire body tighten like a spring. My teeth ached dangerously. Without warning, I snapped open my jaw and sank those incisors into his bare back. *Hard.* My whole body writhed with fury. I felt him stiffen under my clasped fingers, his voice screeching in my ear.

"AAAHHHHHHHH!"

With a quick flip he rolled away from me and off the bed.

Pandemonium broke out. Baby Julie shrieked in her crib, Patrick wailed in sleepy protest, and Grandmamma swooped down on me like a Halloween bat.

"What have you done?!" she screamed. "Don't you know he's your brother?!" With a few quick swats on my behind, she yanked me off the bed and marched me through the house, out the backdoor to the cement steps beyond.

"You wait right there!" she charged. "You can go to *jail* for that!"

Without a backward glance, she slammed the screen door behind her and disappeared into the shadowy interior.

Gradually the cacophony of cries subsided within. I huddled on the top step, my hand hugging the railing. Nervously I peered as far around the house as I dared. I listened. Silence all around....

....I did it big this time. Last time, I pushed Mikey off the bed, and he banged his head on the wooden post on the way down. A huge purple egg appeared. Now he'll probably have blood coming out of all those little teeth marks. Might even get rabies. The police are coming, and they're going to take me away. 'To jail!' she said...

I gazed up at the fading blue sky. The stickiness had waned. Still, the air pressed in on me with a palpable, stifling punch. I gazed all around. Nothing stirred. The brown grass stood perfectly still. Not a sign of life interrupted the landscape. I could feel the air stretching on and on before me, empty and uncaring. All the way to Colorado and our old house and yard. Nothing in-between but strange, dead air.

Mommy and Daddy aren't home. They will come back and find me gone. The police will take me away and I will never see them again.

A tear danced onto my arm, wavering a bit on its journey past my nose...

Creakk. The door swung open.

"Are you going to stay out here all night?" Grandmamma arched her eyebrows.

I stared up at her.

"C'mon inside," she said, jerking her head.

"Are they…are they still gonna take me… is Mike O.K?" I quavered.

"Heck, he's fine – ornery young fella." Her face softened. "You just watch yourself from now on – you hear?"

I nodded; then followed Grandmamma into the house, letting the screen door slam behind me.

Mike

The Babysitter

"Mommy, I'm finished! Can I play at Tracy's till bedtime?"

I pushed back from the kitchen table, anxious to get outside. Early evening lightened the sticky sweat of the San Antonio day. The best time to be outdoors!

"Yes, you may," answered Mommy, still shoveling the last spoonfuls of Gerber turkey into baby Julie's mouth. "But be sure and be back before it starts to get dark."

Mike struggled out of his seat. "Me, too! Me, too!" he cried, scrambling past Patrick, still imprisoned in his highchair.

"All right. But Michael – you stay right with Cathay. She's in charge."

I let out an exasperated sigh. "Why?!"

"If you want to go, " Mommy eyed me, "Michael goes with you."

At five and a half, I liked being in charge…*sometimes!*

"Ohh – *kay*. C'mon, Mike."

Up the dusty back road I stomped, Mike pattering quickly behind to catch up. He grabbed my hand to cross to the other side.

"Let's go on our swing, Cathay!"

I peered down at his upturned face and grinned in spite of myself. It really WAS our swing; the rope swing Daddy had made for our apple tree in Colorado Springs. But much to my disappointment, we found no great tree in our new yard in Texas. Tracy's yard across the road had one (though nothing so wonderful as our old apple tree!) With help from her Daddy we soon had our swing in motion again.

Up ahead now we spied that dangling seat, held taut in the stillness of the air, ready to send us flying at whim. Our own magic carpet ride! As one, our hands let go and we raced each other towards the prize.

"Hey, Cathay! Come up hee-er quick!"

I stopped short just shy of my goal and wheeled around. Tracy. She stood at the top of the wooden stairs that wound up the side of her house. Just then I felt Mike zoom past me and land on the swing with a crow of delight. *Darn!*

"C'mere, c'mere, c'mee-er!" Tracy drawled, leaning over the rail.

I heaved a sigh, and marched over to the swing.

"C'mon, Mike," I muttered, "we have to go *inside* first." I pried his resistant fingers off the rope and yanked him towards the house. Mike began wailing and I instantly buckled towards his ear.

"Don't worry," I whispered. "We'll come right back out in a few minutes. But if you cry," I warned, "she'll make us go home."

I led Mike up the rickety side steps with the peeling

paint. As soon as we reached the landing Tracy ducked inside.

"I thought you'd never get up here!" she called over her shoulder.

Once in her room she gestured downward and promptly squatted on the floor. "Candyland!" she enthused.

I stared at the colorful square board in front of her. Pictures of gumdrops and ice cream cones littered its surface, a rainbow of stepping-stones slithering through them.

"What is it?" I asked.

"It's a game, dodo!"

I could feel Mike's restless hops behind me, but I wavered before that mesmerizing board.

"See?" cried Tracy. "We each pick a marker, and then take a card to see where we go! I'll show you!"

"But what about Mike?"

"He can play, too...IF he *can*..." she frowned at him.

"No!" growled Mike. "Swing!"

I whirled around. "Just for a *minute*, Mike," I coaxed. "See? Gumdrops!"

For the next several minutes we all crowded around the board, busily jumping our colored markers through the titillating terrain of treats. That is, till Mike tumbled forward and propelled the playing pieces and cards in all directions.

"Great! Just great!" retorted Tracy. "Why'd you have to bring him, anyway?!"

I glowered at Tracy – then clicked my tongue at Mike. "Because he's my *brother*," I mumbled. Mike's chin began to jut out. I jumped to my feet.

"Let's play *outside*, Tracy."

"No!"

Mike began to cry.

"Ok," she relented. "But I get to choose what we play."

Once more in the parched backyard, Tracy began barking orders.

"We're playing Doctor – keep away from that swing, Mike – you're the patient."

"Ok," I replied, "but we get to swing afterwards – right, Mikey?" He nodded. "And *I'm* the doctor."

"Why?" Tracy put her hands on her hips.

"Because – because *my Daddy's* a doctor. You can be the nurse. You can take his pulse."

Tracy studied me a moment, head cocked. "Ok." Then she marched over to Mike, took his hand and led him back to the steps.

"Lie down," she ordered. Mike wiggled into place on the board, eyes darting back to mine.

"Good boy, Mike," I called over to him.

Tracy grabbed his arm by the wrist and swung it up in the air. She scrutinized her own wrist and began counting. "Onetwothreefourfivesixseven – eleven – seventy-seven – one hun-erd." She stopped, shaking her head. "Oh, no, Doctor, this patient needs his temp-ature."

"Tracy – where's your doctor's kit?"

She shrugged. "Find something else."

I scrutinized the ground for any choice doctor's tools. There, right before my nose lay the perfect stick! I snatched it up and snapped off the remaining feathered branches.

"Ok, Mikey – sit up," I prodded. "Stick out your tongue and say 'ah'."

Mike complied – that is, until he saw the stick approaching, and clamped his mouth shut.

"Hey!" cried Tracy.

"That's ok," I hastened. "Let's examine his ears."

Remembering my own trips to the doctor, I admonished him. "Hold *still*, while I shine my special light in your ears." Tracy hustled around to the other side and locked his head at an angle in her embrace.

"Ready, Doctor."

"*Hmm*," I mused, my trusty otoscope twig poised for duty. "Looks dark in there." I cranked my head around the side of the stick as I probed further…

"YEEOWWW! OWW – WOW-WOWW!"

Flinging my arm away, the stick flying, Mike wrested from Tracy's grip and tore down the road, shrieking all the while.

"You broke it," hissed Tracy. "You broke his eardrum! You broke his eardrumm!"

Without a backward glance, I scrambled after Mike. "Stop!"

He flew like a banshee. I, on the other hand, moved through molasses. *Why is our house so far away?!* My heart pounded in my ears. *If I could just get to him before he gets to Mommy and Daddy…*

Up the back porch steps Mike stumbled, clutching the side of his head, encased in high-pitched hysteria. Frantically I closed in on him – then froze below the steps as our house swallowed him up.

I dragged my feet over the threshold. All the air inside me seeped languidly out and sidled along the floor like curls of mist. I stood a moment, listening to Mike's trailing cries, becoming more and more muffled. I crept down the dusky hallway, the strange silence pressing in on me. A foreboding cry stopped me in my tracks.

"Walt! I need you! NOW!"

Suddenly the world spun into fast motion again. Daddy's huge frame towered over me before disappearing in a flash down the hallway behind. Sparks zinged up and down my body. I wheeled around and raced after him. *What if his eardrum IS broken? Will he be deaf?!* Black fear raced towards me as I plowed through it. I skidded to a stop in the open doorway.

Ahead of me stood Mike, with Mommy molded around him on one side. Daddy leaned over his black doctor's bag. He pulled out his otoscope (a *real* one!) I watched him flick a button and shine the tiny light with the green cone into his ear. The world stood still. No one looked at me. Mommy and Daddy and Mike crystallized into one solid plate. I held my breath.

"Well, Mike," Daddy began, twisting his head and scrunched-up eye this way and that. "The good news is – your eardrum is not punctured. Your ear canal is probably scratched." He straightened up. "I have some special drops for you. *However*," Daddy turned his head and our eyes locked. "Your *sister*...has some *explaining* to do."

Mommy and Mike raised their eyes. All three of them met my gaze with a cold, unblinking stare.

I shuffled my feet down the loose gravel of our driveway. A week had passed since Daddy forbade my visiting Tracy. The sun's rays grew harsher the closer I got to her house. I hadn't seen her since The Incident.

"You may go to Tracy's today," Mommy had beamed at me after breakfast.

But now my feet refused to be happy.

At the edge of her dirt driveway I stopped. My eyes drifted over to the swing, idly whispering to me. I forced myself to ignore it. Just in time, Tracy appeared. She strolled out of her backdoor, letting it slam behind her.

"So," she drawled, head cocked to the side. "Was I right? Did you break his eardrum?"

"No," I replied, raising my chin. Tracy studied me a moment.

"How come you haven't come over?"

"My Mommy and Daddy wouldn't let me."

Her eyes grew big. "Do they think it was my fault? Did you tell them that?"

"No!" I protested.

"Well, you *better* not have," her eyes narrowed. "Because *you* did it! Not me!"

My foot began jumping inside my shoe. "But *you* made us play Doctor!"

"So? So what?" She wrinkled her face at me and waited. I glanced down at the ground and dragged my heel in a slow arc through the dirt. Echoes of Mike's screams hovered between us.

"YOU stuck the stick in his ear!" she finished triumphantly.

I knew she was right. I no longer wanted to be there.

"Tracy," I swallowed. "I want my swing back."

"What?!" she gaped at me.

"Tell your Daddy to take it down."

"But you don't have any place to hang it!"

"I know that. Just take it down."

I turned on my heel and marched down the driveway. I did not look back.

Once more on my side of the road I halted. My stomach didn't feel so good. I trudged home.

After lunch I slipped out the backdoor and down the cement steps. The sun beat down on my hair. I closed my eyes a moment, head tilted back, and bathed in its warmth. Opening them, I glanced aimlessly about the barren backyard.

I spied a lone stick on the ground, bent down and nabbed it. Squatting, I began to scrape deep lines in the earth. Round heads, arms and legs of stick figures. The line-up: Daddy, Mommy, Mike, Pat, Julie…and then me. *Shall I put a sun? Yes.* The sun's rays splashed down in skinny shards all around the family...except me. I straightened up to survey my artwork.

Crunch, crunch...

Up the gravel driveway lumbered an impossibly tall, lanky grownup in faded overalls. He eyed me intently all the way up. Tracy's Daddy.

I swallowed. I glanced up at the house, suddenly feeling small and very much alone. He stopped before me, clutching a bundle.

"Cathy?" His nasal voice grated. I nodded, not bothering to correct him.

"Here's your swing." Those long arms suddenly thrust his burden towards me.

I gulped. *Why did HE bring it to me? Why not Tracy? Why didn't Tracy just wait for me to come get it?*

His arms extended, he waited. My ears buzzed in the deafening silence around us. Slowly I raised my eyes. His eyebrows lifted, mouth twisted to the side. My mouth felt dry. I tried to think of something to say, but he was too big. My arms finally reached out. He thrust the heavy load between them: the large wooden plank with thick, rough rope twined around it. I stumbled, but caught myself, not willing to let him see me fall. By the time I steadied myself and looked up, he had already turned, and plodded his way down the driveway.

I stood rooted to the ground, hugging my badge of shame as my eyes followed his retreating figure. I squeezed that board to my chest till the coils of rope burned into me, then squeezed some more.

Then, I trudged to the garage. I knelt beside the washer. Slowly I slid the swing along the back against the wall, under the faucets...

...until I could no longer reach it.

TreeHouse Blues

MARYLAND / D.C.
1956-1958

Cathay, Mike, Pat, Julie, Timmy, Mommy

Dad's first military assignment: two years at
Walter Reed Army Hospital in Washington,
D.C. Medical school has given him officer
status (Captain) and the opportunity to stay
"in-country." During this time he completes
his Residency in Radiology. We settle in Silver
Spring, Maryland two weeks before baby #5
arrives.

The Christmas That Almost Wasn't

Tick tock. Tick tock.

A lump under me burrowed into my back…
Scratchiness along the back of my head. Gradually my
eyes opened to fuzzy shadows. Something gleamed out
of the gloom just inches from my makeshift bed on the
loveseat. *Where am I? It's nighttime… It's Christmas Eve!*

Without yet a home, we'd camped at 'bachelor'
Uncle Tommy's one-bedroom apartment in Baltimore.
Daddy shared Uncle Tommy's bed, while Mike and Pat
lay at their feet on the floor. Grandmamma somehow
scrunched up in a sleeping bag in the bathtub. But
I snagged the prized spot: the 'bed' in front of the
Christmas tree! (Only Mommy on the rug below lay
closer, with baby Julie curled up around her giant belly.)

76

Now that gleam looked suspiciously like a face. *Whuh!* I leaped half way up under the covers. A shining face popped out at me, eyes staring wide-eyed at the ceiling. *A doll!* Face framed in golden curls…glowing cheeks, frozen in time. *Oh!* She lay in a gigantic wooden cradle – life-size! So beautiful! So wondrous! So perfectly mine!

A *rustle.* I snapped my eyes shut and held my breath. *What if Santa's still here?!*

"Waaah!" Off to the right the dour wails of Mike pierced the silence.

Boom, boom, thud vibrated down the hall, now drawing closer. *Oh!* My heart pounded in my ears. Uncle Tommy's voice rumbled out, menacing.

"All right. If you won't go back to bed, I'll call Santa."

Uh oh. Mike wailed louder: shrieks of outrage. A fumble in the kitchen beyond. I could feel it through my tightly closed eyelids: the tiny alcove with the massive counter just past the living room. I froze, hardly daring to breathe.

The phone buzzed. *Z-zip. Z-z-zip. Zip. Zip.*

"Hello, Santa? This is Uncle Tommy. We have a very bad boy here who won't stay in his bed. I think you need to come back and take away the presents. All of them."

Oh no! My skin shrieked. *This can't be! My beautiful new doll! I just got it! I never even got to play with it! Please don't! Please don't!* I prayed, quivering in fright.

Huge howls from Mike trailed off as Uncle Tommy stamped back down the hall. A pitter of whimpers, then, silence. I held my breath. *Please, God. I'll be good forever.*

Slowly, Uncle Tommy's footsteps loomed louder as he approached once again. I lay still as death.

Zip–zip. Z-z-z-zip.

"Hello, Santa? It's all right now. I think the boy has decided he's going to sleep. Yup. You don't need to come back after all."

Sighhhhhhh. My tiny breath stream sneaked painfully, but silently out, down to my toes.

Footsteps faded down the hallway.

Tick tock. Tick tock.

All of a sudden, a teensy electric current pricked up and down my body, now faster, wakening my skin like little effervescent bubbles. One eye opened. My golden girlie stared up at the ceiling, unperturbed. The railing of the cradle gleamed in the moonlight. I smiled in the dark.

She's all mine.

Kathleen

*K*athleeeen...

It was a beautiful name. I closed my eyes and savored the sensation on my tongue and teeth as I breathed the word.

Mommy and I stood outside Silver Spring Grammar School, stamping our feet to keep warm. Today was January 3, 1957, and a whole lot colder than San Antonio, Texas! Once again, we had uprooted, following the Army's command, and because school rules about birth dates vary from state to state, I was now permitted into first grade (whereas, in Texas, I was not.)

One consolation for The Big Move was The Name Change. Because *everyone* mispronounced my name, Mommy finally saw the light.

"Now that we're in a new place, why don't you be 'Kathleen'?" she had suggested. "No one will ever know anything different."

Soo happy!! I dwelled on this now as I pictured the priest after Mass "baptizing" me with my new special name and a pat on the head...

Suddenly the classroom door burst open, disturbing my reverie. A stern-eyed blonde woman frowned at us.

"You're late," she snapped.

The chaotic classroom stretched behind her, overflowing with chattering strangers. The teacher ushered me frostily inside. I craned around just in time to see Mommy's face disappear behind the firm hand on the swiftly shut door. My skin itched hot and cold, my throat felt dry. For a second the chatter stopped.

"This is our new girl, Kathleen," Miss McKinley

clipped. "She has never been to first grade, but she is joining our class for the rest of the year."

All eyes stared as one. One boy cranked his head sideways and twisted his mouth at me. Now I wished they would all talk again. I followed Miss McKinley to my designated seat.

…Towards noon, as if to an unspoken signal, the rustle of papers grew louder around me.

"Psst! Did you bring a lunch?" one girl whispered. I nodded.

Just then a bell clanged. Desktops rose and lowered as the odor of bologna and peanut butter mingled in the air. Milk appeared out of nowhere on the teacher's desk. Several children filed forward to claim it.

Miss McKinley rose. "Who wanted ice cream today? Please come see me."

I watched two boys and a girl spring out of their seats and trot up front.

Nobody else? … So rich and creamy! I'd like some! Impulsively, I untangled my legs and leapt from my chair. I strode forth to obtain my prize. But Miss McKinley merely stared down at me.

Suddenly she frowned. "Did you think you were getting ice cream?"

I nodded, uncertain, now.

"No, no, no! You have to *order* it!"

A rousing chorus of titters grew into a roar behind me, warming my back. I wheeled around and bee-lined to my seat, eyes glued to the floor. I studied the round, empty inkwell cut into my wooden desk, tracing its rough-hewn edge with my finger.

When will the day end?!

That afternoon I colored while the rest of the girls and boys labored over "phonics." Miss McKinley moved me to a desk on the far right side of the room, a huge, empty expanse all around me, while she worked with the others.

This became the daily routine. I told Mommy about it, as she stroked her ballooned belly, eyebrows lowered, her face growing redder and redder all the while.

The next day a knock came to our door. Mommy opened it. *What's Miss McKinley doing here?!* She carried a huge pile of papers.

"Here!" she growled, shoving them into Mommy's arms. "Is this what you want? See what *you* can do with her!" She turned on her heel and huffed away. Mommy stared after her, speechless.

Day after day after school I practiced "phonics" on those papers with Mommy, while still coloring in the classroom. Mommy and I "played school," just like we had done at home in Texas, when I was "too young" to be in that first grade.

The one highlight of my school day glowed brightly: reading. Of course Miss McKinley didn't know I could read. She never asked. Every day at 2:00, we broke up into our reading groups: the Robins, the Blue Jays, and the Sparrows. She placed me in the smallest group, with only four boys and no girls. Each boy in turn stumbled through the obstacle course of words in our reader. I alone sat silent, hearing the words in my head, never saying them aloud. My turn never came.

But at last a reprieve: Miss McKinley mysteriously did not appear one morning. A substitute, "Miss Turner," took over. Tall, thin, salt-and-pepper hair pulled back in a bun, she nodded pleasantly to me after the last boy had read in our reading group. *Me?! She means me?!* I took a breath and quietly read the page as if nothing had happened.

The next afternoon, on Miss McKinley's return, we regrouped with the Sparrows. Miss McKinley cleared her throat and began.

"Boys: I understand that Kathleen *read* yesterday. Did you know she could read?" All heads shook in reply. "*I* didn't know she could read." Her eyes bore into me, piercing me down to the bone.

"And by the way, boys," she continued. "Did you know that Kathleen's name is not really...Kathleen?"

Ding! Ding! Ding! Ding! Warning! Warning! A red light flashed inside my head and pulsed its beat up and down, inside and out of my body. *No! She will not say this! She can't!*

"Her name is *Cathay*," *Miss* McKinley oozed.

My chest heaved, my breath spurted in short bursts. My eyes watered.

She didn't! How could she?! Mommy promised no one would ever know!

Eight beady eyes stared at me, dumbfounded.

"Huh?"

"What kind of name is that?"

"Eeuw..."

Snicker, snicker.

I took a huge breath and gulped, gazing down at the floor beside my shoe. *Oh, to be Alice in Wonderland, and fall, down, down into that deep, dark well...*

Never again did I read aloud that year. But when the official testing was graded in June, I surprised them all by my promotion to second grade.

And when the new school year rolled around, I heard Miss McKinley was not asked back.

Military Baby

"*Psst!* Cathay!"

Like a bolt of lightning I jerked awake in the velvet night.

"What is it, Daddy?"

"Time to get up," he whispered. "Mommy's new baby is ready."

"But it's *dark* out!" I shivered in my nightgown on the edge of the bed as I tried to peer through the shadows.

Soon bundled up in our wool overcoats, Mike, Pat and I tottered down the darkened cement steps to the waiting car below.

"It's c-c-cold!" I chattered. Frost glimmered over the frozen ground in the January night. Daddy carried baby Julie over his shoulder, her head drooping in a dead sleep, while he steered Mommy towards the passenger door.

Huddled in the middle seat of the station wagon, I stared out the glass at the silent streets as they whispered past. Slowly we rumbled up the long stretch of roadway flanked by military shrubbery. We eased towards a tiny cubicle that glowed in the dark from within. Inside, a man in army uniform saluted! Daddy saluted back.

"It's a *soldier!*" Mike whispered in my ear.

We crunched to a halt before the emergency entrance of Walter Reed Army Hospital. Mommy and Daddy murmured in low tones to each other while Mommy tried to tuck blankets around us in the back.

"Leave the heater on for the children!" she urged in an undertone. A moment later, the car motor churning, they slammed the doors and vanished.

The car shimmied with the rhythm of the motor as it purred. Wafts of heat trickled into the back. I squinted through the shadows of our compartment. Baby Julie lay curled fast asleep on the seat, her head at one end; with Patrick framed around her, thumb in mouth. Mike sat ramrod-straight beside them, eyes glowing like saucers in the dark. We gazed at each other, unable to move.

And still the car purred.

Suddenly Mike jerked his head to stare past me out the window. I turned. The man in army uniform barreled towards us, growing larger by the second. I caught my breath as his huge hand swung onto the driver's door handle. Mike squealed.

He jerked it open.

Mike shrank against me. I froze. In slow-motion, the long, green arm reached across the driver's seat for the key – and switched off the motor.

The head with the wide, flat military hat rotated towards us. His massive face shone in the streetlight, his nostrils black and looming.

"Where's your father and mother?" he grunted.

"They-they're-Mommy's having her baby, and they're coming *right back,*" I squeaked. "At least – I mean – *Daddy's* coming right back..." I faltered.

"There! *There!*" Mike shrieked, arm pointing.

The man turned. "There's no one…?" He was right. I peered along with Mike through the gloom, willing Daddy to appear. At last, a head popped out of the far-off door, and a familiar figure emerged. Daddy.

The burly man shut the car door and tromped away.

Moments later, that round, dimpled face took his place. Mike bounced up and down.

"Daddy! Daddy!" he shrilled. "A *soldier* got in our car and turned it off!"

Without a word, Daddy reached over and turned that same key. The station wagon roared back to life, and we rolled down the road in the dark to another parking lot.

Amid waves of relief, Mike and I stumbled out of the car after Daddy, with Patrick and Julie in his arms, to wait out the waning night in his office.

When at last I awoke on Daddy's swivel chair, we had a new baby brother.

Timothy.

Mike and Cathay

Reprieve

Ssswoo...ssswoo...

My foot magically disappeared inside the frosty powder. First one...then the other. So silent and still this new world lay! The sparkles winked under the early morning gleam of sky. I lifted my brown lunch sack high above the jeweled landscape so it wouldn't get wet.

On towards Karen's house, down on the corner, I plodded. Mommy had arranged for her to walk to school with me each day, and Karen, a year older, had accepted me. My chin nuzzled inside my wooly scarf as I jerked forward under the quilted snowsuit.

I wondered how we would make the trek to school through the rolling piles of snow.

Ding dong! I stood on her doorstep and waited. Karen peered through the crack she made with the slowly widening door. She was still in her pajamas! *Uh oh…*

My new friend gazed at me with raised eyebrows. She froze like a statue. Her eyes eventually traveled down to my conspicuous lunch bag.

"Ah hah!"

Instinctively I tried to hide it behind my back.

"Didn't you know there's no school?" she chuckled. "Didn't you hear it on the radio?"

"Um…I know…I knew that…" I stammered.

"Then why did you come over here with your lunch, huh?" Karen grinned from ear to ear.

"I…I don't know," I said, suddenly confused.

"Mama," she flung over her shoulder. "Guess what! Kathleen thinks there's school!"

"No – I – I just thought you might want to play." I twisted my thumb and finger together inside my mitten.

Mrs. Angeny's disembodied head suddenly appeared over Karen's shoulder, a cigarette escaping her lips.

"Oh, my!" she exclaimed. "Kathleen, dear, didn't your mother know? It's a snow day, honey. Better go home and tell her."

My face burning in the icy air, I lowered my lids and nodded. I glowered at the object of betrayal still clutched in my hand. *Stupid lunch sack! Why didn't I bury it in the snow?!*

Finally the great door groaned shut. Alone again, I carefully picked my way down the soft steps and studied the long, silent street with its dazzling light. I stood a moment. Suddenly, a whisper of white tickled my brain, sending a shiver of freedom throughout my body. Up ahead now, I glimpsed the frosty hours of play expanding before me. The road beckoned.

With a sudden surge, I willed my boots to plow forward. Ever faster they chugged.

"Mommy, Mommy!" I cried. "Guess what!"

Lessons From The Heart

Electricity crackled in the air of the first grade classroom. Boys and girls around me chattered excitedly in groups of twos and threes. Struggling out of my jacket, I clutched the precious cargo in my department store paper bag. *Finally! Valentine's Day is here!*

Brrringgg! With the ringing of the school bell, bodies shuffled in formation behind each row of desks.

"I pledge allegiance to the flag..." *Mommy was right... Valentines* are *special...* My mind wandered off to the night before...

...White paper doilies for lace and red hearts cut out of construction paper. My jaw clamped, I hunkered down over the kitchen table as I carefully cut each heart.

"Fold the paper in half," advised Mommy. "Then you only need to draw half a heart, like this... When you cut it out, you get two halves – just the same! See?"

Crunch, crrrunch... I hacked and hacked. *Ow!* The scissors pinched my hand.

"That's because with your left hand it can be a bit more difficult – but you do such a good job, it makes up for it!"

At last I unfolded my first specimen. *Ta da!* I grinned in triumph.

Next came the gluing – with special paste we made ourselves.

"Just flour and water," smiled Mommy. *Like making a cake!* I spread the thick goop onto the doily and smacked down the first red heart. It stuck! I peered up at Mommy in astonishment. *We made glue!*

But the best part of all – Mommy showed me how

to draw an arrow so that it appeared to actually pierce the heart and get stuck inside it – the point on one side, the feathers way over on the other side, and a short line right in the center. I pressed hard with the black crayon; then studied my masterpiece. *It worked! It worked! Just like a real cupid's arrow!*

"…indivisible, with liberty and justice for all."

I scooted onto my seat amidst the scraping of wooden chairs. Miss McKinley called out each row in turn to bring their Valentines up to the front. Craning my neck, I eyed the huge Valentine box on her desk. A large red heart, perfectly drawn, adorned each side. Into a slot on top each child stuffed his or her Valentines. I squinted. Most of them seemed to be small white rectangles – with nothing on them! *How could that be?* Mine I carefully threaded through the narrow notch, one at a time, so as not to tear the lace.

"Hurry up, Kathleen. There are other students waiting, you know." *Oh!*

After recess we hustled back into our classroom and shed our coats. *It's time! It's time!* There, on top of each desk lay a zigzag mountain of white envelopes. Our Valentines!

Oh! Were we supposed to put them inside envelopes? Nobody said… I glanced covertly to the right and left. I could see mine peeping out from several other piles. No one else's had lace…

My eyes shot back to my own desk. I picked up the first envelope and tugged at the back flap. From inside I extracted a brightly colored Minnie Mouse gazing up at a beehive, all perfectly drawn. "Bee my honey" splashed the red heart above her head. *This came from a store!*

Slowly I ripped open the others. Almost all of them featured a character or animal from a cartoon.

The boy to my left produced a loud snort. "Eeewww! What's THIS?"

I looked up. From Bobby's thumb and forefinger dangled an all-too-familiar Valentine – mine. He tossed it aside with a wrinkled nose.

"That's DUMB."

I stared down at the white smocking across my red dress and swallowed. My pile of discarded envelopes wavered back and forth before me.

"Ah, ha ha ha!"

I glanced over at Bobby without moving my head. A fully costumed cowboy twirling a lasso decked out his next card. Bobby threw back his head and roared.

Three o'clock. Up the front stoop I trudged, then stopped. In a moment I dragged my feet through the opened door. There stood Mommy, cradling the new baby, poised for news.

"How was your DAY?" she twittered.

The lump in my throat spread across my shoulders and stretched downward. I slumped onto the couch.

"Terrible!" I moaned. "Nobody liked them!"

Mommy listened to my story in silence. "Well," she said at last. "I think those children are unfortunate, because their parents forgot to teach them how to create something of their own. It's sad for them, because they haven't yet learned the joy of making something for others."

I looked up. Mommy rose from the couch and I followed. She set the sleeping baby down in the bassinette in her room; then took my hand. We sat on the edge of her bed.

"Making something for others," she continued, "is

giving someone a piece of yourself. Only YOU can give that gift – and that's why it's special. It's truly a gift from your heart."

Just then baby Timothy stirred. I stood up and peered into the bassinette. His flailing hand found my big finger and latched on. "Timmy, Timmy, Timmy," I cooed.

Suddenly I straightened. I pried open his tiny fist and darted out of the room.

"Be right back," I called.

From under my ballerina jewelry box I pulled out the lacy heart with the Big Mistake. 'TO MOMMY' I had scrawled across the top. Now I scribbled with the blue crayon over the cupid wings that had gone awry. I covered the body with fierce blue loops, as well, turning them into a blanket. Dashing back into Mommy and Daddy's room, I flourished the finished work.

"This is for you, Mommy."

We sat back down and studied it together. A large red heart lay on top of the white lace. Inside, another white heart sat, pierced by a red arrow. Above that arrow floated the smiling face in the crayon covering. I pointed to that blue bundle.

"And this is Timmy. He's your Valentine from God."

Mommy's eyes shone like stars. "Yours is the best Valentine of all."

Redial

The dismissal bell still ringing in my ears, I sauntered from the schoolyard beside freckle-faced Sally, swinging my empty lunch sack. I felt *very* important. Sally acted just like a big girl.

She kept up a steady stream of words. I grunted and tried to keep up.

"That Miss McKinley sure makes me mad!" she glowered. "She wouldn't let me eat my sandwich when I tried to take a bite. I was *so* hungry!" I nodded, wondering how I would ever have the nerve to do such a thing – *before* lunchtime!

It's so nice to have a friend… Sally played jump-rope with me at recess today! That is, she invited me to join them in the queue. I didn't know how to jump in. But she made the two rope turners stop and show me; "…in s-l-o-w motion," she had told them. *I jumped in on my second try! Oh, it was so much fun! Anyway, Sally is nice… Oh! Wasn't that my street?* I glanced back at the road we had just crossed… *That's okay. I'm a big girl now, too! I wonder where Sally lives? I'll just walk a little bit farther with her…*

Sally jerked her head at me. "Where do you live?"

"Oh…on Insley Street."

"But we already passed it!"

"Oh – did we? It's okay. I'll walk you to your house."

Sally smiled at me – then continued on. I did a double skip. Suddenly I felt myself floating in mid-air, delicious space all around me. No longer was I accountable to anybody. I was free to be! *On my own!* With heady delight, ignoring the tiny red flash nagging me from within, I hastened after Sally.

She stopped in front of a white picket fence. "This is it!" Sally strolled up the driveway and around to the back. I followed.

"You want to come inside?"

"Um...no..." A tiny voice deep within me rose just above a whisper. *"Kathleen? Kathleen?"*

I eyed the backyard with its velvet lawn, newly green, snow gone at last... A sandbox lay in the corner! And a tricycle sat ready and waiting.

"Maybe we could play outside for a little while?" I ventured.

"Well...okay, but let me tell my mom I'm home."

I shifted from one foot to another. I wished she hadn't said that.

Sally ducked inside while I played with the back-gate latch, opening and closing the bolt. The voice inside me grew alarmingly loud. I whirled my body back and forth and hummed, "Playmate, come out and play with me..."

Sally hopped down from the porch stoop. Relieved, I raced towards her. "Can I ride your tricycle?"

"Oh, sure – but it's not mine," she shrugged. "It's my little brother's. I have a four-wheeler."

I straddled the seat and grasped the rubber handlebars. Multi-colored ribbons sailed off them in the breeze as I pedaled. *Wheeee!* Sally sat on the stoop, chin in hand, and watched me.

"What's a four-wheeler?" I called out.

"You know – a bicycle with training wheels."

"Training wheels?"

"Yeah. Little bitty ones next to the big one in the back."

"Oh..." No...I didn't know. But I didn't want her to know that. I circled round and round the cement loop, my feet pumping up and down – *I'm a spinning top!*

All of a sudden, an echo burst inside my head. *"Where*

are you, where are you, WHERE ARE YOU?!" I slammed to a dead stop.

"Oh!"

"What's wrong?"

"Uh…I think I have to go home now." Regretfully, I swung my leg back over the tricycle seat.

"But maybe I could come over again sometime and we could play in your sandbox -?" *I didn't know you could have one in your own backyard!*

"Sure, okay," she shrugged. "Bye!" Sally tramped up the steps and disappeared into her house. I scuttled around to the front.

Now the red flash pulsated and pricked my brain. *"You're late! You're late!"* I stumbled forward even faster…

Is this Insley Street? Which way? Suddenly the lack of safety net sharpened and stared me down. I studied the houses in either direction. I swallowed. Never in all my walks to school had I paid attention to the route. I always had Karen to march before me. But Karen went home sick today. I stood still and shut my eyes. "Which way?" I whispered. I opened them and pointed. *This way…* I willed it to be, and scurried onward. *Ah ha!* The familiar cocker spaniel trotted behind the fenced-off yard on my right…

"Where have you BEEN?!" Mommy's voice shrilled. No chance to slip inside the house unseen. There she stood, scanning the road before her.

"I – I…" She swooped down and prodded me up the front steps.

"Inside, inside!" she admonished. At last she halted in my bedroom.

"Now tell me – what happened?"

"I – I…walked home from school with Sally…I …just wanted to see where she lived…and…and I …forgot what time it was..." I faltered.

"You walked home with Sally? Who's Sally? Don't you know you're supposed to come straight home after school?!" She wheeled about, grabbed my gold-backed hairbrush from the dresser and swatted me on the bottom: *whack, whack, whack, whack.*

Ow! I stared up in shock. My chest squeezed tight, then exploded. *Mmwaaahhh...* I stood, hands at my sides, alone and unfriended, my face wet and runny.

Mommy leaned down and wrapped her arm around my shoulders. "I was very worried," she murmured. "Something could've happened to you. What would I do without my little girl?"

"I'm s-sorry," I sniffed.

"All right." She straightened up. "I want you to stay in your room till dinnertime and think about it."

I thought about it all right; I thought about that delicious feeling of slipping away to a friend's house, all by myself – to play and do as I wish.

That evening after dinner I asked Mommy what our telephone number was. "I know our address," I said, "but Miss McKinley said we should also memorize our telephone number. In case we get lost, or...or... something else happens..."

"She's absolutely right about that," nodded Mommy. "You can always tell a policeman, and he will help you find your way home."

She wrote it down for me on a piece of notepad paper. I studied it, rereading it on my bed several times. But what if I forget it? Just to be sure, I folded the scrap into a tiny wad and stuffed it inside my jacket pocket.

I had a plan.

Next day after school I hustled down the now-familiar route home. *Good thing Karen's still sick. I'm glad I don't have to explain anything.* Once in front of my house,

I sped up on dread-filled toes and whispered past. I glanced back. All clear. No one waiting yet. I skipped the rest of the way down the sidewalk, past old Mr. Wall's house, past Janice's house, to the corner. That's as far as I was allowed. There stood Andy Drake's large brick home. I marched up to the front door and knocked. The door creaked open.

"Is Andy home yet?"

"Why, yes, he is," Mrs. Drake's eyebrows flew up. "Kathleen is it?"

"Yes. Can he play?"

Andy's blond head popped up above the banister behind her.

"Yeah. C'mon in," he called.

Andy was an "atheist." He told me all about it the day I said I was Catholic and asked him what religion he was. I had never heard of that religion, and I'm sure he made it up, just to tease me. He couldn't answer right when I asked, "Well, then, who made the sky? Who made the dogs and cats? Who made the people – like Adam and Eve?" But I decided not to make him feel like I won, so I changed the subject, and we played horseshoes instead.

Today he said, "Hey, you wanna play cards? I know how to play Crazy Eights."

"Uh – okay," I stalled. "But first I have to call my mommy and tell her where I am."

Mrs. Drake led me down the hall to a little table in the corner with the big black telephone on top. Thankfully, she turned and left me alone. My hands shook a little, my fingers tingling, as I reached inside my jacket pocket and pulled out the crumpled up wad. I spread the paper until it lay smooth and waiting. BE-9-3247. I breathed a sigh of relief. It was all there. I raised my head and eagerly reached for the phone.

I stopped. *What do I do?* Numbers and letters stared back at me set inside tiny circles in a crazy wheel pattern. They wrapped around the front of the phone in almost a complete circle. I gaped at them. No longer familiar, they glared back, black and unmovable. How do I do the number? I peered back down the hall towards the entry. Mrs. Drake had disappeared. *Darn!* I chewed my lip. But, no…I couldn't ask her, anyhow. Then she would think I was a baby. *Why didn't Mommy show me how to get the phone to work with the numbers?* My eyes finally dropped from that ridiculous circle and slid down to my shoes. I stood there. At last, I sucked in a deep breath and shoved it out through my toes. I trudged around the entry till I spotted Mrs. Drake at the kitchen sink.

"My mommy says I have to go home now," I muttered.

"Oh. Well, Andy will be disappointed," Mrs. Drake cocked her head. "But come back another time."

I nodded. Suddenly the room seemed huge around me. Mrs. Drake grew infinitely tall.

Without a word, I stepped out the opened front door and headed for home. …

Maybe I wasn't so big, after all.

Grandmamma

The Odyssey

"You be a good girl, now," Mommy murmured with a tight squeeze.

Impatiently I nodded, returning the peck on the lips: one, two, three - and slid off the vinyl car seat onto the curb. I glanced back once – to see four little faces peering at me, noses pressed against the station wagon windows.

"Hurry, Kathleen!" Grandmamma urged, grabbing my hand. "A train waits for no man – nor little girl, either." A compact woman with purposefully penciled eyebrows and a cap of auburn hair, my grandmother minced no words.

I trotted after her, lugging my lumpy canvas bag. All

of a sudden, we emerged onto the platform, with people yanking luggage as they stumbled past us through the cavernous space. *Psssssst!* A huge cloud of steam issued forth from the Black Iron Steed. I stopped short and stared. A prickly thrill raced through my bones. My first big adventure away from home!

A tug on my arm zapped me back.

"Up you go, my girl!" Grandmamma prodded. I struggled to hoist my belongings up those huge metal steps.

"All aboard!" A man in blue shouted, big brass buttons fairly bursting off his chest. I scrambled upward and slipped – *kaboom!* – on the last step. With a wink and a twinkle, he leaned down and scooped me back up.

"Ain't no fire, Miss. Just a train."

As we bumped along the aisle between faltering passengers, Grandmamma bent her face down close to my ear.

"Remember, now, Kathleen. You are FOUR years old today – and don't say anything more," she warned.

I bristled with annoyance and glared at her.

"You want to go see Auntie Hal and Uncle Eli, don't you?" she insinuated.

I sighed and jerked my head. *Everyone* always *mistakes me for a BABY. I'm six and a half. It's not fair to say I'm four!* But I knew better than to argue with Grandmamma. If I wanted to go on this trip with her, it had to be for *free* or not at all.

I settled into the enormous tweed seat by the window and peered out. To and fro the last stragglers leapt past.

Chugga, chugga, chugga, chugga.... We were off!

Rummaging in the outer pocket of my satchel, I pulled out three books: all *"Flicka, Ricka and Dicka."* *Which one?...* Ah, the triplets on the farm! Soon the iron and steel around me faded away and I flowed into a new world of wonder.

"My goodness, can that child READ?!" A sharp voice broke into my reverie. Before I could reply, my stern guardian leaned across the aisle and jumped in.

"Oh, yes, it's amazing what she can do for a four-year old. But after all, her father graduated from Stanford. He's a doctor now, you know, at Walter Reed Army Hospital," she professed proudly.

Inwardly I cringed. *I'm six and a half!* My body screamed inside. Instead, I smiled under my lowered lids and hastened back to the picnicking girls in the barnyard. Never mind....

"Cleveland!" the conductor called out. *We're here!* Excitedly stuffing my books and crayons into their slots, I jittered forward on the slowly braking machine.

There on the platform waved a jiggly man and a beaming woman. Auntie Hal enfolded me within her frail arms, her sparkling hazel eyes dancing across my face.

"My dear, I'm so happy to see you!" Fine gray curls fell about her heart-shaped face. My godmother, Grandmamma's sister, she always made me feel special in a world of continuously emerging babies.

Uncle Eli, a plump man with crinkly eyes, a long, slender nose and a slash of a mouth, nodded affably. Bundled into their old Cadillac, we tootled off...

One whole week without *'MikePatJulieTimmy'* everywhere in sight! White lace doilies on the chair arms, pretty bird statues on the coffee table, no baby toys....everything in its place. I sighed, satisfied.

Next morning, light streamed through the guest room window, prodding me awake. "Rise and shine, Kathleen!" Grandmamma's hand shook my covers. With a start, I leaped out of bed. *Today's the day I eat at Uncle Eli's restaurant!*

Hand in hand with Grandmamma, I tripped my way

through the open glass door. "Weaver's Restaurant," in bold blue letters, blazed across the front window.

"Good morning, young lady!" a soft voice greeted me. *Auntie Hal!* With a gentle hand she sat me in a large, wooden chair before a blue and white checkered tabletop.

"No need to give you a menu today," she smiled. "Uncle Eli has prepared something special in your honor." Without warning, a jumble of faces materialized, surrounding the table: two women in white lacey caps and aprons, Auntie Hal, Grandmamma, and a white-jacketed man in a tall chef's hat. Uncle Eli! Bowing low, he flourished a large, white platter in front of me.

"For the little lady of the house," he announced. There on my plate lay the biggest 'Gingerbread Man' I had ever seen. Only it was a pancake man! Two blueberries for eyes and a string of them for a mouth, he stared wildly up at me. People in booths close by ceased chatting and watched, curious. My skin vibrated. Grandmamma prodded me with a bony finger.

"Well?" she queried.

The room grew hot. Faces leered closer, forming an unbroken circle around me. All held their breath, waiting. I cleared my throat, swallowed, and opened my mouth. They leaned closer.

"One leg's shorter than the other," I blurted.

A gasp. A titter. A guffaw from the booth. The circle stepped back. My eyes barely wavered from the 'man' in question. Slowly the plate eased up and out of sight.

Uncle Eli bowed and smiled. "I will fix that for you, Madam," he murmured.

Thankfully the circle disappeared and did not return. Only Grandmamma, who sank, scandalized, into the chair opposite me, remained.

Moments later, the plate reappeared with a *new*

pancake man on board. I studied it carefully. Each leg perfectly matched the other. I tilted my head back and smiled at Uncle Eli.

"Thank you."

Wide-open mornings at 'home' spread before me while I pattered after Auntie Hal in her fastidious daily routine. Content, then, to leave me to my realm of reading, she dusted and puttered around me.

That is, until her friend Marion bustled through the entranceway.

A large woman with a kindly face, Marion chattered away, exclaiming over my big eyes one moment and criticizing the preacher's sermon the next.

But she could braid! *Oohing* and *ahhing* over the angel-fine softness, she wove her fingers through my wispy brown locks. Without missing a beat, Marion briskly braided my hair while I absorbed the music of her voluptuous voice. Once finished, she whirled me about and whisked me in front of the hallway mirror. *Oh, what a cute little girl!* I turned this way and that. Never before had I seen braids that could crawl tightly all the way up along each side of the head. Mommy never did that. It was the most beautiful hairdo I had ever seen! That night, and the next, I refused to let Grandmamma, or even gentle Auntie Hal, undo the vision of beauty.

Three days later Marion paid another visit. With a gasp and a chuckle, she gazed upon my telltale head. It boasted a fuzzy field of stickers with a furry branch angling away from each cheek.

"Would you like me to re-braid it for you?" she asked. I nodded, my shame melting into ecstasy.

That night after dinner the radio interrupted the big band music with a blaring weather report. Auntie Hal swooped up our dessert dishes and announced,

"It's down to the cellar for us, honey. A cyclone's coming."

A cyclone! Was that like what happened to Dorothy in the Wizard of Oz? No, I was told. That was a tornado. Disappointed, I followed down the narrow, steep steps into the basement.

A complete second living room surfaced; large couch, two chairs, a big television set. But no windows. I curled up on the rug while we all watched "I Love Lucy." Moments later, seeing that they were glued to the set, I crept noiselessly up the stairs… but they caught on to me. I only wanted to take a peek out the window! We couldn't even hear the wind downstairs.

Next day we learned Mr. Carson on the corner had half his roof blow off. Now *that* was exciting!

My sojourn slipped languidly by with reading, playing fetch with Lulu, the black poodle, and trips to the restaurant. One day I discovered two brothers, Mark and John, who lived right behind the eatery. We chased each other late into the evening.

"Let's play tag!" Mark whooped.

"You're it!" John yelled back.

Gleefully, we fanned through the parking lot. Weaving my way in and out of the rows of cars, I gained speed and raced for "home" – the side wall of the building.

Uh, oh. My back prickled. I glanced behind. Mark was gaining on me. His face contorted. He yelled something I couldn't understand. *Huh?*

BAM! The night flashed white. I tumbled in a heap on the pavement beside a parked car. My eye had made close contact with its tail fin.

The side door of the restaurant flew open and Auntie Hal tore out. I stared up at her furrowed brow as she carefully pressed my face with her fingers.

Grandmamma appeared from behind, and the two of them carried me down the street to the house.

"How many times have you been told not to run in a parking lot?!" Grandmamma exclaimed. "Land's sake! And in the dark, too! You could've been *killed.*"

Stretched out along the length of the couch, I tentatively touched my cheek. *Ow!*

"There, there, now," Auntie Hal soothed. "We're going to get a nice piece of steak for you." She motioned to Grandmamma, and pointed to the kitchen beyond.

I moaned. I certainly didn't feel hungry now! A moment later Grandmamma arrived, cradling a huge hunk of red flesh. Without warning, she raised it towards my face till it blocked out all sight of her. *What?!* She pushed it right onto my eye! I wriggled away in alarm.

"It's all right, Kathleen. This will help it to feel better."

I sank back against the sofa.

Grandmamma chuckled. "You'll have a real shiner there tomorrow. *Ooo-wee!* Wait till your mama sees that."

A black eye! Wow! Suddenly it didn't hurt so much. I smiled to myself. *I only heard of boys getting black eyes before. Wait till I show Mark and John.* I snuggled down into the springy cushions as Auntie Hal stroked my head.

"Are you homesick?" she queried.

Home. Sick. I pondered the new word. *I guess I'm sick – same as I would be if I were home."* Slowly I nodded. She patted my hand.

"Don't you worry. I know you miss your Mommy and Daddy. We can put you and your Grandmamma on a train first thing tomorrow morning – and you'll be home in no time."

I jolted up. *No, I was wrong! I didn't mean that! Oh! Don't make me go home yet! I made a mistake!* My heart pumped in staccato fashion.

"Would you like that?" Auntie Hal asked.

"No!" I squeaked. "I like it here!"

"Ah," she smiled. "Let's settle you down, then." With a tug and a tuck, she cozied me up like a cocoon. *Close call! I better not answer any more questions like that!*

Three days later I did catch that train, right on schedule. Grandmamma and I plopped down on the platform in Silver Spring with our array of goods.

"Hurray!" someone shouted.

There waved a dimpled man with a toddler on his shoulders and two small boys hanging onto his belt. A jubilant woman juggling a bobbing infant reached out her free arm to me.

"Mommy! Daddy!" I dropped my satchel and skimmed up the platform to kisses and hugs. Boy, it felt good to be home!

Mike, Mommy, Timmy, Cathay, Julie, Pat

105

Mom, Aunt Mary, Timmy and Julie

Mommy, Mike and Pat

Deal Breaker

"Climb down here with me, Kathleen. I want to show you something." Andy Drake gestured towards his neighbor's basement stairwell. I leaned over the wrought-iron railing and peered down into the narrow abyss.

"Okay." *What could be down there? Maybe some sort of treasure he hid under a rock?* I followed him down the steep steps. At the bottom Andy turned to face me.

"If you show me yours, I'll show you mine," he blurted.

Huh? I stared at him, my feet straddling a drain. "My what?" *Does he think I have a treasure too?*

"*You* know." He glanced down at my shorts. *What did he mean?*

"You mean a treasure?" I squeaked, confused.

"Well…" he shrugged. "Not exactly."

I cocked my head. "I don't have any pockets."

He snorted. "If you take off your clothes, I'll take off mine."

Just then a shout rang out from above. I gazed

skyward. Three faces squinted down at us over the handrail: Karen, six-year-old Janice, and Andy's friend Rick.

"Do it! Do it!" Rick crowed. All three of them took up the chant.

I turned back and raised my chin. "Okay…"

Andy planted his feet apart, arms folded, and leaned against the wall. "Go on," he encouraged.

"You have to, too," I reminded him.

"I know. You first."

I glanced up and caught Karen's eye. "C'mon, Kathleen!" she grinned.

Slowly I peeled off my tee shirt and hugged the bundle to my chest.

"Okay, drop it."

I let go and stared back at Andy.

"Keep going," he prodded.

Biting my lip, I tugged at the elastic band of my seersucker shorts and wriggled out of them, my underpants bunched up inside. I tossed them down and watched them land without a whisper. I could feel his eyes and glanced up. But Andy's gaze had already passed down my chest and riveted below my bellybutton.

A cheer rose from above. "Yay, Kathleen!" All three repeated the chorus.

I swallowed and tossed my head.

"*Your* turn, Andy."

But before he made a move, an outraged cry filled the sky. We jerked our heads upward. The distorted face of Janice's mother grimaced down at us. *Oh no!*

"What in heaven's name are you DOING?!" she shrieked.

Andy took one bug-eyed look at me and tore up the cement steps. Evading her grasp, he disappeared from view.

"Get your clothes back on, Kathleen!" the voice thundered.

I didn't need any encouragement. With fervor I tugged on my rumpled shorts and yanked my tee shirt back over my head. Inwardly I glowered at Andy. *It's so unfair! I did* my *part of the bargain! He should've had to do his!* I trudged up the steps, feeling cheated.

As I tried to sidle past Mrs. Miller, she grabbed me by the shoulders and squinted into my face.

"You go home this instant and tell your mother what you did!" she hissed.

I looked away. "Yes ma'am, " I muttered. *Of course I won't!* Still, she did not let me go.

"Because if you don't, I WILL!" she spat between her teeth. I wrenched away and spun around.

"I will! I will!" I screeched over my shoulder, secretly imploring her not to tell, while I sped homeward.

I breathed a sigh of relief as I slipped through the front door and surveyed the family scene. Mommy bustled about the kitchen, preparing supper, while baby Timmy gargled Gerber turkey in his high chair. Mike and Pat lay stretched across the living room floor, glued to *The Lone Ranger.* Quickly I sought out Julie in our room and offered to read *Mother Goose* to her. Everything normal. I relaxed...

That is, until the doorbell rang.

Mommy pulled open the screen door. "Why, hello, Mrs. Miller!"

I stiffened; then scurried into the hallway just out of sight from the front door.

"Did Kathleen tell you what she did today?" The disembodied words darted in, unannounced. Janice's mother's eyes roved around the doorframe till they caught up with mine. I leaped from the hallway.

"Yes!" I squeaked. "Yes! It's okay!" *Now go away! Go*

away! I shut my eyes and whisked her out the door in my mind. But Mommy's voice blazed them open.

"Why, no!" she lilted. "I don't remember anything...?"

Mrs. Miller barged right through the open doorway, spilling into OUR living room.

"Well!" she began. "I discovered *your* daughter at the bottom of a basement stairwell with Andy Drake – COMPLETEY *naked!*" Her voice rose in a whisper that bounced off the walls and kept on ringing. All sound sucked out of the room. I stopped breathing. At last Mommy cleared her throat.

"Thank you, Mrs. Miller," she enunciated. "I will speak to Kathleen about it. Good night." With a firm thrust she bolted the door... then turned around. Her inquiring eyes sought mine.

"Kathleen," she said slowly. "Would you like to tell me about it?" *No... !*

I studied the intricate swirls in the worn Oriental rug. My foot traced the dizzying loops while my voice followed them. "Andy...just...wanted...to see...what I looked like..." My words trailed off.

Mommy's eyes popped out. "Why?"

"I don't know..." Suddenly I felt confused. She gave me that knowing look.

"Darling," she began. "There's no need for that. Everyone looks just the same. There's nothing to see."

My head jerked up. *What's wrong with Mommy?* I *knew* that was not true. Didn't I have three *brothers?* Well, she might've fooled Andy Drake with that one – after all, he was an "only child." But I knew better.

Now it was my turn to give her a knowing smile.

"Okay." I tilted my head a moment; then ambled down the hall towards my room.

Suddenly I felt sorry for Andy. I didn't need to see

Andy naked. He would look just the same as Mike and Pat. And baby Timmy. Nothing new about that.

My hand on the doorknob, I stopped short.

…But he would've always wondered about girls *– if* I *hadn't helped him out!*

Comeuppance

"Hail Mary, full of grace...."

My first bout with Catholic school education took some getting used to. St. John's Grammar School posed a radical departure from the public domain.

"Blessed art thou amongst women...."

One rainy gray afternoon after lunch found me in typical position: standing next to my desk in the back row of the second grade classroom, ramrod posture, beads in hand. The chanting murmur of uniformed boys and girls echoed around me.

Bored, I glanced down at my feet. My shoe was untied. *Hmmm. Shall I bend down now or wait till after the rosary?* I nudged Patsy, the girl next to me.

"Look at my shoe," I whispered.

She glanced down. "Don't trip."

Suddenly she tittered, "What if I tied them together?"

I stuck my tongue out at her and grinned.

"I wish I had your shoes," I muttered under my breath, eyeing her Mary Janes.

Without warning, an irrepressible bubble lurched upwards from my chest, banging insistently, dangerously close to my throat. Unable to control it any longer, my lips parted ever so slightly as I succumbed to an attack of the giggles.

Patsy soon joined in.

"Hey – let's trade for a day!" she chortled. Quickly we crouched down on the cold linoleum and began removing our shoes. The rest of the world faded away as we dove into our brilliant exchange game.

"Maybe we could wear them home tonight," I whispered, with a longing glance.

"Yeah!"

We busied ourselves about the task at hand, absorbed in buckles and laces.

All of a sudden a long, dark wall interrupted my gaze. Beneath it two ebony shoes pointed straight at me. Slowly, my eyes rose up along that vertical expanse of impenetrable black, only to meet the visage of Sister Mary Margaret, surrounded by crinoline.

"Patsy McCoy and Kathleen Gunn!" she thundered. "What in the name of Jesus, Mary and Joseph are you doing?!"

The rest of the room crystallized into view. Fifty pairs of eyeballs stared in horror, mouths gaping beneath.

Uh oh.

I felt the heat rise in my face, burning my cheeks as my breathing shot to a halt, everything on hold. The room began to vibrate menacingly, with a *wong-wong* beat. You could have heard a pin drop. *Why doesn't anyone say something?!* About half a century later, the thundercloud face leered down dangerously close to mine.

"Would you like to tell your mother about this, or shall I?"

"I will," I squeaked.

"Just to be sure, I will write her a note," she trilled in her Irish brogue. "In the meantime, both of you girls will keep your feet exactly as they are now for the rest of the day."

I stared down at the culprits in question. Patsy wore one of my shoes and one of her own. I had only one shoe on – hers.

"But – "

"Recess time!" she announced, marching to the front.

Patsy and I exchanged glances. The rain had stopped, but the schoolyard was reduced to puddles.

"My sock!" I whispered in alarm. Patsy 'zipped' her lip with an imaginary key and gestured covertly towards the teacher.

Sister MM stood guard at the outside door, already ushering out the unusually quiet students. I hesitated at the threshold, eyes peering upward at Sister. With a firm prod in the back, she commanded, "Out!"

I loitered on the cement stoop just outside the door, while Patsy, out of sympathy, returned repeatedly to my 'home base' to offer moral support. Wistfully I gazed out at girls swinging the giant jump rope: "Mabel, Mabel, set the table. Don't forget the red...hot...peppers!" A maze of rivulets lay between us.

Once inside again, I hunkered down at my desk in the back until Sister MM frowned and marched towards me. With a sweeping gesture of her long black sleeve, she compelled Patsy and me to our feet.

"You two will sit up in front of the room facing the

class, so we can all see who disturbed our rosary today."

The afternoon wore on interminably. Faces lifted ever so slightly, one by one, as boys and girls sneaked curious glances at us. One boy, Kevin, began snickering comments to his desk buddy, Jimmy.

"Kevin Baker!" Sister glowered. "You have talked one time too many! Come up to the front!"

To our amazement, the long-threatened punishment for garrulous behavior came to be. Quite determinedly, our teacher placed several large strips of masking tape across his mouth.

"Now, back to your seat!"

At long last, the 3:00 bell rang. Freedom!

"Not so fast!" the 'sergeant' called out. "Kathleen and Patsy will stay behind to complete a disciplinary assignment. You will write 'I will not disturb our classroom rosary again' one hundred times before you leave here today."

Panic set in. *What will Mommy think when I'm not outside when she comes?!* My protests were to no avail. Feverishly I scribbled with heated pencil and sinking heart. Now I would *have* to explain the whole sordid affair.

Tick, tick, tick... Only the methodical clicking of the large wall clock broke the silence.

At long last, I stood up and shakily handed my paper to Sister. She nodded curtly, observing my work.

"You may go." She relinquished the missing shoe.

Mommy's brow furrowed as I flew down the sidewalk, shoelace flapping in the breeze.

"What happened?" she cried.

I sobbed the whole story out, but refrained from admitting exactly WHAT ACTIVITY I had interrupted with my behavior. She eyed me carefully a moment.

"Never mind," she said. "I know you will never do

that again."

I nodded vigorously, eager to put it behind me.

The next Saturday Patsy arrived for a specially requested play date. Her mother dropped her off with her bundle at our front door.

Excitedly I ushered Patsy into my bedroom.

"Ok," I exulted, "Let's play school!"

Patsy knew the routine, as we had mentally rehearsed our plan all week.

"I'll be the teacher first," I declared. My supplies were ready.

My chum retrieved her schoolbook from her satchel and sat at my makeshift desk and chair.

"Class, I want you to turn to page fourteen in your reader," I mimicked.

Patsy opened her book and trilled, "La, la, la," while gazing all around the bedroom. I drew myself up into all thirty-nine inches of me. With raised arms I swooped down on my 'student' and yanked her out of the seat. She began to giggle.

"You think this is funny, Patsy McCoy?!" I glowered.

She shook her head. I carefully peeled the scotch tape off my roll and slapped it across her mouth. Her eyes widened as I pressed layer after layer across the offending aperture. At last I stepped back and surveyed my handiwork. A smile of satisfaction spread throughout my entire body.

And the next Monday at school, upon entering Sister Mary Margaret's classroom, I felt the surge of power that came with wearing *her* shoes.

The Spell

WHOOSH! I bolted upright in my twin bed, eyes
wide open. Familiar shadows spread around me. But
something felt different. It was no longer Christmas Eve.
It was almost Christmas morning!

I listened. Rhythmical breathing flowed from the
bed opposite. Julie. Cautiously I lowered first one leg,
then the other over the side of the bed. Creeping ever
so silently across the rug, I reached for the edge of the
door. With a quick glance over my shoulder, I slipped
into the long grayness unfolding before me. I turned a
corner. Gradually shapes appeared: living room couch
on the left, a lamp, the big overstuffed chair... and
against the window, imperceptibly waving a branch at
me was my secret friend.... the Christmas tree! My heart
leapfrogged. *Dare I venture forth?*

Suddenly a warm hand grabbed my arm. I jerked
back with a start.

"Cathay?" a small voice quavered.

"Mike!" I admonished. "Why aren't you in bed?!"

The four-year-old's eyes gleamed. *"You're* not in bed...."

"Ok, ok." I relaxed, feeling in cahoots with my little brother.

Taking his hand I led him through the murk around the protruding coffee table... to the Entrance of Magic. A thrill zinged up my spine. The tree seemed to wink at me, opening its arms to display its goods in the pale moonlight. Mike and I bent down and carefully fingered the wrapped boxes. Tons of them lay tumbled on top of each other everywhere!

"Too bad we can't turn on the light," I murmured.

"Why not?" piped up Mike.

"Someone might *see* us!"

Suddenly, a shimmer of light caught my eye. Tucked back under the tree behind the packages on the left glimmered the most amazing apparition I had ever seen.

Not daring to believe my limited vision, I whispered, "Mike! Let's look at just one!"

I stretched over the heap and lifted up a delicate structure crowned by a puff of white. Then I darted over to the nightlight on the dining room wall. Mike followed. I set the gift on the rug beneath the golden glow and we huddled closer. A tiny fairy tree fashioned out of real branches stood its ground. Nestled on top was a fluffy cloud of cotton. I fully expected an elf to peer through at any moment. Something shiny glistened in the pale light. I leaned closer. Silver dimes dangled from various branches.

"It's a money tree!" I whispered wondrously. My hands shaking, I carefully turned it around. There on the back was a tag.

I read it aloud: "To Mike. From Santa." Slowly I raised my eyes and gazed at my little brother with newfound respect. *What a magical gift!*

We each cradled the treasure in turn, twirling it softly to watch the dimes dance and shine in the fairy light.

At last, with regret, I nudged Mike. "We'd better go back now; before someone else wakes up."

We lay the miniature tree under its parent, and crept silently into the waning night with our secret.

Tonsillectomy

Every decade boasts its medical fads; the 1950's ushered in the "cure-all" tonsillectomy. One too many ear infections and a subsequent hearing loss earned me a ticket on that ride.

I fidgeted back and forth in the sterile steel medical chair. Gargantuan gray 'earmuffs' squeezed my head, like two magnets irresistibly drawn to each other. A white-haired nurse in matching uniform tilted her head at me.

"Now remember, honey," she bleated, "raise your hand on the same side as the tone you hear. Keep it up the entire time you hear it."

I waited. I strained as hard as I could, but no tiny sound entered my ear. "Where is it?" I finally asked.

The nurse stepped in front of me and leaned into my face. "Little girl," she glared, "Are you playin' with me?"

What does she mean?! "N-no," I whimpered.

"I showed you what they sounded like," she eyed me. "You're not paying attention."

"Yes, I am! I don't hear anything!"

She frowned and pursed her lips. "Then we will keep doing it until you do."

Clutching Mommy's hand, I treaded nervously beside her down the huge hospital corridor. Nearly blinded by the White, I squeezed my lids a moment; white walls, white hats, white uniforms stiffly starched, ready to walk off without the wearer. All too soon, we approached 'The Room.' I peered around Mommy's skirts. To my surprise, it was filled with five beds! All for children! Janet greeted me from her bed by the window.

"I'm ten years old," she stated importantly. "And I'm the oldest one in here." She introduced me to Betty-with-the-comic-books, age eight, in the bed next to her, and quiet Jane, age seven (like me!) along the opposite side of the room. Sally, 'the baby,' (who was three) she indicated with a dismissive gesture. My bed was smack in the middle, opposite the doorway. *Maybe this won't be so bad....* I was right; after a kiss goodbye from Mommy, I unpacked my suitcase of books and became the instant hit with *Little Red-Haired Witch's first Day at School* and other stories. We swapped them around, along with Betty's comic books.

"Lights out! " boomed an authoritative voice. All too soon, we lay in wait of the night, whispering our fears and rumors about the impending operation. "...Do they put that big plunger over your face..."

Next morning a nurse wheeled me down the long corridor into a HUGE refrigerator. I shivered uncontrollably until someone laid nice, warm blankets - fresh from the oven! – on top of me. A masked crusader stuck a needle in my arm: "Count backwards!"

But I never got a chance...

Beep, beep, beep.

My head is fuzzy... Someone is plastering a giant stethoscope over my heart with great strips of white tape...

The room seemed to be slowly sinking as I gradually rose to the top. It swiveled to a stop. Carefully I opened an eye. A large face peered over the bed rail, grinning at me. *It's Daddy!* But I couldn't quite see all of him... *There's something in the way of my eye...* I reached up and felt my face. *That patch! It's on my eye!*

121

"Daddy!" I burst out. "They put a big patch over a stethoscope on my heart – but now it's on my *eye!*"

"Not to worry," he soothed. Later he informed me a corner of the bedsheet scratched my eyeball during the operation, and they covered it up to protect it. Small comfort as I now had to contend with blurred vision in addition to a smoldering sore throat!

Some of the rumors were *not* true. We did *not* get "all the ice cream we can eat, *any* time we want." ONCE only, did they bring me a brick of vanilla ice cream. That was it. Somehow, I decided, the shape of that brick made it less appetizing. And that pale yellow. *Couldn't they have brought chocolate? Or strawberry?*

The day crawled by in a haze, with the burn in my throat that began as a smolder quickly raging into a fierce forest fire. *No reading today…*

The next morning burst on the scene with a flurry of activity: nurses coming and going with last minute thermometers and bowls of gruel, followed by suitcases snapping shut on the hospital hiatus. Chatters of hello and goodbye filled the air as, one by one, parents arrived to bundle their little patient and baggage together and out the door, homeward bound. All but me. Soon the room increased in size; the sounds dissipated, with the occasional noise seeming strange and echoing. *How white the walls are!* I could see down the hallway (with my one good eye) the nurses still bustling back and forth.

Abruptly two of them strode into the room. They stopped short.

"What?! You haven't been picked up yet?!" The redhead exclaimed.

"I'm sorry, honey, but you can't stay here," the curly blonde remarked. "We need the bed."

The redhead rolled her eyes, irritated. "Just get her a different bed."

Curly-Locks pushed little Sally's high-railed bed over and thrust out her arms for me. Reluctantly I made the change. *A crib! It's a crib!*

Without a word, Curly-Locks heaved, and the bed charged out the doorway and down the hall, with me in it. *Where are we going?* A creeping cold finger snaked up my legs and arms, and seized my chest. Nothing was familiar. The din echoed through the corridor, as the wheels churned in rhythm with the elevator bells and nurses' chatter. All of a sudden, we angled into a deserted room, huge and white, with no other beds. We stopped. Prattling amongst themselves, the two nurses disappeared, without another glance in my direction. Their voices slowly retreated down the hall.

I am alone. No one knows where I am. Why is Mommy not here? All the other girls left ages ago.

"*Mmmm-uhhHHHHHhh.*" An ominous moan invaded my ear. *It's coming from the doorway… the room opposite. It – it looks like a torture chamber!* A woman 'floated,' tied up – her limbs extended – over a bed, with nothing on but a bit of sheet dangling off her. No one paid the slightest heed. The sounds grew louder, becoming unearthly. Finally a nurse darted in there, murmured something about "burns," and disappeared again.

Where am I?! This is not like the place I came to have my operation! My heart pounded; my sore throat raged. I scrambled for my book, half-hidden in the sheets. I tore it open to my bookmark and stared, unseeing, at the page. My eye watered furiously, angry at having its mate covered. The words blurred. *I can't even read.* Hot tears welled up under the bandage. I swallowed. My mind struggled to repel the hideous thought now leering up at me. Suddenly it danced in my face: How *will Mommy know where to find me?! I'm not in the right room, and if she happens to pass by this one, I'll just look like a baby in this crib, with a strange patch on its eye!* The room screamed *White* at me now. The noise was deafening…

A whirlwind of color flew through the doorway. In a blur, it loomed closer and swiveled into focus. Dark wavy hair, wild eyes matching my own, searched me out with a cry. *Mommy came!* Rushed words about a train, Grandmamma's friend Aunt Mary arriving late; waiting, waiting at the station.

Waiting, waiting. Two separate worlds. Waiting apart, not knowing. Not knowing.

Mike, Cathay, Pat

Midsummer

"Paddy caught a toad!" shrieked Mike.

I glanced up from my hopscotch lines, chalk in hand. On the other side of Insley Street, five-year-old Mike hopped up and down.

"Where is he?" I shouted. Mike pointed towards the neighbor's house behind him. I could see a smaller figure crouched beside the cement basement stairwell. He straightened himself and shambled towards the curb, hands cupped close to his chest.

"Bring it, bring it, Pat!" I hollered. The four-year-old shuffled back across the street with his precious cargo. At last on our side, he dared look up, eyes shining.

"I *got* it!"

He stopped beside me and cracked open his fingers to give a quick peek. Blinking balefully up at me sat the ugliest brown lump of bumps I had ever seen.

"*Wow*, Pat! That's a GIANT frog!"

"Not a frog!" retorted Patrick. "It's a *toad!*"

"Ohhh…" Sensing something special, I stepped back and allowed him to march importantly into the house before me.

"Mommy, Mommy!" he cried.

Soon 'Lumpy' was outfitted with a name, an oatmeal box home, and orders to remain outdoors. Patrick complied. Mike and I followed behind him up the sidewalk like the Pied Piper.

"Can we count his bumps?" I asked.

Patrick glowered at me. "No! I have to take him for a walk!" With a burst of speed, he scurried ahead, his bare feet spinning.

All of a sudden the gravel-colored lump flew up before his face – and down on the sidewalk in front of him. But Pat's feet had already begun bicycling so fast to get away from me that they helplessly continued their rotation. I stared in horror as his bare foot came crashing down on top of Lumpy.

Squish.

Chaos ensued.

"Oh, no!" Pat screamed.

"Is he dead?!" shrilled Mike.

RRIBBITT! croaked Lumpy, as he zigzagged off the sidewalk, above the grass, over the curb and into the street.

I wheeled around, twisting this way and that, but Lumpy had dissolved into thin air somewhere across the abyss of Insley Street.

"Where is he, where is he, where is he?" blubbered Patrick.

I didn't know if he was dead or alive – *he didn't look squished!* – but I thought maybe, *maybe* he just leaped straight into frog heaven. I didn't know if that was a good thing to tell Paddy, though.

"He's gone, Pat."

Patrick wailed even louder and stumbled back into the house. Mike and I looked at each other and slowly followed.

Patrick eventually stopped crying over Lumpy. Instead, he took up stomping on bugs. No crawly insect in his path was safe from "Bigfoot."

After lunch I caught him outside our house aiming for a shiny black beetle – one of his previously professed favorites. *Squish.*

"Pat. Why do you do that?"

"I dunno."

"But you *like* beetles!"

His bottom lip protruded. "*I* know."

Suddenly his pace quickened. "Oh, look! A ladybug!"

That was too much. "Not a *lady*bug!" I protested.

Too late. *Splat.*

I stamped back into the house.

"Mommy! Paddy's stepping on *ladybugs!*"

But Mommy was busy changing baby Timmy, and couldn't be the 'heavy.'

"Tell him to come inside and play with Julie."

Toddler Julie scurried out after me. "Ladybug? Where da ladybug?"

"Never mind, Julie. It's gone." I stood on the cement steps halfway down the front lawn and called to Patrick below.

"Mommy says you have to come in and play with Julie!"

Pat pretended not to hear. He gave a little skip and sauntered on down the sidewalk. Heaving a sigh, I grabbed my metal roller skates, squatted onto the bottom step, and tightened them over my shoes with my silver skate key. Ready for business, I pushed off towards Patrick. He saw me approaching and padded faster away from me. Just then Mommy's voice rang out.

"Patrick! Into the house!"

He slowed. I sailed past, grasped the light post and pivoted to a stop. I glanced back to see him trudge towards the steps – then hop short.

"Ooh!" he cooed. Pat raised his bare foot and slammed it down – ending in a shrill screech that pierced the sky. He tumbled onto the grass like a roly-poly doll. Mommy raced out and scooped him up.

"Oh, Patrick! That was *not* a good idea!" I watched from afar as she examined his foot. "If you step on a *bee*, it stings you!"

I hesitated a moment – then turned my feet around and charged forward in the opposite direction. *Maybe NOW he'll stop doing that!*

Several long strides later, the mournful wail from behind snagged me to a standstill. I jerked awkwardly around with a backward gaze. There in the distance a lone figure sat sobbing on the top step, hands clasped in his lap. I wavered. *Maybe I should go back... Mommy must've gone in to get the Mercurochrome.* I shuddered at the memory of that medicine...the little glass rod with its red-orange sting. Quickly I blinked it away. *No! I will NOT stay here!*

With a twist I swung myself back around, bent my knees, and powered my way down the sidewalk. I could feel the vibrations over the bumpy cement buzzing through my wheels and on up my legs like little bolts of lightning. Faster now I zoomed, my arms slicing through the air in tandem with my fiercely striding skates. The breeze rushed past me, momentarily clinging to my clothes in a last-ditch effort to stall my progress.

At last! I was free! No one, not even Patrick, could stop me now!

The street whizzed by me on the right. On the left, I

spied Mr. Wall's oncoming low brick wall. (*Funny: the only house on the block with a WALL!*) It rushed towards me. The bricks narrowed and melded into each other in their race to pass me by. All the houses blurred into one long watercolor. I alone was alive, and in focus!

Up ahead I spied Andy Drake's house: the 'end of the road,' the corner, the turning point. *Do I go beyond?* I'd never ventured so far before. The scent of the unknown now grabbing my nostrils, I gasped with the thrill of sudden decision. *Yes!*

Leaning into the curve, I swayed like an undulating ribbon around the corner. There! Before me! A grand new space to fill for the first time! Houses stuck to the ground that could not follow me, *me*, a stranger in their midst. I, alone, could zoom right on by! My knees bent, my power flowed full on into my thighs. *Faster than a speeding bullet...* I was Supe-

The sky suddenly distorted; the houses leaped sideways up in the air. An abrupt silence surrounded me in a momentary bubble as my wheels left the ground, and I flew...*UNGH!*

The world swiveled to a stop with a glaring jolt. Rabid flames raced up my knees and palms. I couldn't breathe! The huge concrete and tar world reared up around me – *WUHH!* – and the air suddenly forced its way back into my lungs.

My body shivered and shook with hot pain and cold menace. The strange houses now stared smugly down at me. No one else was in sight. No people, no dogs, no movement. I, alone, trembled with life too big for my body.

Mommy, Mommy... I knew she was far away... too far away. She couldn't see me, or hear me. She did not know about my knees, about my fall. About... *NO ONE ELSE AROUND.*

At last I began the long journey home. My skates clutched to my chest, I hobbled slowly back. By the time I stumbled over the threshold, hours seemed to have gone by. My injuries were stale; only caked grit embedded in my hands and knees remained. Silently I allowed Mommy to attend to them.

During naptime I lay on my bed and listened to Paddy's cries through the wall as he bemoaned his own injury. In the semidarkness that lonely figure on the steps once more loomed up at me. I swallowed, feeling akin with the boy I had abandoned in his own time of need. *But I ran away...* Slowly, his voice faded, as he drifted into slumber. Or perhaps it was I...

I stayed in my room the rest of the day. I didn't feel like playing outside. I played on the floor with my paper dolls cut from our Betsy McCall dress pattern catalog.

After dinner I finally ventured out onto the front stoop. The day's colors slowly seeped into tones of gray. A warm breeze tickled my cheek. Chin in hand, I gazed down at the sidewalk below.

Shrill cries sliced the air as the boys next-door raced their bikes up the driveway. Down the block Andrea hula-hooped as she bumped her way home. Across the street the big boys tossed a football to each other. The whole neighborhood buzzed with expectancy.

I glanced about, searching for Patrick. Even he had shed his day's insults. Limping slightly, he toddled across the cool, soft lawn. "C'mere, c'mere, c'mere!" he cried, his arms outstretched. Tiny, intermittent sparks darted before him.

Spiraling around, I grabbed the glass jar Mommy had set out by the front door. Quickly I unscrewed the lid, now punctured with holes.

"Here, Paddy!" Leaping out, I soon overtook him. Together we raced towards the glow, all four arms reaching, reaching... Finally I thrust the jar forward faster than the little night travelers could go, and managed to slam the lid shut, with Patrick's hand slapping against mine. As one, we loped toward the steps with our prize. The two of us huddled with the treasure balanced carefully on our knees. Patrick leaned closer.

"Look, Kathleen!" he whispered. "Fireflies."

There inside the glass jar three tiny sparks fluttered and glowed. I caught my breath. *Just like little fairies!*

"This is magic, Paddy!"

He nodded, his eyes shining into mine.

I glanced up at the sky. Ribbons of pink and orange cotton candy floated by. Just then Mike zoomed out of nowhere and tapped me on the shoulder.

"Hey! Do you know what *time* it is?!" he whooped, his eyes dancing. I shook my head. "Nine o'clock!"

"Nine o'clock?!" We were *never* allowed up that late! "Yeah!"

A bubble formed in my chest – then grew and multiplied, oozing streams of fizz that shot through-out my whole body. I leaped up and tapped his arm.

"Tag! You're it!" With a toss of my head I let out a laugh; and with Patrick in tow, I raced down the grassy slope to the sidewalk below.

Independence Day

"It's Fourth of July, Mike, and tonight we get *fire crackers*!" I whooped. We trotted over to our new next-door neighbors' house for backyard festivities.

"Well, no, not fire crackers," laughed Mommy. "But maybe something better."

As the sky darkened, squeals filled the air. We lined up in a solemn row, bubbles of excitement percolating beneath the surface. Mr. Boyle passed out sparklers. The "older kids" got *giant* sparklers. *I* was included! Suddenly, the regular ones grasped by Mike and Pat and little Debbie Boyle looked puny, dull. My chest filled with pride.

Mr. B lit our special torches for us. How mine flared up, seeming to light the sky! I spread my arms, eyes on the prize, and twirled. Magically, I danced my sparkler into a multitude of stars, as I spun, faster, *faster*! The world swirled around me, blurring behind the diamond sparks that fanned outward from my outstretched hand. My stomach lurched with giddy delight; I felt airborne and free!

All of a sudden, the earth tilted, lop-sided, in a rush of brown and green as I tumbled in a heap onto an instant hot poker! A scream like a siren pierced the air; I realized it was mine.

A tangle of legs appeared above me.

"Debbie?!" A man's voice called out. *No, stupid, it's me!*

Daddy appeared then, my hand swiftly turned over to reveal the unrecognizable mess on the palm. Black ashes! Red, white bubbly skin and black - *ashes?! How did they get from the fireplace to my hand?!*

My head swam…Voices…bright lights…a doctor murmuring in low tones about a "third degree burn." A bandaged hand. Not being allowed to see the hand. But through it all crystallized a *huge* proclamation: NO WATER SHALL TOUCH THIS HAND FOR FOURTEEN DAYS.

And on the thirteenth day….

I enviously leered at the backyard children's pool down the street at Karen's house. Karen, boasting at least one year on me, delighted in reminding me of the Proclamation.

Once again, standing in her yard, she admonished, "*Remember*, Kathleen, you're NOT ALLOWED in the water for FOURTEEN days!"

I sighed. So close…and yet so far. I left…

…and sneaked back awhile later.

I found myself deliciously alone on the grass, approaching the plastic pool with tentative steps. I stopped, one hand (the good one) gingerly fingering the rim. With a sudden burst of adrenaline, I swung first one leg, then the other over the side. I was in! The water felt exquisitely cold and forbidden. Nervously I stretched my right hand high, never letting it stray into contraband territory.

No one need ever know.

Pat, Mike, Julie, Cathay, Mommy

The Adventurers

"Oh, a-camping we will go, a-camping we will go, hi-ho the derry-o, a-camping we will go!" belted Daddy, pulling into the parking lot of 'Camper's World.' Mike and I threw open the car doors and scampered through the grand entrance. I stopped short. Row upon row of canvas tents of all sizes greeted us.

"It looks like a little town!" I breathed.

"Wait till we get in the campground. Then we'll *really* be in Tent City, " Daddy grinned.

I raced towards the biggest one, an apricot-colored rectangle, trapped inside a skeleton of shiny metal poles. "C'mon, Mike!"

Hopping up and down, we urged Daddy on as he bent to unzip the large front flap. Mike and I stumbled

135

over the canvas threshold and stared. It was huge! Like a regular room! I twirled in the orange light, arms outstretched, hearing the crickets chirp around us.

Daddy popped his head in the flap and peered about.

"It's just right – don't you think, Daddy?"

"I dunno – it's awfully big…"

"But we *need* it, Daddy – don't we?" I wheedled. "We have *seven* people!"

"Yup…yup… 'course Timmy's only a baby, and Julie's not any bigger…" he mused.

"Let's lie down and try it out!" I eyed Mike. Instantly he whooped and dropped to the floor. I joined him, and the two of us rolled like little logs from one side of the tent to the other. *Ooh! It feels hard!*

I sat up. "Don't we need sleeping bags?" Soon Daddy, Mike and I had tossed five orange rolls inside the tent.

"Timmy and Julie can sleep with Mommy," decided Daddy.

"This one's mine!" I cried.

"I get the blue!" Mike dove on top of another one.

I burrowed inside the green plaid flannel, luxuriating in the soft haven surrounding me. "*Mmm,*" I giggled. I rolled from side to side within the cocoon.

"Daddy, it fits."

"Looks like we'll all fit," he replied.

Home again, Mike and I bounded into the house. "We got it! We got it!" I hollered. Daddy brought up the rear, lugging the bags inside so we could all try them out. Soon the entire living room was strewn with beds. Pat and Julie clambered from bag to bag, checking out their favorite. Eighteen month-old Timmy toddled in a spiraling circle around us. "Where mine? Where mine?" he chattered.

Mommy hurried out of her bedroom with a rolled-up bundle. "Look, Julie," she trilled, "Here's one just your size!" Carefully she unrolled her handiwork: an old gray and white blanket folded in quarters and sewn together just like a sleeping bag.

"And, *you*, Timber," cooed Mommy, "You get this great big one with *me*!"

"Yippee!" I squealed. "Carol Ann's coming with us!"

Our favorite babysitter, fourteen-year old Carol Ann, told the best stories. Now she was to be the camp 'Mother's Helper.'

Our red and white Pontiac station wagon, overflowing with children and supplies, pulled up in front of her house. I shoved open the car door. "Hi, Carol Ann!" She wormed her way inside and managed to stuff her sleeping bag under her knees with her lumpy duffle beneath her feet.

"Let's roll 'em!" Daddy declared.

"Kookaburra, kookaburra, in the tree-ee,
Looking at all that he can see-ee,
Laugh, kookaburra, laugh, kookaburra,
You're so fine to see, ha ha ha..."

Carol Ann warbled to us all. Soon Mike, Paddy and I had the song down pat. I swayed back and forth amongst the pillows and car toys, grazing shoulders with Carol Ann.

"Kookaburra, kookaburra, In the tree-ee,
Eating all the gumdrops he can see-ee,
Stop, kookaburra, stop, kookaburra,
Save some there for me, yum, yum, yum."
*...I could stay like this for hours...*And for hours, we did

137

– drive, that is.

"When are we gonna get there, Daddy?" Pat piped up.

"I have to go to the bathroom!" grumbled Mike.

"Me, too!"

"Soon, soon," answered Mommy.

"You know," asserted Carol Ann, "my brother still sits on the toilet like a girl. For – *everything.*"

"How old is he?" asked Mike.

"Five."

"That's like me!"

Carol Ann nodded. "But that's because there's four of us girls, all older than him, and Jackie is the only boy."

"Does he mind that he's the only boy?" I queried.

"Well, the funny thing is, he likes to wear dresses all the time."

"Really?" Mike's eyes popped.

"Yup. That's because he sees all us girls wearing dresses, and he thinks he should, too. He follows us all around, asking to wear a dress, so we dress him in some of ours." She giggled.

I glanced behind at Mike, hanging over the back of our seat, his face twisted sideways. I tried to imagine him in a dress. Or even Patrick. But I just couldn't do it.

Carol Ann picked up the song.

"Kookaburra, kookaburra, on the rai-ell,
He's got splinters in his tai-ell,
Cry, Kookaburra, cry, kookaburra,
You're so sad to see, boo hoo, hoo."

Gravelgravelgravel. The car ground to a halt.

"We're here!" Mike cried.

We shoved open the doors and managed to climb out, amidst tumbling sleeping bags and pillows.

"We're in the woods! We're in the woods!" Mike and

I shrieked.

"Everyone, this is Letchfield State Park, in the state of New York," Daddy rubbed his hands with glee.

I gazed all around at willowy white trees amidst the more chunky brown ones.

"Birch trees," stated Mommy. Through the branches on either side I could dimly make out other tents.

Daddy marked out a large rectangle on the ground for our tent. "We need a crew to pick up the stones," Mommy decided.

"Why?" asked Patrick.

"So they don't dig into our backs while we are sleeping."

Mike, Pat and I immediately scoured the ground for any rocks. Even two-and-a-half-year old Julie gathered a few. She laid each carefully in her growing pile and set off for a new one.

"I found nine!" Pat announced.

"Nine!" echoed Julie. Pat glanced over at her.

"No you didn't, Julie." He bent down to count them.

"I did too!" she retorted.

"You have four, Julie."

Julie toddled back with another and dropped it onto her pile.

"Nine!" she crowed.

Daddy unfolded the canvas bundle and spread it out flat on our patch of earth. We all stared in silence.

"How do we get in it?" puzzled Pat. "It's too...too close to the ground."

"Ho ho!" chortled Daddy. "Wait and see. First we need to pound the stakes."

"I looked over at Mommy changing Timmy. "Why are we making dinner *now*?" I turned to Daddy. "I thought we were putting up the tent."

Daddy picked up a rock from one of our piles. "We

are! Come help me with the stakes, Cathay." *Whoa!* I shook my head back and forth.

"But – how can you put up the tent with *meat?*" I knew now it could go on a black eye, but this was silly.

Daddy guffawed, and led me over to a sack of giant nails. "*These* are stakes." *Ohh.* I tried to pound them into the ground through the gold rings with my biggest rock. (Daddy helped.)

At last our forest house sprang into view. It just fit under the overhanging branches.

"Yippee!" Mike roared. We both raced towards the tent, Patrick and Julie at our tails. Mommy handed Timmy to Carol Ann and grabbed at them.

"Stop! No one in the tent until it's swept out!"

"But it's not even dirty!" I protested.

"I'll just make sure." Hoisting the broom through the flap, she entered the tent without us.

"You kids go get sticks for the hot dogs," suggested Daddy. We needed no further invitation. Fanning out, we scoured the debris between the trees.

"C'mon, Carol Ann!" I yelled. She followed with Timmy in tow…

Mmm…I could smell the meat roasting on the end of my stick. I stared into the flames, watching the orange fingers lick my hot dog like dancing light beams. So fast they pranced! Like they were playing hide-and-seek… *Oh!* I yanked my stick back.

"It's *black!*" I bellowed.

"Oho!" Daddy chuckled. "That's the *best* kind! It's barbequed."

"*Tsk.* You mean *burned*," I glowered.

"No, no!" soothed Mommy. "Quickly – put it in a bun. Here's the mustard…"

…It was delicious!

Cur-ric-ket, cur-ric-ket, cur-ric-ket…

Deep shadows filled he tent. The air still smelled of burnt marshmallow smoke. I wiggled inside my sleeping bag, bare toes curling and uncurling against the soft flannel lining. I smiled to myself. This was *better* than I imagined!

"Hey, Mike!" I whispered.

"Yeah?" a voice floated out of the darkness.

"What's your favoritest thing in the whole wide world?"

"The Lone Ranger."

"Mine is camping."

Mike shifted in his bag next to me. "Yeah," he said. "The Lone Ranger and Tonto went camping, too."

"All the time!"

We thought about that in the dark.

"Yeah," whispered Mike. "Camping with the Lone Ranger. That would be the best."

I woke up to silence. The crickets had disappeared. My face felt cold – but my body was snuggly-warm! I opened one eye. Nobody moved.

Zzzip. All of a sudden the canvas door flapped inward.

"Rise and shine! Rise and shine!" Daddy's face beamed through the dark opening. "Time to hit the road!"

"What?!" I stammered. "It's not even morning!"

"Sure it is!" he countered. "Very *early* morning."

Moans and groans slithered out of various sleeping bags. Only Timmy sat up. He struggled to his feet and waddled about the other bodies in his sleeper sack. "Mo'ning! Mo'ning! Mo'ning!" he chanted.

On the road again, the car once more loaded down

141

with overflowing gear and sleepy campers, Mommy leaned over the front seat back and passed out breakfast. In silence we munched on Danish and bananas. I turned to my window in the dawning light and watched the trees race backwards…

Slam.

"We're so close to those mountains!" I exclaimed. Daddy and I trekked out to the back of the car to begin unloading once again.

"We're *in* those mountains," smiled Daddy. "Adirondacks."

"Add-a-wrong *ducks?"* I mused. He threw down the tailgate.

Just then Carol Ann popped up around the side of the car.

"Hey, Carol Ann! I cried. "Let's race!" The two of us pounded the rocky ground, chasing each other around the campsite.

"We'll find the rest rooms for you!" she yelled back to Mommy.

Moments later, we spied Mike and Pat bent over a boulder, in total absorption. We grinned at each other and snuck up behind them.

"Boo!" I shrieked. Mike yelped. "Ha ha!" Patrick simply stuck out his lower lip and bent lower.

"It's a caterpillar!" he exulted.

"Neat!" We all crowded around him. I gently touched the red and green bumpy body. It felt bristly under my finger.

"Let's take him to our campsite and put him in something," I suggested.

"And we can feed him some leaves," added Paddy.

"Naw," Mike grimaced. "Let's play Tag."

A hand suddenly reached out from behind and tapped him on the shoulder.

"Tag – you're it!" Carol Ann teased.

"Hey!" sputtered Mike. But Carol Ann had darted away, laughing back at us. Mike leaped up and bolted after her. I joined in pursuit. Without warning, Mike switched directions and lunged towards *me!* I shrieked, and the chase was on! Carol Ann popped into view and I sprang after her. Laughing now, we wove in and out of trees and campsites, spurring each other on. At last out of breath, I stopped and clutched my side.

"Truce! Truce!" As we all dragged to a halt, I took stock of where we were. *All these campsites look strange…*

"Hey, I think we'd better get back," Carol Ann said.

We hesitated; then set off on the path in front of us. The circular trail seemed to lead farther away from what we remembered.

"No," Carol Ann frowned. "Let's try this way."

"I don't like this," tremored Mike.

At that moment a high-pitched wail wavered in the air ahead. I stopped short.

"That's Pat!"

As one, we charged ahead, scrambling across the road and through campsites toward that familiar warble. At last we broke into the clearing where we had begun the game. There sat Pat, his little legs bent behind him, tears streaming down his face.

"You left me here!" he blubbered.

"Oh!" Carol Ann darted towards him.

"And I can't find the cat– a-p-pill-ll-ar!" sobbed Paddy.

She reached down and grabbed his hand. "It's okay, Pat, we'll go back now." Carol Ann tugged at him.

Just then, Mommy appeared.

"Children, where have you been?!"

"Um, looking for the bathrooms," I muttered.

"The bathrooms are RIGHT *here."* She pointed to an old gray building that we hadn't noticed till now. "And Carol Ann – I need you to help *me* – NOT to run off with the children!"

Without a word, we hung our heads and trudged behind her toward the campsite.

There, back at camp, Julie jiggled up and down, clutching her shorts. "I have to GO! I have to GO!" she clamored.

Hand in hand, she and I worked our way back to the wooden restroom. I stepped inside and stopped short.

There was Mommy, squatting in the shower stall, beating diapers against the cement floor as the water sprayed down. I turned toward the toilet. A still-dirty diaper lay soaking inside.

"Oh, good, you're here," Mommy's voice echoed out. "I need your help, sweetheart."

"But – we need to go to the *bathroom!"* I protested.

"All right." She leaned out of the shower stall and wiped her forehead with her arm. "Go quickly in the other toilet, then ask Carol Ann to bring the second bucket back here and help. You can watch Julie and Timmy for me – *in the campsite!"*

...I held my nose and scurried back out with Julie.

The next morning I crawled painfully out of the tent, stiff from cold. "It's still too early!" I moaned.

"We've got to make it to our next campground," prodded Daddy. "You will like it!"

Something white caught my eye. Rectangular sheets of snow seemed to have enveloped the bushes surrounding our campsite. *Ooh! No wonder it's so cold!* Then Mommy leaned down and lifted up each frosty layer – in one complete chunk!

"My goodness!" she exclaimed. "The diapers are nearly frozen!" No snow, after all.

Back on the road, we nibbled on cups of dry cereal and apple slices, staring blearily out the window…

At last we edged around an old stone campus sprawled across fields of green. I stared. "Where are we?"

Daddy chuckled. "This is Middlebury College. "Lunch time!"

Anxious to uncurl our cramped legs, we bolted out of the car like jack-in-the-boxes. *Freedom!* Mike and Pat flew so fast that Mike tripped over the curb and Patrick stumbled over him. He rolled right onto the grass without stopping. *"Whee!"* he chortled. Daddy suddenly tore onto the field and flung himself down on his back. He grabbed Patrick and tossed him in the air. Mike charged towards them and leaped into the fray. Squeals emitted from all sides. "Me, too! Me, too!" Timmy crowed as he toddled after them. I bounced on my toes, wavering, then pushed off towards the pile of wiggling bodies.

"Kathleen!" called Mommy. "Come help me with the lunch!" I lurched to a halt – *ugh!* - then raced around the roughhousers one time before dragging myself back to the picnic table.

"Okay, Julie – you and me are on a search party," I cooed down to her, "to find the bathroom."

At last at the campground in the White Mountains of New Hampshire, we promised Mommy to scout out for it and come *right back*. Mike and Pat had already split off on another path, sure that our way was wrong.

Julie finally stopped and tugged my hand. "What we gonna do? No baffoom?" She gazed up at me. "Mommy said, 'No more diapers!'"

Hmm...I bit my lip. "Don't worry, Julie. There's *got* to be one somewhere."

I trudged a ways farther past more tents, with Julie dragging her feet beside me. At last she sat right down in the dirt.

"No, no, no!" she pouted. I stood still and gazed all around.

A woman lugging a water bucket cocked her head at us. "My! Are you two little girls lost?"

"No. We just can't...do you know where the bathroom is?"

"It's just past the next campsite on your right," she pointed.

I turned and squinted. A tiny wooden shed stood next to the garbage cans. *That?!* I turned back.

"Are you sure?"

"Yes, dearie. It's certainly not like at home, though!"

We treaded across the road to the strange hut. With a twist I yanked open the door. We stood in silence.

Gingerly we squeezed in. Flies buzzed erratically.

"Where's da toilet?" Julie burst out.

"It's..." I peered down at the wooden seat into the hole. A fly zoomed out. Quickly I looked away and held my breath. "...right here."

"It's stinky," complained Julie.

"Here – you first," I offered. Julie scooted backwards. "No – *you!*"

I heaved a sigh; then yanked down my shorts, scooted over the hole and peed. I squeezed my eyes tight.

"Now you, Julie – here – I'll help - " I pulled down her shorts and lifted Julie up and over the edge of the seat. *Oof!* She slipped in my grasp – *oops!* - and fell down hard against the edge of the hole. "Oww!" I shot down my hand and managed to slide her back a bit – but a gaping slice of the hole loomed ominously along side of her. With a big breath I squeezed her harder around the waist and held tight.

"Okay – *go,* Julie!"

Then suddenly my hand slipped and her bottom sank with a rush deep inside the opening.

"*AHHH!*" Julie screamed.

With a twist and a grunt, my knees shoved into the edge of the toilet, I tugged her back up and onto solid ground.

"Bees!" she cried.

"What?"

"Bees! Dere's bees in dere!" She began hopping up and down.

"They're just flies!"

"Let me out! Let me out!"

"Let's pull up your pants," I grunted, tearing at them. Julie fumbled frantically at the door handle. I finally yanked the shorts up, then twisted the lock. Julie stumbled out the doorway and up the path as if bees indeed zoomed after her.

Wheeling around the trail towards us sped Mike and Pat.

"Hey!" yelled Mike. "Did you see the outhouse?!"

"It's *stinky!*" Pat added with glee. Julie screamed louder, hopping up and down.

"What happened to *her?*" asked Mike.

I sighed. "She won't *go* in the outhouse."

"Why? - Julie, *I* did it," Patrick patted her shoulder.

"Yeah, Julie," Mike bent towards her. "We *both* did! It's fun!"

I growled at him. "It is *not!*" - then thought better of it. "Well, yes-s, Julie…it's kind of like a *ride*…isn't it, Mike? Maybe we could try it again, and we'll *all* help you."

Julie swung her head back and forth, her bottom lip out. Mike took one hand and I the other, while Pat pushed her from behind. Julie wailed, her feet dragging through the dirt as we propelled her back to the little 'closet.' The door open, I pulled down her shorts and all three of us reached toward her. Hands flew in a blur as we grappled with the squirmy body twisting in our grasp over the gigantic hole.

"No, no!" She screamed like a banshee. "Mama, Mama! Bees! Bees!"

We could hold her no longer. As one we fumbled her back onto the ground. I sighed, defeated.

"Okay, Julie. Let's go to Mommy."

Mike and Pat dashed back alongside Julie. I trudged behind.

Later, Mommy sat down over the hole with her clothes on, her arms wrapped around Julie, and held her between her legs over the front of the hole. Julie's terrified screams finally subsided.

...*Ice...frosty diapers*...My legs scissored against each other inside the sleeping bag. I opened my eyes. *So cold!* Darkness, silence filled the tent; filled my ears. My arms hugged tighter as I twisted rhythmically back and forth, then up and down in dismay. A voice rose out of the stillness.

"Mommy!" Julie tremored. "I'm cold!"

"Scoot closer to me, Julie," whispered Mommy.

"Can I sleep in your sleeping bag?" she pleaded.

"Timmy's already in mine. Here - " I heard the bag slide as she tugged Julie closer to her. "You'll stay warmer this way."

Hmm... Using my elbows, feet and bottom, I bumped my way towards Mike. I pushed myself as close as I

could against that next lump in the dark. With a twist
of my shoulders I wiggled into position, my knees up
against my chest. Mike grunted and was silent. I closed
my eyes and let out a long sigh. *Was it really…better…?*

"All aboard!" Daddy's voice boomed with the dawn.
We huddled closer to each other as we shuffled toward
the waiting station wagon. *It may be early – but at least it's
bound to be warmer inside the* car! Much to my surprise – it
felt the same!

"Daddy, do we *always* have to go to a new camping
place *every day?!*"

"And do we always have to get up so early? It's so cold!"
"Yeah!"

Mommy heaved a deep sigh. "Walt, this is really
getting very wearing. And *please.* No more campsites
without hot and cold running water. I desperately need
to wash the diapers!"

Daddy turned around and faced us all. His eyes
twinkled with sunshine. "We're taking an unexpected
detour."

"Oh, no!" Mommy slumped.

"The camp host has told me about a very special place
in Vermont. We're going to stay in a cabin on a lake for
three days."

"Oh, thank goodness!" sighed Mommy.
"YAAY!"

At last we anchored in the driveway of our own
cabin in the trees. Lake Champlain glistened through the
branches just beyond.

"It's beautiful!" Mommy breathed.

One after another, we streamed out of the car, with
Mike, Pat and I heading down toward the lake.

"C'mon, Carol Ann!" I exclaimed. "Come with us!"

A wide swath of white pebbles stretched endlessly

along the water's edge.

"Look at the beach!" whooped Mike. "It's gigantic!"

"Hey, Carol Ann!" I yelled. "Let's race!"

A light breeze pulled at us as we crunched along the shore. Carol Ann began weaving like a snake, zigzagging across the pebbles. I tossed back my head and laughed as I tried to follow in her footsteps.

"C'mon, Carol Ann, let's wade in the water!" She wove her way straight toward the lake. I darted after her. With a shriek, she sloshed through the water. Laughing, I drew up behind her. Carol Ann bent down, then turned and shoved a sprinkling of water towards me. *Ooh!* With two hands I shoved it back, splashing her blouse. She raced away with a parting hit. Back on the shore, I caught up with her. We chased each other in ever widening circles on the huge beach before she suddenly lunged off.

"Come back!" I yelled.

She laughed, shaking her head, zigzagging back towards our cabin.

Up ahead, Mike and Pat looked a long way off, miniature figures on the shore. At last we drew up to them, heaving and out of breath.

"That was fun!" I gasped. "Let's do it again, Carol Ann!"

Just then Mommy emerged from the trees.

"Carol Ann!" she snapped. "Who was watching Mike and Pat?"

"Uh, I'm sorry, Mrs. Gunn," mumbled Carol Ann. "But they were right here..."

"Never, *ever* leave them alone by the water."

Up in the cabin, we claimed our rooms. *I get to sleep with Carol Ann!* I surveyed our built-in bunks with great satisfaction, envisioning late night whisperings under the covers. *And we can play lots of games...* I turned around, but she was gone. Galumphing through the cabin, I discovered her in the kitchen. Mommy was showing her the stove.

"Isn't this wonderful? Three days of cooking with a *real* stove!" Carol Ann nodded in reply.

"Hey, Carol Ann!" I exclaimed. "Let's play cards!"

"Uh, no, Kathleen," she said. "I need to help your Mother now."

Under the Formica dinner table I swung my legs back and forth.

"*Mmm,*" Daddy sniffed. "Mommy has prepared something very tasty." She smiled at him, "Why, thank you." We munched our chicken and rice in ravenous silence.

"Hey, Carol Ann," I smacked my lips. "Why did the moron throw the alarm clock out the window?"

"Uh, I don't know - why?"

"Because," I smirked, "he wanted to see *time fly!*" I laughed uproariously amidst the groans and chuckles.

"Hey – Carol Ann," I continued eagerly, "why did the moron throw the butter out the window?"

"Uh – you tell me."

"Because…" I stalled, "he wanted to see the *butterfly!* Ha ha ha!"

"Okay," inserted Mommy. "Finish your dinner, now."

"Wait, wait – hey, Carol Ann, Carol Ann!"

"Yess," She looked at me.

"What's black and white and read all over?"

""I know! I know!" Mike burst out. "It's - "

"Not *you!*" I elbowed him.

"Hey!"

"Kathleen, that's *enough,*" warned Mommy.

"It's a *newspaper!*" I shrieked. "Did you get it? Did you get it, Carol Ann? Not *red,* but *read* – like a book!"

Mike kicked me under the table and I kicked sideways back.

"*Cathay!*" Mommy raised her voice. "I said, 'that's ENOUGH!'"

In the bathroom after dinner, I leaned my elbows on the sink and watched Carol Ann brush her teeth.

"I like the way you do that, Carol Ann. You do it really *fast.*"

She garbled gibberish through the toothpaste.

"We get to play games in the living room after we get jammies on," I chattered. "What game do *you* want to play?" I followed her into the bedroom. "Do you like Candyland?"

"I don't know, but I think you should get *your* pajamas on." Then Carol Ann stepped out of her shorts and blouse. She wore a bra – just like Mommy! – and she took that off, too. I froze, mesmerized by her naked body. Suddenly, eons of years poured into the gap between us. I stared at the two round bull's-eyes staring blindly back at me. She was a *grownup!*

"Uh, Kathleen," her face wrinkled kind of funny. "There's something on the wall over there that you can look at that's really keen." *Huh?* She pointed to the wall behind me. "See that little hole there?"

I turned and walked over to the wall. Sure enough, my hand found a small, round hole I could almost put my finger through. "This one?" I turned back to her.

"Look through it," she said. "You can see the moon! It's really neat. Keep looking…"

Hmmph! I could feel the heat building up in my chest and radiating down my arms and legs. *She thinks she's tricking me! But I'm not a baby! She just wants me not to see her naked!* But I squinted through the hole anyway.

Sure enough, I could see the moon out there, a great shimmering orb. I kept staring at it. My eye began to ache from squinting. I switched eyes. *What's she doing? Why doesn't she let me go?* I didn't dare look away, in case she was still naked.

What's taking so long? Now I *really* felt irked. My legs cramped, my neck hurt, and my eyes watered. I bit my lip and pulled back just a bit. *It's so quiet.* I studied the wood grain lines in the wall for variety...

Suddenly her voice burst out loud and clear. "Hey! *There* you are! Are you planning on staying there like that all night?!"

I wheeled around. She stood there, hands on her hips, robe on, *laughing* at me!

"Why aren't you playing games, like everyone else?"

I swallowed. *Because you...you...*

...She had squashed me like a bug and scraped me off her shoe.

I turned away from her, my cheeks burning, and slipped into my nightie. Hastily I shoved my way past her out of the room.

On the living room floor I squeezed in between Mike and Pat. "Goodie! Candyland!" I murmured.

"Here's your marker, Kathleen," Mike offered. "I saved it for you." He held out the little green wooden man – my favorite. I bumped shoulders with him and smiled.

"Thanks, Mike."

Two days later, we lugged out the suitcases and supplies, and helped Daddy stuff them into the red and white station wagon. Back in our cramped quarters, we peered out the windows for one final look at our surprise paradise.

"Goodbye, cabin!"

"Goodbye, lake!"

The camping adventure's homestretch beckoned us onward.

Our final night we set up camp at Hammonasset State Beach in Connecticut. Mommy rummaged through the few remaining food supplies.

"Oh, dear!" she sighed. "Whatever can I make?"

Julie and I crouched in the sand, busily drawing with shells and sticks. Mike and Pat raced back to the campsite cradling their sand dollars. "We're bringing these home with us!" Carol Ann bounced Timmy on her lap while Daddy pounded the stakes into the tent. "Up we go! One last time."

"*Hmm…*" Mommy mused. "Let's see what I can do with these." With renewed energy, she set water to boil on the camp stove. "Open these cans for me, will you, sweetheart?" She thrust them towards Daddy…

Soon we all gathered 'round the picnic table. The ocean lapped in rhythm against a pink and blue sky. Mommy, illuminated by lantern light, ladled out the dark green and orange concoction. Warm and savory on the palate, nothing on the entire journey tasted finer.

"Yum!"

"*Mmmm…*what is it, Mommy?"

"Well," she paused. "I found a can of spinach, a can of cheese soup, two cans of tuna and a package of macaroni."

"And what do you call it, my sweet?" asked Daddy.

"I call it – Tuna Rockefeller!"

…And so…a great family tradition was born.

The sky had blackened as dark as the tree shadows behind the beach. Smoke wafted in great plumes from the fiery core before me. Straight ahead, grotesque, distorted faces wavered in the firelight. I gazed at my marshmallow, watching it turn from snow white to black ash in mere seconds. (My favorite!)

"So – what do you think of camping?" Daddy suddenly asked.

"Let's do it again!"

"Yeah!"

"I like camping."

"But no stinky baffoom, Daddy."

We stared into the fire. Mommy's voice broke through the night.

"Look at the stars!"

I turned my head. Above, in the blackest sky, thousands of sparkles glimmered back at us. In silence we drank them in.

Better than any dessert.

Overnights

Mrs. Angeny sucked hungrily on her cigarette. Her arm drooped back onto her bare stomach, sandwiched between leathery folds of mahogany skin. Karen and I lay next to her mother, stretched out on our towels on their front lawn.

Her mother's bikinied body glistened in the sun under liberal coatings of cocoa butter. I tried not to stare at that figure of dark, polished wood. I had never seen such a suntan!

Mrs. Angeny raised her head and squinted over across the street. There, six-year-old Janice with-the-short-blonde-bob busied herself in the sandbox, setting up her baby dolls. Janice was a year and a half younger than me.

"That child is too old to be playing with dolls," announced Mrs. Angeny. "Her mother should know better."

I caught my breath and carefully averted my head. *Did she hear her?* Suddenly I didn't want Janice to see me here. We played together. But sometimes we argued, like when she told her mother, Mrs. Miller, I had "committed a sin" for not saving her swing when she went to the bathroom, like I said I would. I told her mother it was only a "venial sin," and not a "mortal sin." But they were Protestant, and didn't understand that.

Janice knew I played with dolls, too, of course. Sometimes we played with them together. *What's wrong with dolls?*

Karen rolled over on her towel. "Let's go down the basement," she yawned. "It's too hot out here."

Relieved, I leapt up after her. Once inside the door, she flattened herself against it.

"I just got a great idea!" Karen exclaimed. "Why don't we ask my Mom if you can spend the night?!"

"Really?!" I'd never, ever slept over at a friend's house. *Could I??*

Minutes later, I flew down the sidewalk, my heart pounding. I didn't know anybody who had had an overnight yet. *Would they let me? What was it like?*

Soon it was all arranged. Family dinner came first, though. Hints of Tuna Rockafeller wafted from the oven. Impatiently I gobbled down my share; one of the few times I finished first.

Mommy accompanied me back across the street. I proudly lugged her white overnight case, toothbrush and nightie neatly tucked inside.

"Good night, little darling," Mommy kissed me at the door. "Remember, you can always call us if you change your mind."

I drew back in dismay. "I'm a *big* girl!"

Mrs. Angeny laughed. "Of course she's a big girl!"

Karen nabbed me at the threshold and hustled me down to the garage. "Mom's taking us to the A & P to get snacks!"

Karen and I had free rein of the store, racing up and down the aisles, with *no* little children for me to look after. *Just us!* We picked anything we wanted, and tossed it into the cart. Potato chips, sugared "orange slices," marshmallow "peanuts," caramel Sugar Babies... Karen heaved a carton of Coca Cola over the side. I glanced up at her mother. She didn't bat an eye.

"Do we each get our own bottle?" I whispered to Karen.

She frowned at me. "Of course!" Suddenly she raced off again.

I wandered on my own, gazing at all the shapes and colors on the shelves. I never really got to look at them before...

From around the corner popped Karen. "C'mere, c'mere!" she gestured. "Come see!"

I followed her down the next aisle. Behind a table at the end stood a pudgy lady in an apron with pink apple cheeks.

"Cocktail sausages!" she sang. "Try one!" She thrust out a tiny wiener on a toothpick. *For me?*

"Go on!" urged Karen.

"I don't think it's for children," I whispered in her ear.

"It's for *anybody!*" Karen's eyes danced. "Take it! Take it!"

It smelled so good... The lady smiled encouragingly. I grabbed that little sausage and popped it, lickety-split, into my mouth. *Yumm...*

Karen seized my arm and shrieked with delight. "It's FRIDAY, Kathleen! It's FRIDAY!"

I stiffened. The delicious mound in my mouth instantly turned to mud. I darted to an empty aisle and there, against the wall at the end, I spat that Catholic offense. *She tricked me!* 'No meat on Fridays...No meat on Fridays...' echoed in my ears.

I could still hear Karen cackling in the other aisle. I knew she wasn't Catholic, and, somehow, could not get into trouble for eating it. I stared at the evidence, then slunk the long way 'round to Karen's aisle.

I decided not to tell her what I did.

Back at the house, we hurried into our pajamas; then arranged our treats in front of the TV. A rainbow of brightly colored metal bowls surrounded us on the carpet. I had never seen such forbidden indulgence at my disposal! Karen threw back her head and guzzled from the green bottle. I sipped slowly after each sugary nibble, wanting to make it last.

As the music faded at the end of *Bachelor Father* Karen snapped off the TV. "Let's go to my room," she said.

"Yes, let's go to bed," I giggled.

"Mom!" hollered Karen. "We're going to bed, now."

We barreled down the hall to her room. Karen threw open the door and leaped onto her giant double bed. I clambered up after her.

"*Whee!*" I cried. We bounced higher and higher, our eyes glued to each other like magnets. My stomach flip-flopped with delight. At last, breathless, we flung ourselves backwards onto the bed.

"What now?" I gasped.

Karen immediately jumped off the bed and sashayed towards the door. "I have to kiss my honey goodnight."

There on the wall she had taped a magazine picture of Elvis. I had seen it there before. Just his face.

I stared. This time a red smudge spread across his left cheek. Karen stood on tiptoe and kissed that smudge. I drew closer and studied it. The mark looked just like a lipstick kiss!

"I made it myself!" grinned Karen. "Wearing my Mom's lipstick."

"Why?"

She shrugged. "So I could see where I kissed him."

"Oh."

"Hey, let's go play music in the basement and dance."

"N-no. *Umm.* I don't like dancing." It seemed so grown up.

Karen rolled her eyes. "You're such a baby sometimes."

I chewed my cheek. "Why don't we play 'School'?"

"That's boring. Oh, I know!" she cried. "Let's play 'Fortune Teller'!"

Our handmade game cards finally ready, we knelt on the bed in the semi-darkness, side by side on top of her pillows. Eagerly we grouped the pieces of paper in piles on the windowsill: boys' names, different states, types of houses, and numbers of children.

All of a sudden I looked up. The sky pressed shiny black upon our window, sprinkled with diamonds. The only light in the room shone down from the huge orb before me.

"Look at the moon!" I whispered. "It's spilling onto our cards!"

Karen and I watched in silence. It seemed as if the whole sky smiled on us. My eyes flickered down toward the clues to our futures. "Let's play!"

"Okay…" Karen pondered as she shuffled the first pile. "You have to give me a number…"

At that moment my stomach seemed to grow inside me. I rubbed against my nightgown, willing the bubble to melt away. But the churning persisted. *Oooohhh…*

"Karen," I hedged, "Do you think your mother might have some medicine for a stomach ache?"

Without a word, Karen took me by the hand and dragged me down the hall to her mother's room. Mrs. Angeny lounged across her pillows in her kimono, cigarette in hand, gazing at a tiny TV.

Before I knew what was happening, Mrs. Angeny had grabbed the phone, called home, and prodded me out into the black of night into Daddy's arms.

"I knew she wouldn't last the night!" she huffed.

"Oh, no, no, no!" I moaned. Slowly we wove our way down the darkened street, Daddy's arm around my shoulder. *I didn't even get to stay the whole night!*

"The fresh air will do you good – you can do it," encouraged Daddy.

"Daddy," I murmured. "If I feel better when we get home, can I go *back* to Karen's?"

"N-nooo…" he mused. "Not tonight."

At last we scaled the stoop and I stumbled into Mommy's waiting arms. "You poor darling!" she exclaimed.

In that instant a tidal wave of pressure reared up inside my stomach like an angry monster. It charged full up to my throat. *Unnnn...*

My cheeks puffed out like balloons, my eyes cried out to Mommy.

Like lightning she darted to the coffee table, pushing me onto the sofa, and thrust the now-emptied fruit bowl under my chin.

Bblaaahh...

Under the blankets I tossed, in my own little room now – so hot, my cheeks on fire. The nightlight glow jumped: an eerie dandelion fuzz that grew like a sun with spiky rays. They seemed to elongate and draw me in, holding me fast in their sea of yellow. *"Mommeee..."*

Instantly she appeared. An icy washcloth weighed down on my forehead in the dark, then dabbed with wet coolness on my cheeks and neck. The heavy blanket whipped away; the sheet sailed up and down, sending a welcome breeze over my legs. I sighed...

My eyes flashed open. Like a raging river, an icy chill undulated through me, stealing my heat. My teeth chattered; my body jiggled like a milkshake. "What's wrong with me?" I squeaked.

Back came the blankets – more this time. Mommy's hands snuggled them around me. "There, there," she murmured. Her fingers found my hair and stayed there. I could see her shadow leaning over me; her familiar fragrant smell surrounded me. One warm hand stroked my head...

Her voice tremored in the darkness:

"Twenty froggies went to school,
Down beside a rushy pool;
Twenty little coats of green,
Twenty vests all white and clean..."

...Softly the sun filtered through the curtains and played with my lids. When at last I peered out, the room shone with daylight.

"How's my little sweetheart?" Mommy had just tiptoed in. A glass of water loomed in her hand.

I rubbed my stomach gingerly. It felt stretched like a rubberband. I had thrown up twice more in the night.

I dozed in shadows, then woke to stillness. *Was it still morning? Was it almost nighttime?* My room was so hushed... Beyond its walls the distant clamor of Mike and Pat seeped through. I heard a baby crying. *Was it Timmy? Or Julie?* Mommy's far-off voice murmured like a purring kitten. Then silence.

My bed held me like a magnet. So big...so empty. Just me.

Shadows, now, across the floor. No more sun rays. The door creaked open.

"I brought you some soup," smiled Mommy. She nestled next to me on the wooden chair, a tray on her lap.

"Try a spoonful."

I peered into the bowl. *Chicken noodle! My favorite!*

Mommy leaned back while I slurped, and read to me from *The Velveteen Rabbit.* Her voice washed over me in cool colors as the savory soup soothed my stomach.

I lay back once more, warmed inside and out, and floated away in a cloud of white...

Next morning, my head popped up. Biggie Bear eyed me from the foot of my bed. Baby Annie and Buhtricia doll slouched next to him, all smiles. I grinned back. My stomach growled like a tiger. *I'm HUNGRY!* I tossed off the covers and leaped from my bed.

The sunshine had climbed back in to stay.

That afternoon Karen knocked on the screen door. Mommy set baby Timmy in his playpen and ushered my guest into the living room.

"You're just in time for snack," she beamed.

The two of us sat on the couch while I described my rocky night to Karen. "I *wish* I could've stayed all night with *you*," I sighed.

Out of the corner of my eye, I saw Mommy set a tray of milk, grapes and saltine crackers on the dining room table.

"Come on in here, girls!" she called.

Suddenly I pictured Mrs. Angeny draped over her bed with the cigarette. Turning my head, I watched Mommy as she carefully set each place at the table.

I whirled back to Karen. "Maybe next time you could spend the night at *my* house." With sudden inspiration I leaped up and reached across the coffee table.

"*And*," I declared, "You know what this is? If you ever get sick, you can just use our silver throw-up bowl!"

The Last Supper

*There are three religions. I know that. Catholic (that's us),
Protestant, and Jewish. Andrea is Jewish...* I thought about
that as I sat hunched on the cement steps halfway down
our front lawn.

*She gets eight presents at Hanukkah. One each day for
eight days, when they light those skinny candles.* I mulled
this over. *We only get* one *day of presents. On Christmas.
That doesn't seem fair. But then...maybe...maybe we get
more presents...*

I stared off into the street, the cool breeze tickling my
shoulders, as I ticked off the months until Christmas:
October...November...December.

"Hey!" A familiar voice assailed me from down the
block. Up the sidewalk bumped Andrea, her yellow
hula-hoop swinging rhythmically around her waist as
she undulated her way towards me. I studied her. *How
does she do that?* I could hula-hoop. Around my waist,

164

around my neck, even around one wrist (that hurt a little, though.) But Andrea could keep it going all the way down the block and up the steps!

At last she halted, the yellow hula-hoop stilled in her hand.

"Mama says, you wanna come over for lunch? We're having waffles!" Her eyes widened.

"*Waffles!*" I stared back at her. Her face sparkled, then blurred as I flew backward in time...

Last Sunday morning after Mass we had all gathered 'round the dining table for scrambled eggs and bacon. Daddy had just finished serving from the platter when a knock came to the door. I leaped up to see Gina, the next-door neighbor girl, through the screen. Gina was a year younger than me and twice my size. We never played together.

"Can we borrow a cup of flour?" she blurted. Mommy jumped up and filled a cup from the kitchen. I handed it over. Letting the screen door slam, I scurried back to my seat. Five minutes later, another knock sounded. This time Gina's voice demanded, "Do you have some maple syrup?" I produced the bottle from under the cupboard, then raced back to the table and jabbed my fork into the quickly cooling eggs.

Before I could raise my juice glass, a third knock pounded. Heaving a huge sigh, I slid off my chair and trudged towards the door. Gina cocked her head at me.

"Can we borrow your waffle iron?"

I stared. This time I knew the answer without glancing at Mommy.

"No. Cuz...we don't have one!" I watched her stomp away, then turned to join the family.

"Imagine that!" Mommy exclaimed. "What were they thinking?"

I giggled. But deep down, I ached for those same,

unattainable waffles...

Andrea's face popped back into view.

"Let me ask my Mommy!" I scrambled up the front steps and tore open the screen.

Once inside Andrea's house, we padded across the white carpet past her two gigantic older brothers, David and Jacob. They lay sprawled along the settee, arms draped over the back. In the corner the record changer dropped a black disc onto the growing pile of plates spinning round and round. I stopped just long enough to watch the big silver arm magically swing around and plop – all by itself – onto the record. "You ain't nothing but a hound dog!" I jumped.

Just then a large balding head popped out of a doorway. "*Jesus Christ!*" their father roared. "What, ya gotta make that racket in the house?!"

"C'mon," Andrea prodded. "Mama says we get to eat in the basement." I scurried after her.

Dark wood lined the cellar staircase that wound down to the cement floor below. A card table with vinyl placemats popped into view. Only instead of plates and forks, bowls and spoons lay there. *Wait a minute...*

"What about the *waffles?*" I exclaimed.

"Oh – Mama says we have to have chicken noodle soup first."

I was so hungry for waffles I could almost taste them. I could just see all those perfect little windows, each one filled with a golden drop of butter and a thick pool of syrup...

I gnawed the inside of my cheek and sat down. Mrs. Weinstein appeared over the railing, bearing a steaming silver pot. She ladled the soup into our bowls and set out a basket of bumpy white cracker pieces.

"Eat, eat," she urged. *"Then* you have the waffles."

Andrea picked up a chunk of cracker and broke it up into little specks. They fluttered into her soup like snowflakes.

"What are you doing?"

"I'm crumbling my Matza,"

"Matza? What's Matza?"

Her eyebrows lifted. She pointed to the basket. *"That's* Matza."

"They look like Saltines." I opened my mouth and shoveled in a great glob of noodles.

Suddenly she giggled. "Noo-o. That's-a-*Matza*." Andrea bobbed her head from side to side, her eyes rolled back: "Soup is hotsa. Eat lotsa Matza." Her face turned into one of those jiggly doll heads that bounce up and down on the back seat of cars. I snorted. We both erupted into giggles.

All of a sudden, the glob at the back of my throat jammed. I couldn't breathe! My stomach heaved, quivered, and exploded upward. My tongue lunged forward, propelled from behind as a tidal wave of white lava roared out of my mouth and into my bowl! In disbelief I stared into my soup at the re-surfacing foreign matter. I raised my head and peeked at Andrea. Her frozen face wreathed in black curls stared back at me, mouth gaping, eyes bulging in a moment of shocked silence.

"It's just crackers," I croaked. *Maybe she didn't see that. Maybe she'll think it's just "lotsa Matza" – like hers.*

The split-second had passed, and like lightning, she roared back to life.

"Mamaa!"

Andrea pushed back and flew up the basement steps. *Oh no, oh no...*

Lickety-split, Mrs. Weinstein galumphed back down

and hustled me out of my chair.

"You gotta go now! Go home quick! Tell your mama!" she bellowed.

"But – what about the waffles?" Little windows with maple pools faded slowly before my eyes.

"What you talking about? What? You want to eat waffles when you're *sick?!*" She prodded me up the steps and out the front door.

Once down to the sidewalk I turned back. Andrea stood behind the screen door waving her hand at me.

Rap! Rap! Rap!

A week later a knock came to our front door. I peered through the screen at Andrea. Hula hoop in hand, she gazed back at me.

"Mama says, are you still sick?"

I clamped down on my teeth and shook my head. *I was never sick!* But I didn't want her to get mad. Besides, I didn't want to think about those waffles right then.

"Hey!" I exclaimed. "You want to play inside?"

"Okay."

I opened the screen door and Andrea followed me down the hall to my room. "I've got a great idea!" I said. "Let's play 'Mass'!"

Her face wrinkled up. "Huh? What's 'Mass'?"

"I'll show you!"

I'd been waiting for this. In April I had made my First Holy Communion, and ever since I'd wanted to try it out at home.

"You can be the altar boy, and I'll be the priest."

"I don't want to be a *boy*!" frowned Andrea.

"It's okay. The priest is really a man. But we'll change it. Besides," I added. "You have the best part. Cuz you get to ring the *silver bell!*" I dangled Mommy's dinner bell before her.

Together we set up our altar on top of my dresser, with the two candles from the dining room table. "And…" I turned back to her, "You get to light the candles - just *pretend* -" I whispered, "- and *put them OUT!*" Triumphantly I flashed the metal measuring cup with the long handle that I had swiped from the kitchen drawer.

Next we lined up Biggie Bear, Clarabel the Clown, Goldie, Buhtricia Doll, and Baby Annie against the wall on my bed.

"Are they watching the show?" asked Andrea.

"No, silly," I retorted. "They're praying."

"Oh – just a minute -" I poked my head outside my door. "Mommy! Can we have some *red* Kool-Aid and some Saltine crackers for a snack?"

Carefully I carried the little cups to my room, along with the basket of crackers and a saucer I took from the drainer. These I arranged on the altar next to the glow-in-the-dark crucifix I had 'won' at school by selling magazines.

"*Now…costumes!*"

Andrea reluctantly agreed to wear Mommy's white petticoat around her neck – "Are you *sure* this is what they wear?"

"Yes! It's – almost – just like it!"

I donned my winter nightgown and, rifling through my drawers, at last snatched up my pink pajama bottoms. These I wrapped around my neck, each leg limply hanging down my chest. *Now* we were ready!

"You just kneel beside me,' I advised, "and whenever I say, 'Dominee, dominee', you say: 'speary tutu oh.'"

I faced the altar and raised my hands up high. "Dominee dominee!" I cried.

Andrea knelt quickly beside me. "*Ow!*" she

exclaimed. "Er – speary…speary."

"Speary tutu *oh*," I hissed. "Now get up and light the candles." On tiptoe, she reached up above the dresser.

The candles 'lit', I waved my hands over the Kool-Aid and crackers.

"Dominee dominee – dominee dominee," I chanted.

"Er – tutu speary – *oh*."

"Get ready to ring the silver bell," I whispered. I raised a cracker over my head. "*Now!*"

Tinkle – tinkle – tinkle… My whole body sang with the sound. *Magic is happening!*

I then raised up one of the Kool-Aid cups. "Again!"

Andrea dutifully obeyed.

Tinkle – tinkle - tinkle…

"Now we get Holy Communion!" I exulted. "And you get to hold the Special Plate!" Andrea cocked her head at me.

"I'll do you first," I explained. "See?" I picked up a broken cracker with one hand and the saucer with the other, holding it under her chin. "Stick out your tongue." I laid the cracker on her quivering tongue, wishing I had chosen a smaller piece. "Now don't chew it," I admonished. "Swallow." Andrea's eyes widened as she stopped in mid-chew. Her lips tightened, then slowly she attempted to swallow – without success.

"Oi…kennt…" she muffled. Her eyes glowered as she resumed the grinding of teeth.

"*Stop!*" I cried. "You're hurting Jesus!"

"Then gimme thum Kool-Aid!"

"No! That's only for the priest. It's Jesus's *blood*." I took one of the cracker pieces, placed it on my own tongue and forced it down. Then I reached up for one of the cups on the dresser and swallowed the red liquid. It slipped coolly down my throat.

"Here - " I held out the little plate. "Now we give the

dolls – I mean – the people – Holy Communion. You stick the Special Plate under their chin."

But Andrea just stood there, eyebrows flattened, mouth open.

"That's not fair!" she burst out. "Your Mama gave you *two* cups!"

"I knowww. But that's because you're the altar boy, and he doesn't - "

Andrea clamped her mouth shut, whirled around and charged out of the room.

"Wait!" I cried. "I was gonna give it to you *after* the game!"

But the screen door slammed, and then she was gone.

That evening after supper the phone rang. Mommy tapped on my bedroom door. I glanced up from the rug, having just put Annie to bed with Goldie in her cradle. Mommy perched on the edge of my bed, watching me.

"That was Mrs. Weinstein."

I stiffened, and studied Baby Annie's nose.

"She was very upset."

I stared sideways at Mommy's legs. "You...mean because I wouldn't let Andrea have the Kool-Aid?"

"Kool-Aid?"

"Our snack – but it was part of the 'Game'..."

"Was your game called 'Mass'?"

I looked up at Mommy. She was not smiling.

"Yes."

"Sweetheart. Andrea is Jewish. She cannot play a game doing something that is Catholic."

"Why?"

Mommy's face softened. "Because it's about Jesus Christ, and Jews do not believe that Jesus was God."

I knew she must be wrong. I'd been to Andrea's house.

"That's not true!" I protested. "Mr. Weinstein –
Andrea's daddy – is *always* saying 'Jesus Christ'!"

Mommy studied the rug a moment.

"I'm sorry, sweetie," she sighed. "I tried to tell her it
was only a game. But Mrs. Weinstein said that Andrea
will not be allowed to play here again."

The next morning I slumped on the cement steps
in the middle of the front lawn and gazed down the
block. A small figure in the distance bumped in time
with the swirling yellow hoop. She faced the street. Her
voice wafted towards me: "…eighty-eight, eighty-nine,
ninety…" I raised my hand and waved, hesitantly at
first, then expanding into giant rainbow arcs.

"Helloooo…"

But never once did she glance in my direction.

Finally, I looked away from Andrea, picked up Annie,
and trudged back up the steps and into the house.

Cathay, Patrick, Michael
Easter 1957

*Julie, Nana, Tim (top); Mike, Pat, cousin Holly,
Cathay (bottom) 1958*

Cathay, Mommy and Timmy

Mommy and Timmy at the shore
1958

Birthday Party Friends December 3, 1958

IN TRANSIT
1959 (January – February)

Cathay, Tim, Mike, Julie, Pat

Dad's new military assignment: Letterman
Army Hospital at the Presidio of San Francisco,
California. A long way to go!

Pat, Mike, Julie, Cathay

Westward Ho!

"Goodbye, house!"

I gave a last, lingering look about the vacant living room around me. *How funny it sounds in here....almost like an echo.* Just like it did when I first ventured in, all excited, a mere six-year old, two years before. Now it was time to follow the Army's calling, once again, and head back to California.

"Load 'er up!"

I broke away from my reverie and dashed out the front door to the cement steps. Swinging on the wrought-iron railing, I gazed at the moving van below. Two burly men in sweaty T-shirts (even though it was January!) grunted beneath the old brown sofa. Mike and Pat danced past them on the sidewalk.

"We're leaving! We're leaving!" Pat chanted. Mike didn't look too sure.

"Where are my Lincoln Logs?" he muttered.

"In the big truck," I pointed out.

Finally the tailgate clanged shut on all our worldly goods. We waved goodbye in the waning winter light as the heavy weight heaved and groaned on down the street. At last it disappeared around the corner.

Daddy rubbed his hands back and forth, grinning sideways at us.

"Ok, everybody! It's time to roll!"

I joined the throng of eager bodies shoveling themselves into the already packed Pontiac station wagon. The roof rack bulged with suitcases and odd-shaped bags. Mike and Pat grabbed the third seat, folded down and blanketed for sleepyheads. Satchel in hand, stuffed with Little Golden books, I bounded into the middle, next to three-year old Julie. I knew my job would be to entertain her. Mommy settled toddler Timmy in the front between Daddy and herself. Daddy turned around in his seat to inspect the troops.

"Everybody ready for the big adventure?" he beamed.

"Yes, yes!"

"Let's go, Daddy!"

"Let's hurry and drive to California!"

With a laugh and a wink at Mommy, he propelled our own heavy load away from the curb and down Insley Street.

"Bye, house!"

"Bye, sidewalk!"

"Bye, trees!"

"Bye, froggies!"

"Bye, Silver Spring, Maryland!" Mommy finished.

We were off!

❦

Four hours and three bathroom stops later, the novelty had worn off.

"I'm bored!"

"I'm hungry!"

"You just finished your peanut butter and jelly sandwich!" reminded Mommy.

She whispered something to Daddy. He announced: "Special dessert is waiting for us when we get to our Virginia motel!"

Thirty minutes later we raced into the tiny room crammed with beds. Gleefully I dove onto one of the doubles and bounced up and down. Mike and Pat scrambled up the other one - "*Whee!*" - when Mommy entered the room, juggling suitcases.

"Off the beds!" she commanded.

"Aww...."

Mike hurriedly hopped from one bed to another, just out of Mommy's reach, before disembarking.

Bed partners were designated: Mommy, Daddy and Timmy in one big bed; Mike, Pat and Julie in the other. I proudly accepted my station as the sole occupant of the foldout rollaway. A hue and cry swiftly ensued.

"Why does SHE get her own bed?!"

"It's not fair!"

Mommy leaped in with her usual Solomon-like judgment.

"We'll trade off. Michael gets the cot tomorrow night, and Patrick the night after."

"Ha, ha!" Mike stuck his tongue out at me.

I smiled smugly at the boys. "But *I* have it tonight."

Mommy rewarded us with Oreos as we settled in for the first of several such nights on the road.

Morning erupted as we bombarded Mommy with demands for breakfast. Instead, Daddy surprised us with "portable cereal bowls" – individual-sized boxes of Sugar Pops, Sugar Smacks, and Sugar Frosted Flakes that could be cut open down the middle. Plastic knife and spoon in hand, we gleefully attacked our boxes like happy vandals.

"Along the DOTTED LINE!" Mommy admonished.

To our amazement we were allowed to pour the milk right inside the waxed paper lining. None of it even soaked through the cardboard!

The second day on the road droned on. By nightfall Timmy's sleepy wails began to subside. Mommy faded out her rendition of "Twenty Froggies Went to School," while Daddy began warbling "A Hundred Bottles of Beer on the Wall." For the tenth time Julie tossed *The Little Engine That Could* onto the floor.

"I want my 'iddow Piddow!" she pouted.

I searched under all the books and sweaters piled up around us. Nothing. A snicker escaped from the third seat. Craning around, I peered through the shadows behind me. I first noticed Patrick noisily sucking his thumb in slumber, snuggled against the bunched-up blankets. Mike lay beside him. He stared up at me with a grin; then snapped his lids shut and pretended to snore. A suspicious-looking bulge stuck out from behind his ear.

"That's Julie's!" I yelled. "You give that back!" Mike rolled away from my grasp, laughing and pummeling the pillow under his tummy.

"MommEE!" I cried.

Mommy wheeled around wearily once more. "Michael Thomas, give Julie back her pillow!"

Instant silence as Michael feigned sudden sleep. Daddy's usually mellow voice broke the stillness.

"IF I HAVE TO STOP THIS CAR, THERE WILL BE ONE VERY UNHAPPY LITTLE BOY!" he bellowed.

Without a word, the miniature pillow shot up in the air and over the seat. Julie grabbed her special friend and thrust it behind her head, spreading herself full out along the seat beside me. With rhythmical precision, she bounced her head up and down on it as she serenaded herself to sleep.

"Mamamamama...."

With a unified sigh, we all settled back to the mundane lull of the road.

Soon Daddy pointed out the bright lights of a small hamburger stand.

"Fast food ahead!"

I stared, mystified. *Does that mean we have to eat very quickly? Or if we don't, the waiter takes it away before we are finished?*

Once inside, we lined up hungrily on the benches straddling a wooden picnic table. Daddy vanished, only to reappear moments later bearing a whole tray of hamburgers! What a treat! Moans and sighs of contentment filled the air as happy bodies munched in unison.

Suddenly an inner alarm exploded in my brain. I leaned across the table.

"Mommy!" I shrieked in a whisper. "It's *Friday!*"

Mommy stopped in mid-bite. Mike and Pat froze, watching the meat quiver in her outstretched hands. She swallowed, glanced at Daddy and calmly replied,

"Remember the new baby in my tummy?" My eyes wandered to her latest bulge with tentative interest.

"Pregnant ladies don't have to stop eating meat on Fridays," she said, "because their babies need the protein to grow."

But…."But what about us?!" I blurted. *Were we committing a sin?*

Mommy caught Daddy's eye. He frowned a moment, furrowed his brow and pursed his lips. Then he raised his eyebrow and smiled at us.

"The Army gives us a dispensation for traveling," he stated. "When we move from place to place we can eat whatever we can find."

Mommy shot him an appreciative smile.

"Ohhh…." I resumed munching. We all breathed a collective sigh of relief that we didn't have to toss out our much coveted and rarely received hamburgers.

At last we spotted the welcome sight of our Tennessee motel. A single bulb glowed through the dark above the porch steps of our unit. Immediately car doors sprang open as cramped bodies cried out for release.

"Last one there's a rotten egg!" Mike sang.

"Everyone carry something!" Mommy called out.

Julie scrambled off the seat of the car and onto the curb.

"Julie, wait!" commanded Mommy.

Too late. Giggling in her desire to be first, Julie toddled through the gloom towards the motel. Faster now, as Mike raced her, she suddenly shot forward and fell with a thud against the intruding cement step. An earsplitting shriek cut through the air. As one, the stragglers leaped forward toward the sound. Mommy reached her first and turned her over. Julie's face was covered with blood.

"Walt! It's all right, Julie, there, there, little sweetheart…"

I stared, open-mouthed, while Daddy swept past me and swooped her up into the motel. The sound of running water met my ears as I entered. Mommy pressed a wet washcloth against her face, Julie screaming all the while. I watched, fascinated, as the white of the cloth slowly bled bright red.

Mommy helped Daddy bundle Julie up in blankets and carry her back to the car.

"Where are you taking her?!" I cried.

"Cathay, quick – you be a big girl and come help Julie," ordered Daddy.

Uncomprehending, I let Mommy settle me into the backseat while Daddy lay Julie next to me, her head in my lap. Mommy pressed my hand over the cold, damp cloth on her forehead. She blew us kisses, then hurried the boys towards the lighted porch. Daddy got behind the wheel and roared off.

I gulped, and peered down at Julie. Her face was white, her eyes big as pancakes as she wildly searched my own. Her voice had sunk to a whimper.

Cautiously I patted her arm. I swallowed.

"Daddy! What do I do?"

"Talk to her."

"It's ok, Julie," I muttered. "It's ok, it's ok…."

Now what?

A tiny voice eased out of my mouth in song. "Playmate, come out and play with me…." I quavered. Julie seemed to relax.

Up ahead glaring lights stabbed at us in the dark. 'E-M-E-R-G-E-N-C-Y' I read above the entryway of the building. Daddy scooped Julie up while I hung onto the tail of his jacket. Once inside, the smell of alcohol assaulted my nostrils. For a moment I couldn't see for the dazzle of all the lights. Daddy murmured something to the gray-haired nurse at the desk, and we sat down on the metal chairs along the wall. Julie began to whimper again.

There didn't seem to be anything going on – just lots of people waiting. On the wall opposite us a big clock ticked. Finally Daddy leaped up, Julie folded in his arms.

"What's the story here?" he demanded.

The nurse glanced up from her chart scribbles.

"I'm sorry, sir, but two of our doctors were taken ill," she drawled. "We're dreadfully overworked at the moment."

Daddy's face tightened. He fumbled in his jacket and pulled something out of his wallet to show her.

"I'm a physician," he declared. "I will do it myself!"

With a stern look over his shoulder he caught my eye.

"Come along, Cathay."

I scurried after him as he strode past the startled nurse, cradling Julie in his arms. We stopped inside a curtained room with a high bed surrounded by a metal rail.

"Up you go, Cathay," he urged.

My eyes widened, "ME?!"

"I'm counting on you to help me." He smiled for the first time. "You're my little assistant. Julie needs you to hold her for me."

I stole a glance at the waiting nurse who shrugged, then lifted me up onto the side of the bed. Daddy laid Julie next to me.

"Your job is to hold her head still."

I stared in horror as Daddy raised a giant needle and stuck it right into the gaping cut on her forehead! Julie yelped and tried to pull away. I pressed against the sides of her head with both my hands, and squeezed my lids shut. *I don't want to do this! I don't want to do this!* When I opened them, Julie was staring up at me, her own eyes appealing to me for help. I gulped.

"I'm sorry, Julie," I whispered.

She wailed. I started shaking. Any moment now, I

knew I might cry, too. Then Daddy's voice rose calmly through the fear.

"We'll have Julie good as new in no time. She's so lucky to have her big sister here with her."

I relaxed. Then I caught sight of a curved needle with black thread in his hand. Closer now he approached her face. I held my breath, horrified but fascinated. Deftly in and out of Julie's skin he wove that needle. I didn't even know he could sew! *Just like Grandmamma!*

All of a sudden I felt prickly. Tiny spots of light winked before my eyes. A shadow crept up, up around me as my body slid sideways over the rail. Two big arms pressed in on me and laid me back on the bed.

"Whoa! Looks like we have two patients!" Daddy chuckled.

Dizzy now, I slowly sat up and realized… Julie was gone! I glanced wildly about.

"Where is she?!" I squeaked.

"Not to worry," Daddy patted my arm. "She's waiting for you in the next room."

I climbed down and followed Daddy into the adjacent alcove. Suddenly I realized it was I who had been moved! Julie lay on the same 'operating' bed, eyes closed in slumber. A lumpy white bandage covered her forehead.

I stared down at my shoes.

"I'm sorry, Daddy."

Daddy bent and gave me a tight squeeze.

"You were there where she needed you," he reassured me. "She'll always look up to you, now."

Back in the car, Julie's heavy head weighed down on my lap. But I didn't mind. I peeled a strand of hair away from her bandage. She sighed and shifted, nodding up and down in her sleep.

"Mamamamama…."

Three days and three nights later found us nearing the end of our journey. As night fell along with the rain, tired children succumbed to the rhythm of the road. All but me.

Shadows flowed all around me. I leaned into the window, eyeing the rivulets that trailed, one by one, down the maze of raindrops. With a single fingertip I tracked their movements along the cool pane.... my own private crystal curtain, shimmering in the streetlights. Off in the distance a mournful train whistle sounded. Car wheels grew louder as they approached us, splashing on the wet pavement, then faded slowly off again.

Tomorrow we will be in California... Maybe I'll be 'Cathay' again... Cathay...

I glanced down at the sleeping child next to me; her rhythmical breathing flowed between her slightly parted lips. I turned back to my crystal curtain. Pressing my mouth to the glass, ever so quietly I allowed my song to escape.

"Playmate, come out and play with me..."

Mommy and Grandmamma

California Trail

"We're here!"

North Hollywood. The car doors swung open in front of the whitewashed wooden house with a picket fence hugging the yard. Mike, Pat and I charged ahead past the gate, while Mommy and Daddy extricated sleepy Julie and Timmy from the car. I skidded to a stop paces before the large, pillowy woman on the doorstep. Nana. I knew that; but, suddenly, I felt shy. Her face dimpled broadly as she folded us inside her ample arms.

"My, my! How you've grown!"

Just then, a willowy man with glasses poked his head

out the doorway with a smile. "Well, well...Well, well," he murmured. Grampa.

Amid the confusion of hellos and bodies bustling into the house, I wandered into the kitchen. Everything white. The screen-door to the left led outside. I pushed it open onto the back-porch. *Oh! They have a porch-swing! Just like in Texas!* With a hop, I wiggled my way onto the seat of that swing, grasped the wooden arm, and leaned back. *So peaceful out here; so noisy inside.* The air in me eased its way out of my body like a slow-moving train. I gazed at the barren backyard and rubbed my back against the wooden slats, content to listen to the muffled chatter within, sight-unseen.

...Daddy said, no, we are not moving here. We still have a long way to go. We will spend the night, and then move on. But we will not *be living near Nana and Grampa. Or Grandmamma...*

"Supper!" Nana's head popped out the screen-door. "Why, there you are! We've got some good cookin' in here. Best be getting it quick, with this crowd!"

I sidled inside and surveyed the kitchen table, now coated with a slick apple-patterned cloth and overcrowded with meat and potato plates. *Too many of us for those white chairs...* But, lickety-split, we doubled up, with Mike and Pat, and Julie and I, each sharing high-cushioned seats. Mommy held Timmy on her lap.

"Apple pie!" Mike, Pat and I beamed at each other, while Nana passed the plates all around. Just as I raised my fork, Grampa's roving arm caught my eye. He had picked up the gravy pitcher and oozed the grainy brown goop back and forth across his pie! Mike and I sucked in air together, eyes locked. Grampa spied us out of the corner of his eye with a sideways grin.

"Oh, it's *heaven*, I tell you!" He nodded up and down. And took a bite.

"Next stop, Grandmamma's!" Daddy rumbled from the front seat.

I leaned down to Timmy beside me and cooed, "Did you hear that, Timmy? We're going to go see Grandmamma!"

Timber bounced up and down. "Gum machine! Gum machine!" he shrieked.

"Ah-hahaha!" Mike guffawed.

"No, Timber," I shook my head. Timmy eyed the two of us with suspicion, then stood up and yanked on Daddy's shirt over the seatback.

"Gum machine, Daddy!" he pleaded. "I wanna See Gum machine!" By now, shrill laughter had engulfed all of us in the back, while Timmy wailed his repeated request.

"Stop it, now, children," insisted Mommy. "He'll see when we get there."

"There it is! There it is!" I shrieked Grandmamma's red-tile-roofed house with the arched entrance and the palm tree beside it. Just like I remembered. I bolted from the car and flew up the cement path. Gandmamma pulled back the front door and cackled.

"Well, my little chickadees, how the heck are ya?"

Moments later, the troops poured past her into the antique-filled living room that had once been home to us, as well. Within minutes, Grandmamma had settled us around her mahogany dining table. She fed us corned beef, carrots and potatoes… and *cabbage!* The smell of it smothered me, but we forced ourselves to eat it, so we wouldn't waste food "for the starving children in China." *How do they get our food...?* Really, though, we swallowed with our eyes peeled for that lemon meringue pie gleaming on the counter...

Yum! I swung my leg back and forth while sucking that last wiggly yellow bite off my fork. Julie smacked her lips, perched on the phone book beside me.

"Grumma! Grumma!" chattered Mike. "Tell us a Charlie and Joe story!"

"Yeah!" Pat echoed.

We were the only ones left at the table. Mommy was busy with Timmy, and Daddy had gone to the car.

"Well, now, let me see..." Grandmamma scootched her chair in-between Pat and Mike. "Now, Joe, as you know, was a beautiful blue bird –"

"A BIG blue bird!" blurted Mike.

Grandmamma poked him with her long fingernail. "You bet. A great *big* bird, with wings as long as your legs."

I pushed my plate aside and watched her drawn-on eyebrows dance and her eyes twinkle.

"Now, Charlie, the spider, of course, was Joe's best friend. He was a big, *friendly* brown spider, who would do anything for Joe. But Charlie had a problem. He was so poor, that he had no shoes. And, you know, he needed eight of them, because a spider has eight legs." Patrick nodded, his eyes big as saucers.

"So one day, Joe heard him crying from way up high. He swooped down to the ground in front of him and said, 'Climb aboard, my friend! I'll take you to the land of the magic shoe tree!' Charlie wiped his nose with one of his legs and climbed up on his back.

"Hold on tight, Charlie boy!" Joe cried. Then he rose high in the sky, higher than Charlie could ever have imagined..." I closed my eyes and floated along with them...

191

All too soon, it was time to move on. Mommy herded us all out, and we packed back into the station wagon. We still had a ways to go this afternoon.

Grandmamma waved us goodbye from the curb, shaking her head with a chuckle. "Oh, my! My, my, my!" She had promised to meet us the next day 'to say a real goodbye' at Auntie Jo and Uncle Freeman's in Bakersfield. Auntie Jo was her youngest sister.

"We're almost ther-ere!" warbled Daddy.

Orange trees surrounded our car!

"Look, Daddy!" I pointed. "It's an orange forest!"

"Yep. Orange groves."

"Are these Auntie Jo and Uncle Free's?"...*Maybe we could climb them – and even pick some!*

"N-no... but I believe their neighbors have some."

Without warning, we pulled into a rambling yard of pines, firs and palm trees, bordered by a tall wooden fence. The car doors bounced open and Mike, Pat and I tumbled out. We raced in circles, weaving around the various trees and bushes. My chest puffed. It felt so good to *runnnn!* A carpet of needles spread lushly over the ground. *Oooh!* My feet scuffed and slid. *Perfect for 'ice-skating'!*

I stopped short, caught by the liquid eyes of a velvet brown horse-head gazing at me over the fence. "Ohhh..."

"Children! Come! Let's go in, everyone!" called Mommy.

"Can we ride him? Can we ride him?!" I refused to let go of his gaze.

"Cathay, it's not theirs. It belongs to the neighbor." *Oh...*

Auntie Jo looks just like Grandmamma! Only skinnier.

But, unlike Grandmamma, her feet seemed to dance when she moved, and her arms flew with her words.

"Free, get them a high-ball, will ya?" Her husky voice floated out on the tails of her cigarette.

Uncle Free tipped his head at her. "Certainly, my dear," he lilted with his clipped Canadian accent. His lips crinkled beneath his pencil mustache. In his grey-flannel suit, he looked like he was about to leave for church. He must've felt like going to church a lot, because that's all he seemed to wear.

Patrick burst through the still-open front door. "Guess what! They have a lake with GIANT goldfish in it!"

Mike, Julie and I rushed back out after him. Timmy toddled to catch up. Sure enough, cushioned by overgrown plants, a pond glimmered on the far side of the house. Plate-sized orange fish sashayed before us.

"Oooh!" Timmy cooed. He stretched over the edge and flicked his chubby hands in the water. "Here, fishie, fishie!"

Just then, Auntie Jo loomed up behind him. "Oh, ho! No, you don't, young fella!" She scooped him up just as Mommy bore down on us.

"The pond is not to be played with, children! Come back inside!"

No sooner had we joined the grown-ups in the house, when a long, melodic whistle split the air. *Whittt – Wheee-ooo!*

Who did that? Mike raised his eyebrows at me. We studied the grown-ups, but they were all talking. Again... the whistle. Suddenly Auntie Jo chuckled.

"Hey, kiddos. Check under that towel over there." We followed her gaze to a shapeless mass on the corner table.

"Go on. Lift up the towel."

We shuffled towards it. Patrick glanced back at her;

then slowly raised it up.

"HELLO!"

Pat leaped backwards, tumbling into Mike and me. There inside his cage, a *huge* black bird had spoken to us!

"It's a Mina Bird," laughed Auntie Jo. "His name's Inky." The bird blinked at us and cocked his head.

"What'd he charge ya?" he squawked.

From then on, we glued ourselves to his corner.

"They're cooking dinner in the *fireplace!*" I whispered in Mike's ear.

Uncle Freeman smacked his hands together and sprinkled something from a can into their living room fireplace. Orange flames shot up when he dropped the match. *Whoa!* We raced into the kitchen where Mommy and Auntie Jo huddled over the counter.

"Here – let me get it ready for the children, Jo. I'll be fine - "

"What are we having for dinner in the *fireplace,* Mommy?"

Auntie Jo whirled around. "Why, steak, kiddos! Your Uncle Freeman knows just how to do it right."

"Steak?!" wailed Mike. "I don't like that kind of meat! It's too chewy!"

I couldn't wait to try it. "You're strange, Mike. You like *liver* – yuck! And you don't like steak."

Auntie Jo hustled us back into the living room. Just then, Inky piped up. But I couldn't quite make out the words.

Mike jerked around. "See?! Inky doesn't like it, either! He said, 'For lasagna!'"

"What?" Auntie Jo squinted.

"For lasagna! For lasagna!" repeated Inky… maybe.

"See? See?!" Mike shrieked. "He wants lasagna!"

"Are you sure?" I strained my ears.

Uncle Freeman chuckled. Auntie Jo guffawed.

"No, kiddos," she finally snorted.

Uncle Free winked at us. "Mike, Inky was saying, 'How much on ya?' – I told you, Jo, that bird would catch up with you someday." She swirled her drink and laughed at him.

Mike's face crumpled.

"How much on ya? How much on ya?" I leaned in and taunted.

"For lasagna! For lasagna!" Mike taunted right back.

Daddy interrupted. "Honey? How's the meat coming?" he called to the kitchen doorway.

Beaming at us all, Mommy marched in with a large platter. "It's all ready for you!" she sang out.

Daddy's jaw dropped. "What did you *do?!*" On the platter lay an array of small pieces of raw meat.

Uncle Free shook his head back and forth in disgust. "I don't believe it! No, no, no!" He stared at Daddy, then at Mommy.

"What?" Mommy looked confused.

"Why did you cut it in little bits?!" roared Daddy.

"Well...well, for the children! They can't eat a big piece of meat!"

Nooo! You COOK it first! THEN you can cut it!" Daddy's face glowed bright red.

"Bonnie, Bonnie, Bonnie." Uncle Free shut his eyes and shook his head.

Auntie Jo leaped in. "Oh, fiddlefaddle, Freeman. Just get on with it."

I nudged Mike. "C'mon. Let's go outside!"

We tripped out the backdoor of the empty kitchen and joined Patrick, chasing Lulu, the black and white bundle of fur...

"Dinner!"

...I stood on tiptoe over the kitchen counter and inhaled the most succulent aroma wafting from the serving platter. Bodies milled around me.

"Where's Patrick?" Mommy's head swiveled back and forth.

"I think he's still outside." I peered out in the yard, my lips to the screen. "Dinner! Dinner, Pat!"

From a distance, Patrick jerked up in surprise and sped towards us. But something was wrong, because the closer he got, the faster he zoomed... until –

BAM!

Patrick roared right into the house like a sledgehammer with the screen-door wrapped around his body! Total shock covered his face. *"Waaahhh!"*

"Oh, my goodness!" cried Mommy, cradling him. "Didn't you see the screen-door?"

"N-noooooo!"

After that, Auntie Jo plastered a big, black "X" onto the screen.

Dingg-dong-dong-dingg!

I glanced up from the rug after dinner to the front door. Auntie Jo continued clearing glasses, cigarette clamped between her fingers, and disappeared into the kitchen. Only Mike and I were left in the room. The bell rang again. We looked at each other, then back at the kitchen. *Hmmm...* I unfolded, sauntered to the front door and tugged it open. No one there. I sat back down again.

Dingg-dong-dong-dingg! This time I leaped up and yanked the door open. No one. *Huh?* I turned around, my hand still on the knob, just as Auntie Jo waltzed back in. She took one look at me and exploded with laughter.

"Oh, kiddos!" she gasped. "Inky got you again!"

"Really?" Mike's eyes widened. "He can do a

doorbell sound?"

"Uh oh," I frowned. "How do you know when there's really someone there?"

"Oh, that's not what *our* doorbell sounds like." Auntie Jo strode to the door, twisted the knob, and pushed the bell. "See? Completely different." She grinned at us. "He learned *that* doorbell sound from his previous owner."

"Ohhhhh."

Bedtime. Julie and I snuggled up on the brown plaid folded-out "divan" in the den. I kicked my feet back and forth against each other under the covers, getting cozy. Julie had drifted off, her lips parted. I stared upward through the dark, towards the ceiling. *I wonder if Mike and Pat are awake… But, wait – where* are *Mike and Pat?* I sat up. Voices outside my window wavered…whispers. In the gloom, I leaned against the back of the divan and peeked between the blinds. They crinkled loudly. Three orange sleeping bags stretched along the ground below. One of them was mine. Instead, Auntie Jo's smoky laughter wafted out. She rose up in the shadows and twisted towards the other bags. Through the opened window her words snuck in.

"And then…I climbed up on the back of that horse…" Her voice muffled. Mike and Pat leaned on their elbows in the dark and listened; followed by furious whispers and giggles. *Wait – what?!*

I crept off the divan and ran smack into Mommy in the living room. I glared at her.

"How come the boys get to sleep with Auntie Jo?"

"Well," began Mommy. "Auntie Jo especially likes boys. She's a tomboy." Mommy smiled. "But Auntie Hal likes girls. You're lucky, because Auntie Hal is *your* godmother."

I stared at her. *But Auntie Hal isn't here… And now she's* really *far away from us.*

Finally, I turned around, pushed open the den door, and crawled back into my own bed.

I wished Grandmamma were there to tell me a Charlie and Joe story.

"Time to hit the road!"

Our Southern California sojourn had come to an end. Grandmamma had tootled up that morning from Hollywood for her own visit, just in time to help cheer us on for the final lap of our journey.

"Hello and goodbye, you little dickens!" She squeezed each one of us.

"What'd he charge ya? What'd he charge ya?" Inky marched furiously back and forth on his perch as we tried to say goodbye.

"For lasagna! For lasagna!" we chanted back at him.

Then all five of us tumbled out the front door, and instead of beelining it to the car, we zigzagged wildly for one last hurrah through that outrageously big backyard. *"Wheee!"*

At last settled in our spots in the station wagon, we twisted around and hung over the seatbacks. The five

of us stared out the rear window and waved to the three shrinking figures on the doorstep - natty Uncle Free with his felt fedora hat, flanked by the "twin" sisters - waving back at us... until we rounded the long driveway, and they disappeared from view.

Uncle Freeman and Auntie Jo

Relatively Perfect

"Wake up Cathay! We're going to Mass in fifteen minutes!" I snuggled and stretched inside yet another strange bed.

Where am I?

My eyes popped open. Memories of the night before flooded over me. At last in Northern California, we had invaded the home of our cousins in Menlo Park. Aunt Joan was Daddy's cousin – the daughter of Auntie Hal and Uncle Eli. Mommy and Daddy had decided to leave me with the Hausermans so I could continue school with them while they searched for a house.

I smiled to myself as I gazed sideways from bed to frilly bed. That suited me just fine. Instead of only *one* (very) little sister and three younger brothers, I now had *three* "sisters!" (And two little "brothers.") One was a year older (fair Susie) and one was my own age! (dark-haired Julie.) Mary was two years younger. It was in *her* bed that I lay, having ousted her to a cot in her parents' room.

Julie shook me this time. "Get up! If you're late, no breakfast afterwards!"

I leaped up and fumbled for my suitcase.

After Mass, I trailed back inside the vast kitchen on the heels of my cousins. Susie, Julie and Mary, dressed like triplets in their matching Sunday dresses, bickered over who got to sit next to me. I felt like a queen! Certainly not the respect I got at home! Wedged between Julie and Susie, I graciously agreed to sit next to Mary at dinnertime.

"Order up!" I peered down the long table past three-year-old Danny to brisk Aunt Joan at the end. She sat surveying the scene, head tilted inquiringly. I stared back, mystified.

Mary leaned across the table towards me. "Cathay, what kind of egg are you having?" I hesitated.

"Fried for me!" Julie sang out.

"Scrambled!" Susie added. *Uh...is this a restaurant?!* Julie nudged me. "What's your order?"

"You mean I get to *choose*?" I whispered behind my hand.

Both affable Uncle Dan at one end of the table and Aunt Joan at the other sat in their chairs, unmoving.

"Er, who's making the breakfast?" I mouthed.

"Why, Marty, o' course." I followed Mary's gaze across the room. A young redhead in a black dress and white apron had just settled cousin Timmy in his high chair. She wheeled about and smiled at me.

"How would you like your egg, luv?" she queried in a clipped brogue. *This is really like a restaurant!*

"Um...I'll have – I'll have...what Susie's having," I finished faintly. *Whatever that was...*(We never got to choose at home!)

Minutes later, a plate appeared with scrambled eggs, bacon and the hugest half-moon yellow fruit I had ever seen! Grapefruit. I knew that. *But how do you eat it?* I glanced sideways at Julie. She grabbed her spoon and quickly lifted a juicy morsel. I picked up my spoon and stabbed in the middle – but nothing happened...*ow!* Except a squirt in the eye, and my grapefruit bouncing off the plate, upside down in my lap. My cheeks burning, I carefully eased it back in place.

"Haven't you had grapefruit before?" Julie snorted.

"Yes, I just, uh...um, well, not exactly..."

Susie leaned over on my left.

"Here," she said. "Stick your spoon along the edge – like this." Grateful, I followed her example and plopped a shredded lump into my mouth. Susie and Julie exchanged glances and giggled. I soon joined in.

Nightfall brought a new discovery. I meandered throughout the house, exploring its nooks and crannies, when I slipped into the TV room. Mary and Julie lay on their stomachs gazing at the black and white flickering screen.

"Psst! Cathay!"

I turned. A narrow door stood slightly ajar just behind the couch. I peeled it open and peered inside. Neat stacks of cardboard boxes lined the walls of the closet. Susie, seated on the floor, grinned up at me. Her hands twisted up and down, entwined in green yarn. Two metal sticks flashed back and forth in the glaring light from the bulb above. I stared at her. She looked like an elf busily working away with a sly smile on her face.

"C'mon in," she said. She shifted over and I sat down beside her.

"What are you doing?"

"Knitting."

I stared, fascinated. Her hands flew so fast they almost seemed to blur.

"This is my special place," she confided.

I nodded, drinking in the long, shallow chamber, the musty smell, the tight space just big enough for two children.

"Neat."

"I come here and imagine everyone's looking for me, but no one thinks to look here. I see them walking by, searching, but they don't see me. It's like I'm invisible."

I nodded knowingly.

"Hey…how do you do that?" I pointed at the needles in her hands.

"Oh – here, I'll show you." Susie grabbed another set and some yellow yarn from a corduroy bag behind her. She leaned over my lap and patiently led my hands into the threading of the first stitches. Half an hour later, I had succeeded in creating two even-looking rows all on my own.

"You got it!" Susie exulted. I smiled back.

"What are you making?" I asked.

"A sweater."

"Oh." That sounded awfully complicated.

"I'm…making a baby blanket," I decided. "For my Mommy's new baby."

Susie's face scrunched up. "Maybe you should try a doll blanket first."

"Nope. A baby blanket."

First day of school with the cousins held plenty of promise. I padded through the yawning doorway after Julie, protected by a bubble of association. Julie, who could do no wrong, led the way.

But third grade in California seemed jumbled. I stared up at the bulletin board borders of enlarged cursive letters: *Aa, Bb, Cc*… *That looks like my second grade classroom!* Much to my surprise, Sister Mary Michael had everyone take out their penmanship book to practice "cursives." I waited till the nun, circulating the room, ambled between the rows of desks beside me. Cautiously I raised my hand.

"Sister," I whispered. She bent low and waited. "I already learned these *last* year."

"Well, now," she spoke softly, "this will give you

more practice."

Then, right after that, we did arithmetic with numbers much too big to multiply together! Everyone else scribbled furiously while I stared at the offending figures, defying them to show me the way. At last Sister called me up to her desk and patiently unraveled the mystery. She gave me extra papers to do for homework (which I carefully hid under my sweater as I slipped back to my seat.)

Finally, the bell blaring the end of the day, I gathered my new workbooks and joined the crush squeezing into the open air.

School's out! Now to find Julie. I waited till the mob thinned, then disappeared. No Julie. I peered to the right and left along the open courtyard. No one left in sight. The building opposite grew harsh and unyielding under my gaze. I swallowed. *I know she said she'd meet me after school...we'd walk home together...* Susie, I knew, had a ballet lesson, and Mary had swimming. I didn't dare leave the premises by myself into the Unknown outside.

I dragged my feet across the asphalt to the auditorium opposite. I peered timidly inside an open door. Empty. Backing out, I shuffled over to the other side again. Rows of silver lockers gleamed along the wall in the low winter light. I tried counting them: first forward, then backward. Two strange girls appeared from around the corner of the building. Quickly I set my books against the bike rail behind me and thumbed through a workbook. Maybe they wouldn't notice me.

"Hi. Aren't you Julie's cousin?"

I glanced up. "Um, yes. Do you know where she is?"

"Of course. She's at basketball practice. Well, see you tomorrow."

I turned and watched their retreating backs as they skipped across the courtyard together out to the sidewalk. Solitude once again.

Dropping my books to the ground, I grasped the cold, hard surface of the bar with both hands and slid my feet underneath it. Four quick baby steps backward, and *swoosh!* I slid again, this time my head thrown back, eyes closed against the warm rays above. Over and over I repeated the pattern, becoming one with the dance.

At last, Julie appeared. Enveloped now in shadows, I stopped in mid-swing, gazed up at her, and waited.

"Ready to go?" she asked.

"I didn't know where you were," I blurted.

"Oh, yeah, I had basketball. Three days a week."

"Oh."

Julie smiled and sauntered ahead. I scrambled to catch up.

As we approached the homestead, a high-pitched yell escaped from within. Julie and I glanced at each other and broke into a run. We stumbled around a large white van blocking the entry through the shield of evergreens. Aunt Joan emerged from the open door, eyes wild, cheeks flushed.

"Who locked the TV room closet door?!" she shrieked. I could feel my stomach shrivel and fall. *Uh oh.* Her black eyes darted from Julie to me and back again.

"Well?!" she demanded.

My fingers twitched, remembering the cool, slippery feel of the button poking out of the golden knob. It felt nice to push it rhythmically in and out as I watched Susie pack away the yarn the night before. I must've stopped with the button pushed in. But...*I didn't know it would stay that way if the door got shut!*

The silence weighed heavily on my ears.

"I've had to call a locksmith!" Aunt Joan raged on, her arm rigid, pointing down the hall. Reluctantly I followed Julie to the door in question. A man in white overalls bent over an open toolbox beside it. Instinctively I reached for the knob and wrenched it – to no avail. The workman raised his head and stared straight into my eyes. *He knows! He knows!*

"I'm sorry! I'm sorry!" I gasped. "No one told me it could lock with nobody in it!" I dashed past the man, his gravelly voice guffawing behind me. With a twist I slipped out the patio door, seeking solitude.

A thick blanket of grass stretched before me, flowing farther than any backyard I had ever seen. Tall sentinel trees stood ramrod straight, guarding the perimeter. I faltered, unsure where my feet would carry me. I edged forward. When I sensed an equal amount of space in all four directions, I plopped down in the center of the lawn, legs crossed, my back to the house. *Green. I want it to always be green. Just green.*

All too soon, a door slammed behind me. Footsteps pattered closer and closer.

"Cathay!"

I waited.

Mary danced before me.

"It was you! It was you!" she cried, wide-eyed. I glared at her.

Julie flopped down next to me. "Don't worry, Cathay. Mom's not mad any more."

Mary suddenly lunged forward, her wavy-haired face in mine.

"I did it too, once," she whispered.

"You did?"

Both Julie and Mary nodded.

"But this time it wasn't me!" she crowed, whirling backwards in delight.

"Mary!" admonished Julie. Mary's hand flew to her mouth. She bent down and patted my knee. "I'm sorry!" she squeaked.

Maybe Mary *did* do it, too – but that didn't count. She was practically a *baby*. I was too big to make mistakes.

I did feel better, though.

A week later I decided I could walk home alone. Susie, Julie and Mary all had their after-school activities *(again)* and I didn't like waiting.

The house seemed awfully quiet.

I wandered into the living room. Spacious and beige all around, it flowed before me. Like a half-full carton of vanilla ice cream, soft and plain. Except for the grand piano. Deep brown and gleaming in the corner, it beckoned. I approached.

First I twirled on the stool…slowly, then faster. I giggled, my voice sounding loud in the stillness. I listened. No movements. I reached out and caressed the keys. Black, white. Pretty patterns they made. I remembered hearing Julie practice the day before. *How did she do that?* I took a breath, raised my hands, and let them crash down onto the keys. The sound jangled through my hands, up my arms and electrified my whole body. I was a piano player! I raised them again, and this time brought them down here, there, everywhere at once - like they did in the movies! My hands flew up and down, making notes jump and sing as they stung the air! My heart pounding, notes zinging wildly against each other, I filled the room with as many as I could.

"What is that racket?! *Stoppp!*"

Oh! I glanced up to see Aunt Joan bearing down on me, eyebrows raised, face contorted.

I snapped my hands back. The air rang with the residue. I chewed my lip and stared at the keys.

Her voice softened. "You need *lessons* to play music,

honey. Why don't you go outside and play?" She cocked her head, waiting.

"Okay," I mumbled.

Alone again, I surveyed the room once more. On the wall behind the piano hung a large pastel sketch of all five children, heads only, arranged like a wreath. *How lucky to be drawn by an artist!* I turned to the right. Glancing through an arched doorway, I spied three framed silhouette cutouts of the girls. I stared. They looked just like them! They were perfect! Just like Susie, Julie and Mary. Perfect.

❧

"Cathay! They're here!"

Two weeks had passed since I became a Hauserman. Finally I was going home for a visit. No, they hadn't found a house yet, but I would get to see my family's "rental." Of course I talked to them on the telephone. Mommy and Daddy, that is. But this was different. You can't smell them and hug them on the phone!

Mary hopped from one foot to another. "They're at the door! They're at the door!" she shrieked.

I lunged down the hall just as Uncle Dan pulled back the heavy oak door.

Suddenly I felt shy. *They look different!* Daddy had a funny cap on his head and little Julie wore a pink striped dress I had never seen before. Pat and Mike raced over to the great green lawn without a backward glance. Big baby Timmy (just turned two) was bigger than Julie! But Mommy looked just the same, and I snuggled into her arms. All too quick, Julie tugged her back, while Timmy toddled forward, heading over the threshold. Daddy leaped after him.

Fifteen minutes later, Mommy and Daddy managed to corral the boys and load us into the red and white station wagon.

Uncle Dan leaned in through the window. "Goodbye, Daughter!" he grinned. I glanced quickly at Mommy and Daddy, up front. Then I smiled back, secretly pleased.

An hour and a half! It seemed like forever. Mommy chattered on about the different houses they had seen. Mike and Pat, in the third seat, interrupted with the highlights and pitfalls of each one. Nobody asked me anything – which was good, because I didn't really feel like talking.

"And...we almost got a dog!" Mike exclaimed.

"We *did* have a dog – for one day!" corrected Pat.

"Really?" I swiveled around.

"Yeah," continued Mike. "Daddy's patient gave him to us. I named him Spike."

"But then Mommy said 'no'," Pat added.

"Oh." I turned back and sighed.

I could feel Julie staring at me. I turned my head. Quickly she looked down and bounced her leg on the vinyl seat. I poked her tummy.

"Where'd you get that new dress, Julie?"

"Unnh!" Her arm jerked back and elbowed me, her bottom lip protruding. I stared. *What happened to my little sister?* She flounced over closer to the door, and gazed out the window. But within seconds I knew she was secretly watching me from under those long lashes.

I felt cold.

Finally we arrived, having crossed through San Francisco - ("You used to live here, Cathay, when you were two!" "I did? No I didn't!") - and over the Golden Gate Bridge. 'Corte Madera' the exit sign said. Daddy rolled to a stop before a squat, square building. I squinted up at it. *It's a box. A big gray box.* Slowly I trailed the troops as they raced up the leaf-strewn path and through the simple front door. I stopped. Mommy and Daddy brought up the rear.

"Look around, Cathay," Mommy said. "Then you can join me in the kitchen." Julie scurried after her.

I gazed. Nothing looked familiar. Lots of furniture lay scattered about, but none of it was ours. Mike and Pat appeared out of nowhere, chasing each other in a circle around me. Timmy got in the way and tripped, wailing. Like lightning, the boys darted out of sight again off to the right of the living room. I helped Timmy up (who had already forgotten the insult) and decided to follow Mike and Pat.

Up a narrow stairway they seemed to have gone; I could hear them above, hooting and hollering. I slowly ascended, staring at the tight, angular channel around me. At the top I saw three doors, all close together. *What are these rooms? Where am I?* The door on the left burst open; Mike and Pat tumbled out, laughing as they dashed past and scrambled back down the stairs.

"Where are you going?" I called.

"Outside," Mike yelled back.

I stood a moment; then one by one pushed open each door. Beds. Lots of beds.

But none for me.

Patter-patter pat. Patter-patter pat. Saturday. The rain drizzled down the great front window as Susie, Julie, Mary and I pressed our noses against the cold pane. I watched my breath steam up in a little patch. Aunt Joan and Uncle Dan were out "showing houses" (*Didn't they ever show any to Mommy and Daddy?*) while Marty busied herself with the boys in the nursery.

"What shall we do?" Susie mused.

"I know!" Mary piped up. "Let's play 'hide and go seek'!"

Julie immediately tapped her shoulder. "Okay… and you're 'it'!"

"Aww…"

Laughing, the rest of us fanned through the house, searching for our own secret hideaway. Hunched down low I slunk through the hallway and into the dining room, lest Mary should spy me through splayed fingers.

"…Eleven, twelve, thirteen…"

Wildly eyeing the furniture, I rushed forward.

"*Psst!* Cathay! Under here!"

I glanced over at the table. *Ah ha!* Flipping up the linen cloth, I spotted *both* Julie and Susie beneath it. Susie giggled behind her hand and hid her face in her knees. Without a word I scurried under and squished in beside them. The white cloth glowed with its own special light around us. Suddenly we were in our own secret cave! The underneath side of the table looked strange and protecting at the same time.

"Shh!" Julie warned.

Footsteps. Purposeful… Forward they marched, little black-strapped shoes, as they passed – just inches from us! We held our collective breath. I gazed into Julie's eyes: stern and commanding - but shining. Then Susie's: light and laughing. We eyed each other in pregnant silence. I thought I would burst! Back and forth we watched the little feet, now slower, now stomping.

"Where *are* you?!" she wailed.

At last I could stand it no longer. I buried my face in Julie's back and let loose a barrage of giggles. Susie and Julie joined in, as we hugged each other in our attempt to muffle the evidence. We were in cahoots! Minutes oozed by…

"I give up! Okay?" Mary whined from the hallway.

We succeeded! Howling with laughter, all three of us rolled out from under the table, doubling up even more at the look on Mary's face. Her gaping mouth exploded with a squeal of delight as she, too, soon bubbled over.

"Okay, okay –let's play tag!" she cried.

"Yes –and *you're* 'it'!" I chortled, lunging towards her with my outstretched hand. With a shriek, we all flew off in opposite directions.

"Table is base!" called Julie.

Gleefully I galloped down the hall. "You'll never catch me!" I crowed. Mary stopped short, wheeled around and charged after me. *Uh oh.* Quickly I darted into the girls' bathroom. Just as Mary shoved open the door I grabbed the toothpaste from the sink, yanked off the cap and aimed it at her.

"Don't come near – or I'll shoot!"

Mary yelped and backed up, her eyes glued to the oozing paste.

"Yahh!" I exclaimed, thrusting it closer. She turned tail and ran.

Alone, I exulted in my good fortune and power! I stared a moment at the potent tube in my hands – then impulsively aimed at the sink and squeezed hard. A mint green line came shooting forth, so smooth and shiny. The pressure felt good under my hands. I pressed harder...and harder! With a sweeping flourish, I swirled that line in grand swoops and twirls as I decorated the washbowl with faces and flowers and zigzag designs. I squeezed until the once-full tube lay thin and flat in my shaking hands. *Wait till they see!*

I yanked open the door and gestured to my cohorts running towards me.

"Hey! Julie! Susie! Look at this!" I hustled them inside. Mary brought up the rear, straining to see.

In unison, they all sucked in their breath, eyes wide and staring: first in the sink, and then at me.

Silence. Mary broke it first.

"Mama!" she cried.

"Shh!" Julie slapped her hand over Mary's mouth.

"You *wasted* it!" Mary hissed between Julie's fingers.

Suddenly all the air seemed to go out of the room. The games were gone. I felt heavy. I swallowed.

Julie took charge. "You've got to get rid of it!" she urged. I flipped on the faucet and began frantically swishing the water and toothpaste down the drain. All my designs slowly slipped away – too slowly, as they clung to the sides, laughing at me, till Julie and Susie joined in to finish them off. Then I buried the remaining evidence under tissues in the wastebasket.

"Mary!" I pleaded. "Don't tell!"

"Ohh...*kay*," she mumbled, eyes downcast.

One by one, we all filed out and separated. Susie slipped into the closet with her knitting, Mary flicked on the television, and Julie disappeared into the living room. I pressed my nose against the big front window and watched the raindrops slide, out of focus, while pert piano notes played behind me.

Thursday afternoon after school found us munching Marty's homemade chocolate chip cookies with ice-cold milk. Julie reached for another.

"I can't wait for tomorrow morning," she mumbled between bites.

"Why?"

"'Cause tomorrow we get DOUGHNUTS!" she enthused. "It's First Friday, and *our* school has the *best* doughnuts."

"You get doughnuts at school?" I blinked.

"*Mm-hm* – and hot cocoa, too!"

"They have the yummiest 'twisties'," added Susie. "That's my favorite. What's yours, Cathay?"

"My favorite are twistie doughnuts, too!" I exclaimed. *Mmm*...I could just taste that soft, sugary dough melting in my mouth.

"Well, I like chocolate doughnuts the best," declared Julie.

"I wish *I* could have some," Mary pouted.

"Well, you can't," scolded Julie. "Not till you make your First Holy Communion. Anyway, we have to wait till after First Friday Mass, of course – but by then it tastes extra good, because - "

My laugh suddenly caught at the back of my throat. I stared at Julie's face, her mouth opening and closing, but I heard nothing more. She stopped and scrutinized me; instantly I pretended to cough. *Mass...Communion...the TOOTHPASTE! I didn't go to CONFESSION!*

Next morning I woke up, leaden and bleary-eyed. *If only I could just hide under the covers and not go to school...*

All too soon, I found myself trudging after Julie towards our classroom door. Right outside I stopped.

"Julie!" I blurted.

"What?"

I froze. I glanced at her quizzical face, and all of a sudden it changed to that scary, big-eyed frown that I saw on Saturday by the bathroom sink.

"Uh...n-nothing...um...I forgot."

Julie shook her head with a questioning smile and marched on into the room.

Before I knew it, we all filed down the corridor and stood lined up outside the chapel. My legs wanted to *move*. I glanced wildly around me, searching for a way out. *Maybe I could just hide in the bathroom till Mass is over! But where - ?*

"Settle down now," commanded the Mother Superior, sweeping by as she inspected the students. Too late.

All during Mass I watched the candles glimmer in little red glass holders along the side. I didn't dare look towards the priest up on the altar. *I can't go to Communion... But if I don't go, everyone will wonder why,*

213

and they'll know I've done something terrible… If I DO go, that would be a WORSE sin…

Tinkle, tinkle, tinkle. I jumped. Up front, the altar boy on his knees jingled the little silver bells. Usually my favorite part. Now it meant Communion was COMING!

Without warning, the boys and girls in my row stood up and started shuffling toward the aisle. I froze. Dickie, the boy next to me, scrunched his eyebrows and smirked down at me.

"What are you doing?" he hissed.

With a gasp, I leaped up and stumbled after the others. *God will punish me…God will punish me…*

I knelt at the altar rail, right smack in the middle, pinned in on either side. The altar boy held the golden plate under my chin, in case the host should fall. *Maybe I should let it! Then I wouldn't have to eat it… But no… everyone would stare…the priest would have to eat it…and they'd just give me another one, besides…* With an inward whimper, I resigned myself to my fate, and opened my mouth.

This time I welcomed hiding my face in my hands to say my prayers to Jesus – *I'm so sorry, I'm so sorry, I'm so sorry…* I prayed that Mass would never be over, because I knew I couldn't go to that special breakfast…

Back out in line in the church vestibule, I spied a small door off to the side with the word 'toilet' in tiny letters. Suddenly I sidestepped the line and hunched inside my skin as small as I could, imagining I was shrinking. I darted to the door. I couldn't believe it! It was unlocked! I ducked inside and locked it behind me. My ear at the opaque glass, I listened, my breath rising in staccato bursts. No one called out. No one noticed! Gradually the footsteps faded. Silence.

I flicked off the light. When my eyes adjusted, I sat on top of the toilet and waited. Far off, a dog barked.

Then...nothing. I stared around me in the darkness. The shadowy edge of the sink jutted out on my left. And that was it. Finally I crouched down on the bare floor and hugged my knees. The cement was cold – so cold. Still I waited, not knowing how long, how long...

They must be eating now. I heard their voices in my head, laughing, chattering. I could see them pushing against each other as they reached for their own favorite doughnut. The cafeteria danced in brightness, full of colors. I imagined that 'twistie' doughnut deflating in Susie's mouth.

At last I raised myself up and felt for the wall. I squeezed the knob and peered out through the crack, blinking at the dazzle of light. Just then a shadow flitted by. I slammed the door – without meaning to. *Bam!* I jumped.

Knock, knock, knock! I held my breath.

"Cathay?"

Slowly I opened the door. It was Julie! She slipped into the bathroom.

"Where have you been?!" she cried.

"Julie!" My face felt hot. I tried not to cry. My chest tightened.

"I-I-I..." My words leaped out of me. "I-couldn't-go-to-Communion-because-of-what-I-did-with-the-toothpaste-and-I-never-went-to-Confession-and-it-was-a-mortal-sin" I took a breath. "But then I *did* go to Communion, and now it's a *worse* sin, and I don't know WHAT'S going to happen!" My skin prickled at the out-spoken fear.

Julie flipped on the light, locked the door and turned to face me. She looked very serious.

"Cathay," she began. "I don't think that was a mortal sin."

"You don't?!"

"No." She shook her head emphatically.

"But-but everyone thought it was really bad!"

"Well," Julie hesitated. "A venial sin, maybe – but not mortal. So you could still go to Communion."

I looked at her. "You sure?"

"Of course! Silly!" For the first time she smiled. Suddenly I felt myself in a bubble, ready to rise to the ceiling. I gave Julie a hug. We looked at each other.

"You know what?" Julie whispered, a slow smile spreading across her face. "I thought that was the craziest thing ever! Pictures with *toothpaste!*" She clapped her hand over her mouth to stifle a giggle. Soon the two of us lapsed into an uncontrollable fit of voiceless laughter.

Finally Julie opened the door, looked both ways and prodded me out.

"Coast is clear!"

Miraculously, we slipped back into the classroom at the tail end of the students returning from the cafeteria.

"Sorry you missed the breakfast," whispered Julie, stuffing a bulging napkin in my hand. "But I saved you a doughnut anyway." I took a quick peek before sticking it under my sweater. It was a 'twistie.'

That afternoon I hurried home after hearing that Susie had been picked up right before Mass because of her asthma. Bounding down the hall, I burst into the girls' room. There she was, sitting up in bed, her pale face lit with surprise.

"Hi!" she trilled.

She scooted over and I joined her. Susie told me all about asthma and allergies and how sad she was that she could never have a dog or cat.

"But do you know what I *really* wanted?" she whispered wistfully.

"What?" I leaned closer.

"A horse." She sighed, staring out the window. I

told her all about my terrible day at school, and then stopped.

"Close your eyes," I said. She scrunched them shut, waiting. Carefully I pulled out the slightly smashed bundle from my lunch bag.

"Okay, you can look now... Open it up." Susie peeled away the paper napkin.

"A 'twistie'!" she exclaimed, eyes darting up to my face.

Just then the door burst open and Julie bounded in. Laughing, she leaped on the bed with us and began pummeling me with her fists.

"Did she tell you what happened today, Susie?" she teased.

"Yup," Susie nodded. "And she gave me her 'twistie'."

"What?!" Julie's jaw dropped.

Quickly I divided it up among all of us. "This is *our* Communion," Julie said solemnly. "Sisters?"

I smiled back at her. "Sisters." We looked at Susie. "Sisters," she repeated.

Just then the door burst open a second time.

"What are we doing? What are we doing?" Mary cried, rushing in.

We all laughed. I patted the bed.

"C'mere, Sister."

Even Mary got a bite.

TreeHouse Blues

MILL VALLEY/SAN FRANCISCO
1959 – 1960

Daddy and Julie

After our six-week separation, Mom and Dad finally find our home: a three-story house "in the woods" near the top of the second highest peak of Tamalpais Valley: an unincorporated area of Mill Valley, California. At this time, Mill Valley is considered "the poor cousin" of San Francisco. The price: $22,000.

Mom is seven months pregnant with baby #6.

Julie, Pat and Tim

Mike and Cathay

Night Traveler

*Lights out…the bed splays all around me. I snuggle deep under the covers - but - No! First I swish my legs frantically back and forth against the icy sheets: too cold! Too cold! At last the warmth begins to seep into my skin. Ahhhhhhhhhh…
I listen to the silence.*

*Will the Bigness come tonight? That's my own special 'friend' that sometimes visits. It doesn't always happen. Sometimes it's the Smallness….a sudden falling – WHOOSH! - faster, faster – as I shrink smaller and smaller while the walls rush upward - HUGE! - growing higher and higher as I slip down, down into the chasm. My body shrinks, condenses; arms, legs shorten as they remold into one tiny, tiny DOT –
But not tonight.*

I lie in the dark and stare out into nothingness. I wait. My body sinks deeper into the softness of the bed. Gradually I feel myself spreading bigger and wider as the great, giant hand of 'Bigness' caresses me from all sides. It lifts me gently up, up in the air, holding me aloft in its great hand of softness, as I rise higher and higher, sinking deeper…

    and …

        deeper…

            into…

                the…

                    Land…

                        of…

                          Big…ness…………

California (New) Girl

"Hold tight to Julie and Timmy's hands!" Mommy called to me. "We don't want them to tumble down the hill."

I stared ahead through the billow of fog, as my own feet felt ready to tumble forward. *Like 'Jack and Jill'...* Mommy, I knew, waddled behind me, balanced on either side by Mike and Pat to keep her ballooned belly from pulling *her* down the hill.

This morning we had scrambled out of our gigantic new house, up the terraced earthen steps, and on down the steep road towards my new school bus stop. The trees creaked overhead as they swayed far above us. *We live in the woods! Like a fairy tale... Good woods? ...Or bad...*

Everywhere I gazed those tall, tall trees stood their ground around us. Eucalyptus, Daddy had said. *Mmmm...* So sharp it smelled, so clean! I peered ahead through the wisps of white that languidly lazed before us. *This is a different kind of California!* Droplets of mist stung my face as I pressed forward.

At last we rounded the corner and the road leveled out. Up ahead lay the crossroads of the mountain: our destination. A jumble of children shuffled from one foot to another, bleary-eyed, in front of the row of funny silver mailboxes with red flags on the side. Mostly boys of different sizes. No uniforms. Only one grown-up: a woman.

No one spoke.

Soon, I knew, Mommy would turn away and trudge back up the hill...with only three children instead of five. Standing midst a crowd of strange, silent beings with nowhere to go, I felt my chest tighten. Minutes oozed by. *What does my school look like? How do I know where to go?* My stomach churned. I tugged on Mommy's sleeve.

"Where do I go when I get off the bus?" I whispered. Mommy bent towards me.

"Just follow the rest of the children into the school," she murmured. "Someone in the office will tell you where to go."

I gulped. I no longer had Julie Hauserman to lead the way. *Office? What office? Where is it? I have to ask?! How?!* I could not speak.

The other mother smiled at us.

"What grade is your daughter?"

"Third grade," replied Mommy.

"Why, so is mine. I'm Pat Hamilton. And this is Carol."

I peeped over my shoulder. A girl with tight blonde braids and blue cat's-eye glasses grinned back at me.

"She'll take her to the classroom," Carol's mother reassured us. "And what is *your* name?" She looked directly at me this time.

Uh oh. What do I say?! Now was the moment of no turning back. *Do I really want that name?*

"Um." I glanced up at Mommy. She nodded encouragingly.

"Cath... Cath – AY." I cleared my throat and waited. Carol's face wrinkled quizzically.

"It's the old name for ancient China," Mommy hastened to add.

"Why, that's a beautiful name!" exclaimed Mrs. Hamilton.

Meanwhile, the yellow school bus had rumbled to a halt. I turned quickly to Mommy. My knees quivered. She latched my hand onto Mike's, delivered our lunch sacks, and squeezed us tight.

"You look after Michael now," her eyebrow flew up.

"Make sure he gets to where *he* needs to go." I peered down. Mike's face was chalk-white. I swallowed; then nodded; I took a breath, and pulled him up the tall steps into the big yellow bus.

I stared out the window, Mike squeezed between it and me. Surrounding us the babble of children's voices bubbled up in swoops and staccatos. The trees whizzed by as we zigzagged down the mountain, the bus flinging us from side to side. The bar of the seat before me vibrated crazily under my grip. Mike refused to let go of my other hand the entire ride. *Mommy never drives like this!*

At last the tumult stopped as the bus lurched to a halt at the curb of the school. I stumbled down the aisle after Carol ahead of me, Mike's hand still glommed onto mine. Once on the ground, I scurried after her, not wanting to lose sight of my potential new friend in the mass of children piling in droves through the opened front doors of the school. I trusted her to lead me to the classroom. *But what do I do with Mike?* It looked like I would have to find a grown-up after all.

Carol suddenly pointed to the Big Counter to the left of us. "Go there," she whispered; then sailed off without me.

I stared silently at the woman behind the counter, her back to us. My gaze wandered to the door beside her. 'GUY E. POORMAN, Principal,' shouted the black letters emblazoned across the opaque glass. I re-read them. *Why does it say 'GUY?' Isn't that rude? And what a terrible last name! ...Or is he really poor... Do people make fun of him? Of his name?* I mulled this over while students continued to pour past.

At that moment the door burst open and a beefy man barged out. He swung his arm in the air towards a boy stiffening on a wooden chair close by.

"What?! You again?!" he roared.

"May I help you?"

Oh! My eyes zoomed back to the counter into crinkled blue eyes; and there I somehow found my voice…

At last separated from Mike at the Kindergarten classroom door, I treaded after the secretary to my new classroom. She bent down towards the blonde head at the teacher's desk and whispered. 'Miss Hayes,' my new teacher, rose and smiled at me. Then she took my hand and led me towards the top of the sea of students.

"Boys and girls," she cleared her throat. "This is our new girl – Cathay Gunn." *She said it right!*

A furious hubbub of whispers flurried around the room. I held my breath.

"What?! 'Coffee Bun?" A voice whooped. My eyes darted in that direction. A sturdy boy with huge front teeth and sandy hair swept straight up grinned back at me.

"Hi, Cafeteria!" he called out. I stiffened.

"That's enough, Class," Miss Hayes admonished in a ringing voice. My breath eased out as we stood side by side and waited until quiet descended like a blanket across the patchwork of students.

Under Miss Hayes' protective gaze I slipped into the offered seat and snuck a peek at my new deskmate. It was Carol. A smile lurking around the corners of her mouth, she pushed a shiny new pencil towards me. I smiled back.

Maybe this won't be so bad, after all…

Anggggg…. Recess time! Our teacher clapped her hands. She strode towards the outside door and stopped.

"Class," began Miss Hayes, "Several of you left your rubbers here on Friday. Make sure you take them home today. You may put them in your cubbies right after recess." *Cubbies? Rubbers?*

We trooped out the door past a jumble of mostly

army-green rubber shoes. No straps. No ties. Just long, shallow cups. *Huh? So ugly! Why would anyone want them?*

Before Carol could slip away into the masses I tapped her shoulder.

"Um – Carol," I hesitated. "What were those shoes?"

"Rubbers," she blinked at me. "Don't you have some?"

"Uh – why?" I didn't see any other sign of a uniform...

"In case it rains."

"How do you keep them on?"

"You wear them on *top* of your shoes." She squinted at me. "What do *you* wear?"

"Snow boots."

Carol grimaced. "Well, you won't need those here!" Then she skipped off to the jump-rope line.

I gazed uncertainly at the myriad of whirling colors. So different from uniforms. Beyond the maze a girl stood still by the fence. I thought I'd seen her face at a desk in our classroom. A tight red tube hugged her body from her waist to her knees. *What a funny skirt! She looks like a grown-up!* She started to move off as she eyed someone up ahead, bending with every other step. *Oh! One leg looks shorter than the other!* Sure enough, a gigantic heeled shoe surrounded her right foot as she limped towards another girl in an identical black tube skirt. The older girl hustled her to the bench ahead.

At that moment a sudden wind reached out and clawed its fingers into my sweater. I shivered and picked up my pace in a spiral around the perimeter of the schoolyard.

Anggggg! End of recess. *Finally!*

"Carol," I whispered while we waited in line before the classroom door. "What happened to *her*?" I dipped my head towards the red tube girl.

"She had polio," Carol whispered back behind her hand. "Her leg won't grow anymore."

"Oh!"

We trooped inside and I hustled back to my desk. A new notebook with my name at the top lay there waiting for me.

"Class, take out your penmanship books," Miss Hayes commanded. "Turn to page 24."

A flutter of activity coiled throughout the classroom. My hands cramped with cold as I gripped the new pencil and tried to improve my cursives. *Why do we have penmanship right after recess?! My hands are too stiff! I might not need snow boots, but maybe mittens!*

Back at last on the school bus, I slid into the seat next to Carol. But she twisted backwards to chat with the girls behind us. I stared straight ahead at the dark, plaited hair before me. Two French braids angled from the wearer's forehead and on down the back of her skull. But the braids ended soon after departing her skull, with the look of ponytails hanging beneath the rubber bands. *Her hair is so long!* My hand itched to reach out and complete the braids to the ends...

We crawled up that dizzying zigzag road this time, like a giant caterpillar that screeched and groaned along its journey to the top. At last at the now-familiar crossroads, the remaining few students straggled onto solid ground.

Carol waved goodbye and set off to the right. I turned my gaze to the left. No Mommy this time. And no Mike. The school bus, I knew, had delivered him earlier into the arms of the waiting Mommy. But I was to go it alone.

Up the road I spied the same plaited head of the girl on the bus. She twisted towards me as I approached.

"Hah," the tall girl said. "Muh nae- ih- Rae." *Her words are funny!*

"Um – I'm Cathay." I settled into a pattern of footsteps beside her. We hiked in silence awhile as the blacktop steepened.

"Wheh duh yeh lih-?" she slurred. I pointed up the hill to the left.

"Ah lih- pahh- th- taw- uh th- hih-." I nodded and focused on that stunted braid whose exaggerated tail swished across her back.

"Yuh cah- pwae a- muh hou-," she pointed towards the top of the hill.

"I have to go home."

"Ass- yuh Ma," she said. "Ah wai- fuh yeh."

"Ok..." *Should I? Maybe she could be a friend...*

Rae waited on the porch while I slipped into that new pink house to confer with Mommy. It still felt strange.

"I'm home!" I called, feeling like a liar.

A few minutes later, Mommy beamed her approval.

Dress exchanged for play-clothes, I trudged beside Rae back up the earthen steps to the road and into unknown territory. I did not know what to say to her, but she rumbled on in half-syllables anyway. Finally we scaled the peak of Smith Road and continued round the bend to the right. This was farther than I had expected. *I wonder what her house looks like...* She slowed up ahead.

"Thah- muh hou-," she pointed. A tumbled-down shack half-hidden in the brush crept into view. Wayward boards hung haphazardly from random parts of the structure. Two rusted pick-up trucks sat half-buried in the weeds. Overturned tin cans and discarded food wrappers lay close by. A tire swing dangled in the distance. *Oh dear...* I bit my lip. *I don't know if I want to be here...*

"Meoww..." An orange tabby cat traipsed towards us.

"Thah- muh cah-: 'Maw-muh-lai-'."

Oh. Like that jam with the orange peel in it... I
swallowed and tried to pet it but it hissed at me.

Just then a tan hound ambled over; hair so smooth it
looked like he didn't have any. Tiny triangle ears poked
skyward on his large head. *His eyes!* One brown eye and
one blue eye zipped back and forth between us.

"Heh- Heinh- fih-tih seh-unh-."

"*What*? Is that his name?"

"Naw. Thah- whuh- heh *ih. Heh nae- ih...nnnnnnn.*" At
that moment the dog ambled away. I was glad. I could
not figure out what she said was his name, but my eyes
riveted on the quivering stump on his rump.

"What happened to his *tail?*"

"Thah- *ihh* hih tai-," she insisted. "Muh Paw cuh- aw-
th- tai-. Whenh- awh th- puh-pie- bohnh-, weh cuh- th-
tai- aw-." *They cut off ALL the puppies' tails- ?!*

Rae bent down and tossed a stick into the weeds.
"Goh, boah!" The hound bounded after it. Reluctantly I
joined in the game until a slight wiggle of my own took
charge.

"Um, Rae – can I use your bathroom?"

"Yeh. Cuh- ih-sigh-."

I followed her through the torn screen-door into a
darkened room. A low rumble of voices drawled on to
my left. There, standing beside a sink, two gangly men
in ripped overalls hunkered next to a gaunt woman in a
threadbare dress. *They* talked funny, too. I swallowed.

They paid no attention to us.

"Heh, Ma. Thih muh frienh-." Rae thumbed in
my direction; then turned and pulled me through
the muddle of wooden chairs, crates, and soiled sofa
towards an opened doorway opposite. My skin began
to itch.

"Ah waih- ow-sigh-," she said.

I crept into what seemed to be the only other room in the house: a long, narrow space with tools at one end, a toilet at the other, and a window with cracked glass in-between. Next to the tools, overalls and oily jackets hung from nails on the wall above a pile of mud-caked boots.

There was no door.

I swallowed and peeped back out. No sign of Rae. Just the grown-ups opposite who suddenly seemed *huge*! I turned around and peered out the window past the dirty gauze curtain into a tangle of weeds and overturned cracked clay pots. My leg jiggled uncontrollably. I took a breath and backed towards the toilet. *Don't look, please don't look at me...* With a quick glance behind me at the last moment, I flipped the broken toilet seat down, tore down my pants, and sat. My right leg jerked like a rototiller.

I peed in torrents as the men's voices grew closer. *Are they coming in here - ?! Do they need those tools? Or a jacket? Who ARE those men? Why don't they have a DOOR?! ...* One of them laughed.

At last I finished and tore through the doorway into the jumbled room of gangly figures and flotsam furniture. But I did not stop there; no; I grabbed the screen-door handle and flew outside. I would not be back. Rae was not the one.

"Rae!" I shouted. "I gotta go home!" Not waiting for a reply, I fled down our new road without stopping till I stumbled down our terraced dirt steps, over the meandering stone pavers and on up to the big, pink porch. I threw open the front door and yelled:

"Mommeeee! I'm hommme!" This time – I *meant* it.

Without pause, I clattered down our basement steps and into my new bedroom. I slammed the door behind me, clambered up onto my bed and hugged my knees. I rocked back and forth. Gradually my breathing slowed as my eyes traveled the walls and soaked up the now familiar artwork Mommy had so carefully placed the day before. There they all were. Sketches of little girls; in a special moment of sharing we had dubbed them "Susie," "Julie," and "Mary" – our cousins. My room. My family.

Yet, an unease I could not define had filtered into the back of my head and taken up residence. I swallowed it down and looked the other way.

Carol. Tomorrow I will see Carol.

Then I climbed off the bed, entered the bathroom, and washed my hands for dinner.

The Trap Door

"Place your hand right across this bump," suggested Mommy. The two of us sat side by side on top of her big double bed. I studied her rounded tummy, laid bare for my inspection. It looked like a playground ball – with a triangle flap poking out from the middle. *Just like where they fill the ball with air!*

I laid my hand against it. Smoother than a ball – but *hard!* I glanced up in surprise.

"That's the baby's head," she smiled. Suddenly the side of her tummy jumped! (I did, too.)

"Oh, the baby's kicking!" she cried. "Here – " she grabbed my hand and held it firmly on top of that alien action. Into my hand something bounced.

"I feel it! I feel it!" I yelled. "Do it again!"

Mommy laughed. "When he's ready, he will."

I looked up at her. "When will the baby be ready to come out?"

"Oh, very soon, now."

I stared at that bulbous expanse. "HOW will it get out?" I couldn't see any way…

"Oh…" she mused. "When the time is right, a special door will appear…"

"Like a secret trap door?"

"Well...sort of."

I scrutinized her tummy, searching for some telltale outline. *Three lines of a square...maybe around that bellybutton...*

"But then why can't I see it?" Her tummy glared blindly back at me, so smooth and unyielding.

She paused. "It's not time yet. When it's time, the door will suddenly appear. But *only* then. That's why you can't see it now."

"Why?"

"Why, to protect the baby! We wouldn't want it to come out before it's ready!"

"Ohhh..." Disappointed, I rocked back on the bed and sighed. Then I leaped up.

"Will you show it to me when it comes?"

"I'll try."

That afternoon I scrambled through the eucalyptus to our road above the house. If I hurried I could meet my new friend Carol halfway. She would short-cut over here, I figured, through the neighbor's ambling property across the road. I glanced up and down the lane; then raced to the other side. I soon spied the pig-tailed figure striding towards me through the leaves.

"Carol! Carol!" I called. "I've got something to tell you!"

Carol eyed me with surprise. "Okay..."

We plopped down together on top of a large log lying beneath the trees. I leaned towards her.

"I know what happens when a baby gets born!" I confided.

"Yeah?" She listened.

"There's a *secret* door that magically appears on the Mommy's tummy!"

Carol pulled back, eyes widened. "No, there's not!"

"Yes, there is!" I insisted. "My Mommy showed me!"

"She *showed* you?"

"Well – I mean – she *told* me when she showed me her tummy, and – "

"But did you *see* it?"

"No – because - it's not – it doesn't – " My words got all twisted in my eagerness to make her understand. "You can only see it when it's *time*," I finished.

Carol shook her head and rolled her eyes. "Cathay," she stated. "The baby comes out of the little hole where you go to the bathroom."

I stared at her.

"You're crazy!" *How could it even – what?! – how – how could it even FIT?!*

Carol stood up, arms folded. "It's true. My mother told me."

"Well - my Mommy's had LOTS more babies than *yours* has!" Carol only had one brother and one sister - and they were born a long time ago. *So how would she know?!*

But she wouldn't be swayed.

I decided not to say anything more. After all, I would get to see the real trap door myself – and she wouldn't.

Wednesday after school I burst through the front door. "Mommy, Mommy!" I yelled. "Are you still here?" *Maybe TODAY I'll see that trap door…*

There, her wide back to me at the kitchen sink, stood Nana. Nana had arrived the day before for a special visit. She ambled around, wiping her hands on her apron, and twitched her lips.

"Why, dearie, she's gone to the hospital! The baby's coming!" Her smile dimpled from ear to ear.

…Too late…

It was hard to wait. Mommy arrived home on Saturday. I couldn't ask her right away, of course.

Everyone crowded around baby Eric. I hung back until I got a chance to be alone with her. When everyone else had left her room but us, I carefully closed the door behind them.

"Mommy," I began. "Tell me about the trap door. Is it still there?"

Straightening up from the bassinet she turned and blinked at me. "What?"

"On your tummy!" I urged. "Can you still see it?"

Mommy reached back with her hand and sank down hard on the bed. Her breath slid out in one long stream. A moment. She raised her eyes to me and smiled. "Come here," she beckoned, and patted the bed.

Slowly I approached.

"I'm so sorry," she murmured, "But the door only stays there long enough for the baby to get out." She brushed a stray hair from my face. "It's gone now."

"Can I still look?" I needed proof.

Mommy pulled up her blouse and pulled down her skirt. I leaned very close and grazed my fingers over her warm skin. The bubble seemed much smaller now…still smooth, no lines. And no way in.

She was right. *I guess I just missed my chance.* Disappointed, I tried to figure out how else I could convince Carol of the truth…

Mommy put her arm around my shoulders. "But let's look at the little man who finally decided to come out."

Together we peered into the bassinet. The soft head lay covered with a dusting of *black* hair! Not like Timmy's! A tiny arm stretched against his cheek, a faint squeak escaping his lips. His eyes popped open and grabbed me. I fell right into them… He wouldn't let me go…

…Carol could have her silly old story. I wouldn't say a word.

I had a new baby brother.

Land of the Free =
Home of the Brave

"Good morning, boys and girls! Welcome to the fourth grade!"

I glanced up from my newly designated seat past rows of ordered desks to the woman up front. Solid, stately but relaxed, stood Mrs. Glenn, salt 'n' pepper hair clinging in crimped waves about her neck. She looked nice enough....

The buzz in the classroom slowly diminished before her steady gaze.

"I would like to get to know you a little better," she said. "Mary Jane is passing out a questionnaire. Please answer the questions and Billy will collect them."

I gazed down at the white parchment with the purple ink on my desk. Pencil in hand, I gnawed its eraser-end as I scrutinized each line:

NAME: *Cathay Gunn*
FAVORITE COLOR: *green*
FAVORITE FOOD: *Mommy's chocolate fudge cake*
FAVORITE SUBJECT: *reading*
FAVORITE BOOK: *Charlotte's Web*
FAVORITE PLACE: *the woods*

The next line stopped me in my tracks.

SUMMER IS A GREAT TIME FOR OUTDOOR PLAY. CHECK OFF ALL OF THE FUN OUTDOOR GAMES YOU ENJOYED THIS SUMMER:

__BASEBALL   __SWIMMING
__BASKETBALL   __COPS AND ROBBERS
__KICKBALL   __COWBOYS AND INDIANS

Huh? I stared in dismay at the paper. Feverishly my eyes darted from choice to erroneous choice. *I have to check something!* My pencil hovered above the word

'Indians.' Hesitatingly I checked off the category – then furiously erased it, my stomach heaving at the very idea. *No, no, no! That's wrong!* ... Sick at heart, I made my choice and relinquished the paper to Billy, impatiently shifting beside me.

I couldn't wait for recess.

"Carol!" I called, grabbing my best friend's gingham skirt. She turned around, wearing the same grumpy expression I felt.

"Humph!" she muttered. "What stupid choices!"

Relieved, I concurred. "Yeah. What did *you* put?"

"There was only one – "

I nodded in uncertain agreement.

" – Swimming," she finished.

"Huh?" I stared at her. "We didn't go swimming!"

"No, no, silly," she grimaced. "When I visited my Grandmother's. *I* went swimming."

"Oh...." Suddenly Carol seemed far away.

"So what did *you* put?" she asked.

I sighed. "There was nothing right. But I checked - "I lowered my voice. "Cowboys and Indians."

"Cowboys and Indians!" Carol's eyes widened, incredulous.

"Well...we played *Indians*...." I wavered.

"That was NOTHING the same!" She shook her head emphatically.

"No...." I stared off, unseeing, into the distance, the boisterous banter of the playground fading, as my mind gave way to the portals of the past....

"Hey, Boo!"

"Hey, BooBoo!" Carol had greeted me back as we met up at the crossroads that summer between our mountain homes.

"Ut-way al-shay ee-way oo-day oo-tay ay-day?"
she asked, carefully enunciating with our newfound
secret pig-latin. I gazed about the golden countryside,
tall eucalyptus trees framing my every view. Summer
stretched ahead almost as far as it rested behind us. I
inhaled it luxuriously.

A sudden image from our third grade "American
Indian" filmstrip leaped before me.

"I know!" I cried, forgetting our vow of pig-latin-only.
"Let's play Indians!"

Carol wrinkled her nose. "Indians?"

"Yeah!" I crouched down and snaked up the path
from the road into the tall grasses. Turning around
without a sound I motioned with my finger to my lips
and a cock of my head for her to follow.

"What are we looking for?" she whispered.

"Food. But watch out for enemy tribes."

Remembering the black and white footage rolling in
the darkened classroom, I breathed, "We're Hunters and
Gatherers."

"I'm Running Deer," Carol responded solemnly.

"Ok – you be the hunter," I decided. "My name is
Little Bird. I'll be the gatherer."

I promptly sat down on the ground and snatched
several fronds of tall grass from their resistant roots.

"We need to weave baskets for gathering," I informed
her. I tried to remember the hand movements of the old
Indian women seated together in a circle, but to no avail.

"Running Deer," I said, eyeing her blonde pigtails.
"Show me how to braid."

"I don't know how."

"What?!"

"My Mom braids my hair."

Stymied, I tossed down the grasses, then pulled my
white tee shirt up over my head.

"This will be my basket!" I remarked with satisfaction.

"Yeah!" Carol exclaimed, whipping off hers, also. "Indians didn't wear shirts anyway." She tucked it into the waistband of her seersucker shorts, letting it hang down in front like the flap of the Indian braves.

I carefully pulled up four corners of my own shirt into a solid bunch, and swung the 'basket' over my shoulder. Straightening up, I felt the warm rays of the sun graze against my eager skin. A slight breeze caressed my chest, carrying with it a sense of freedom and delight.

"*Now* we're Indians!" I exulted. "Let's go hunting!"

Running Deer forged the path ahead, slipping stealthily through the wavering grasses and into the foliage beyond. Heading towards the tall trees on the right, I listened for intruders. The sudden cry of a blue jay pierced the air. I froze; then relaxed, convinced no humans accompanied it. Through the thick ground covering I foraged, searching for acorns. *Hmm. Must not be the right territory…*

But what's this? Tiny buttons. I wonder if our tribe has tried these. Eagerly I pounced upon the eucalyptus droppings strewn through the wooded edge of the meadow. I scooped up a handful, filling my cloth 'basket' full of booty. On top I tossed a few red-brown eucalyptus leaves. With silent, exaggerated steps, I made my way back through the open meadow, and to our 'camp' behind the squat of bushes along the edge of the road.

Raising my hand to my mouth I emitted our secret call: "EeOo, EeOo, EeOo." Within seconds the air echoed back to me my baited response: "AhHah! AhHah! AhHah!"

Moments later the brush parted and Running Deer appeared, her eyes sparkling. She raised her arm triumphantly.

239

"Raccoon for dinner!" she crowed, lifting high a fallen bough with two knotty pinecones still attached.

"Good hunting, Running Deer!"

Swiftly she set to work preparing the 'fire' with a collection of fallen debris. Meanwhile I scoured the hillside for my 'kitchen' tools. At last I had gathered several large rocks and arranged them in a circle. Still squatting, I poured the eucalyptus buttons into the center. With one oblong-shaped rock I viciously stabbed at the 'acorns,' jaw set, breathing in snorts.

"These acorns must not be ripe yet," I frowned.

"Little Bird – just stir them," Running Deer suggested. "They make good soup." Carol set her 'raccoon' across the 'pot' circle and left it there to stew with the 'acorns.'

"We need beads for necklaces," she remarked.

I nodded, remembering the pretty beads the Indians strung together on bits of deer-hide. A sudden idea flashed before me.

"Wait here and stir stew," I ordered.

I leaped into the air; the grass tingled against my bare legs as I sprang like a gazelle. My eyes spotted their quarry: wafting in the breeze ahead stood a multitude of cattails. I snipped them at ground level, making sure to have plenty of slack. Hurrying back to the camp I shared my find. With legs crossed before the 'fire,' we painstakingly wove the stems of the cattails into small, knotted loops, intertwining them in succession till they created a circle large enough to fit over our heads.

"There!" I burst out. The oblong cattail shapes did indeed look like beads! (A little itchy, though.)

"And look!" I cried. "We have feathers!" I snatched up the red-brown eucalyptus leaves that had spilled out of my 'basket.' With care I slipped one under the elastic on each of Carol's braids. She, in turn, used her bobby pins to attach one to either side of my straggly brown locks. We jumped up and frolicked around the 'fire,' spontaneously intoning our Raindance cry....*Woo-Ah, Woo-Ah, Humma Humma, Humma Humma....*"

Suddenly Running Deer grabbed my arm.

"Shh!" she warned. "Strange boy warriors nearby!"

I stopped, instantly aware I had no shirt. We sank down into the tall shield of grasses and held our breath. Gradually their voices receded as the strange boys disappeared down the mountain road. No sense in having them laugh at us....

The elementary school playground slowly crystallized back into view. The babble returned. Billy jeered at Mary Jane on the monkey bars, while Johnny chased Susie through the sandbox. "This is the LAW!" he roared. "Stop, or I'll shoot!"

"You're right, Carol," I sighed. "It was NOTHING the same."

Cathay with her cousins and Aunt Willie, the bride

Wedding Surprises

"Uncle Tommy's getting married!"

I stopped dead in my tracks on the Oriental rug. *What?!*

By the end of our first summer back in California, our bachelor uncle had moved into a "singles' complex" down in Mountain View, 50 miles away – not far from our cousins. We loved to visit him there, especially as he had a swimming pool! (Mike even slipped and fell into it while running in his dress clothes, and then had to wear my green pedal pushers out to dinner!) Around the pool, beautiful women with their tinkling laughter lounged in their bathing suits and paid Uncle Tommy a lot of attention. But he never seemed to have a girl friend (as far as I could tell, anyway.)

This was news, indeed!

I hovered behind the grownups surrounding Uncle Tommy by the front door as they scrutinized her snapshot. Grandmamma pointed a finger at him.

"Are you sure you want to marry her, Tom? She's

got some excess poundage on her." She gave him a knowing look.

Uncle Tommy stared down into her face. "Oh, yeah?" He raised his chin. "Well, I love every ounce of fat on her."

Mommy and Daddy exchanged glances; then nodded. Yep. He loved her.

Grandmamma chuckled. "Well, I'll be. ...OK; so how'd you meet?"

Uncle Tommy leaned to the side, cracked his knuckles and surveyed his audience.

"Up at Ashland, Oregon. On a whim, I drove up to the Shakespeare Festival. And - by the way, Ma – " Uncle Tommy smirked at Grandmamma. "She's an opera singer. You would like that. Anyhow, before the show, which is outdoors, you know, there was a chorus of troubadours milling around in front of the audience. Mostly women, don't ya know, singing like troubadours of the times would do. And suddenly, right in front, steps up the most beautiful woman in the world! And, lo and behold, she is singing right to ME!" Uncle Tommy's face glowed. "I couldn't understand it. So, after the show, I stuck around, we started talking, don't ya know, and the rest, as they say, is history." He smacked his lips with a satisfied smile.

"So. Coming to the wedding? It's in December."

Back down the red-carpeted aisle of St. Raymond's I tripped my way ahead of Mommy into the blinding sunshine. Daddy had already processed out as the Best Man, outfitted in his Army dress uniform. From our family, only I got to go with them to the wedding. I couldn't wait to get back to the Hausermans' house! But everyone clumped around the bride and groom, kissing and chattering. I sighed.

243

The bride, (surprise, surprise!) our new "Aunt Willie," did *not* wear a long white gown and veil like my bride doll. Instead, she wore a short white wool skirt and jacket with a leopard fur collar and matching pillbox hat. But she did have beautiful black hair and flashing black eyes crowned with thick lashes. And that big booming laugh! Kind of scary at first – but she laughed a lot, and it made you feel good.

"Well, hello, Daughter!" Gentle Uncle Dan greeted me as he pulled back the front door. *At last!* I grinned up at him and pranced inside the already crowded home. So many people! All talking at once! Suddenly I felt shy and followed close to Mommy...

"Cheers!" Julie exulted, holding up her glass.

"Cheers!" I giggled back as we clinked glasses. A waiter had shrugged and poured champagne for all of us – Susie and Mary included, as well. *Just like the grownups!* We eyed one another with secret giggles as we sipped and posed for the camera. Susie, Julie and Mary, dressed like triplets in their red-trimmed, white embossed dresses, had welcomed me back into the clan.

"Come into the living room, folks," Aunt Joan cajoled. "We have a treat! Tom's beautiful bride is going to sing 'Ave Maria' for us!"

As I wiggled my way in, I spied *Julie* scooting onto the piano stool! Susie, Mary and I wormed up to the front of the crowd and placed ourselves beside the piano. I stood right next to Aunt Willie. Now I could watch both of them!

Julie's fingers hit the keys, and without warning, a deep, voice rumbled overhead like thunder! I jumped. Never had I heard such a gigantic sound indoors! It surrounded us like the ocean. I could feel the floorboards vibrate under my feet. Mary, Susie and I sneaked nervous peeks at each other and tried not to giggle.

So that's what an opera singer sounds like!

"Psst!" Julie leaned down into my ear. "You want to come help us put shoes on their car?"

Scarfing down my last bite of wedding cake, I gazed up at her in wonder.

"What do you mean?"

I tried to picture Uncle Tommy's white Triumph convertible with shoes in place of tires. The car was small – but not *that* small!

She raised her eyebrows. "Follow me." I jumped up and we tiptoed through the throngs and out the kitchen door to the backyard. In the middle of the lawn sat Susie surrounded by paper bags. I peeked inside. *Lots* of shoes! I scrunched up my face at Susie. She grinned.

"We're tying them all together," confided Julie. "In two lines. Then we'll tie them to the back of their car. It's a surprise."

"Yeah!" giggled Susie. "It'll look really funny when they drive down the street. I made a "Just Married" sign to put on the back, too, so everyone will know!"

I promptly plopped down next to Susie and we busied ourselves about the task…

"Hey, who's that, and what are you doing?"

I glanced up to find an older boy about Susie's age standing there, frowning at me. A little girl younger than us stood a ways off.

Susie leaned over and whispered behind her hand, "They live across the street: Bobby and Kathy."

"She's our cousin," Julie answered him. "And it's our uncle's wedding. We're stringing shoes for the car."

"Hey, can I do it, too?" He reached for the shoes.

"No, we have enough help." Julie pulled the bag closer.

"Huh. OK." The boy gazed around the yard a moment. "Huh. So. Do you have a bomb shelter yet?"

I peered up at him.

"No," replied Julie.

"Well, we do." Bobby twitched his lips and nodded up and down. "Just finished digging it this week. It's got a door and everything. In our yard."

Nobody answered.

"You need to make one, you know."

I glanced up. "Why?"

"Why? Because the Communists could bomb us at any time."

I quickly returned to tying the knot in the shoestrings.

"Hey, do *you* have one?" He prodded my foot with his.

"No," I mumbled.

"Well, you better get one," he warned. "Or you'll be sorry."

"Why do you think they're going to bomb us?" Julie raised her head.

"Well, heck. Everybody knows that," he smirked. "My dad says it's always in the news."

Julie remained silent.

"You know what the siren means, don't you? On Tuesdays?" continued Bobby.

I knew. The Tuesday siren at noon we also heard in Mill Valley. No voice; just a siren. But everyone knew what it meant. It was a sort of practice, always at that time – like a fire drill – to warn everybody if the Communists were about to attack us, and to make us get right back home if they did. I wondered what would happen if they tried to trick us and attacked us on a Tuesday at noon. Would nobody believe it? I said nothing.

"And don't you have air raid drills at your school?"

Of course we did. Just like we had fire drills. Only

in the air raid drills we stayed inside. Immediately I
visualized the underneath side of my desk while we
each crouched into a tight ball, waiting for that loud
siren to stop.

"Yeah… So?" Julie raised her chin at him. The little
girl stood behind him, eyes down, swinging her arm
back and forth against her side.

"So that's why you need a bomb shelter."

I thought about the prayer for world peace that
we recited every school morning at the end of Mass.
It finished with: "…and protect us from the evils of
Communism."

"We pray about Communism at school," I offered.

Bobby snorted. "Big deal that is!"

Julie stood up. "You need to go now. If you don't, I'm
calling my mom."

Bobby backed up slowly and taunted, "You'll
be sorreeeee!" Then he turned and ran, with Kathy
pattering behind him.

"Don't pay any attention to him," Julie glowered.
"He's a jerk, anyway."

"Yeah," said Susie.

I nodded. But secretly I vowed to say an extra prayer
every Tuesday at noon.

"…OK! That's the last shoe!" Susie announced.

Julie jumped up. "Great! Let's go tie them on!"
Relieved, I leaped up, too. Off we scurried with our
booty.

Our secret deed done, we stepped back and admired
our masterpiece.

"So many different shoes!" I exclaimed. "So funny-
looking!"

"Yeah!" remarked Julie. "OK, let's get back before
they all come out!"

I dawdled, and gazed back at our handiwork.

Hmmm... A tickle inside my brain grew until it zapped like lightning bugs. *Oh!*

I lunged forward and nabbed Susie before she could slip inside the door; then whispered in her ear.

"I've got a great idea! We can play a trick on them!"

Susie's eyes sparkled. "What is it?"

"You and me can hide in the back of the car, and when they drive away, they won't even know we're there!" We giggled behind our hands, now in cahoots. Susie nodded, breathless...

"They're coming! They're coming!" Susie squeaked in a whisper. Something tiny hit my head. *Zit! Zit!* I rose up from the rumble seat and peered out. Sure enough, hordes of guests poured out of the house towards us. Uncle Tommy and Aunt Willie led the pack!

"Get down!" Susie hissed. I sank inside the pocket and burrowed into Susie's back.

"Rice!" I mumbled. "They're throwing rice!"

Gay voices tumbled over each other.

"B'bye!"

"Farewell!"

"Good luck!"

"We love you!"

I could feel them getting closer...

All of a sudden, Aunt Willie cackled right near my ear! *Uh oh!*

"What have we here?!" *Caught!*

Susie and I grimaced at each other and slowly rose. *Darn!* There stood Mommy next to the rumble seat, shaking her head and smiling. We stood up. Susie lifted her leg and struggled to climb out while Uncle Tommy and Aunt Willie settled up front. I opened my eyes wide at Mommy, half-crouched, and pleaded up at her. She hesitated. "Please!" I whispered. My head swiveled up front and back at Mommy. Her eyes suddenly twinkled and she gave me a tiny nod. I yanked Susie's skirt. "Down! Down!" I hissed.

"What? ...Oh!"

Quickly we scrunched ever lower, our eyes glued to each other in excitement. We were doing it!

The engine roared and leapt forward; people's screams of delight engulfed us as the wiggle-waggle bumps of the road just inches below us vibrated our bodies and rattled our souls. *We did it! We did it!*

"At last, just you and me, eh, Honeybun?" crooned Uncle Tommy.

Susie and I snorted; then held our breath to keep from exploding, her eyes growing into mine.

"Gee, Tom, what's that sound coming from the back of the car, I wonder?"

I could hold it in no longer! As one, we popped up like a two-headed jack-in-the-box, the car whirling around the corner.

"SURPRISE!!!" Shrieks of laughter ballooned out of the rumble seat.

"Oh, my goodness! Stowaways, Tom!" Aunt Willie's cackle never crackled so loud.

Uncle Tommy craned his head around.

"Haw Haw! Why, I never!"

Giggling and waving like queens, we rounded the block and re-entered the Hauserman driveway – right into the reception of laughter awaiting us.

It was the best wedding ever!

Grandmamma and Uncle Tommy

The Fall

"Wow! It's like Santa's Workshop!"

Gleefully we burst through the shop door as if shot from guns, and fanned out in all directions. Mike and Pat leaped into the display of balls while I whirled from one treasure to another in the Army Post toy store. Colors galore! Dark wooden shelves and storage bins exploded their wares upon us. Such a feast for the eye! Teddy bears of all sizes and textures, cars, trucks, and dolls, dolls, dolls! Where to start?!

Quickly I approached the display area of old-fashioned dolls, dressed in their finest lace and calico. Eyes that opened and closed, 'real' hair. Then there were the baby dolls, rag dolls, skinny 'big girl' dolls.... Carefully I turned them over, one by one.

"Cathay! Where are the boys?"

Mommy frowned down at me, tugging back against the insistent pull of little Julie on one arm and Timmy on the other. Although one year apart, they were still the same size and looked like bookends.

I glanced around and shrugged. "They were here a minute ago...."

Mommy sighed, "All right. Take Julie and Timmy to the car. Daddy's waiting there for us with Eric."

Reluctantly I yanked the 'little ones" hands toward the shop door. Moments later I scurried back – bells ringing merrily to announce my re-entrance into the land of bliss. Once again, the magnetic pull called to me from the shelves....

On the left I spotted Mike and Pat crouched down against a glass case, their backs to me. With a skip, I circled around to the opposite side and mimicked them, my nose squished against the glass, staring bug-eyed at their down-turned faces.

"Neat-o train set!" Mike whispered to Pat.

"Yeah!" he replied. "Look at it go through the tunnel!"

Suddenly they caught my eye – and protruding tongue.

"Hey!" Mike spluttered.

I burst out laughing. "Ha, ha!" We all leaped up and chased each other 'round and 'round the glass case until....

"Cathay Laurel Gunn!"

Guiltily I stopped short and bumped right into Mommy, with Mike and Pat colliding into me from behind.

"*You* are nine years old. You are supposed to be setting an example!"

Oops. My finger flew to my lips, head in the air.

"Boys! It's time to go!" I announced.

Solemnly we headed out the door; then made a dash towards the waiting car.

On the ride home the red and white Pontiac station

wagon could scarcely contain the excitement within.

"Santa's coming! Santa's coming!" Timmy crowed. Almost three, he bounced up and down between Mommy and Daddy, nearly upsetting baby Eric on Mommy's lap.

Soon we crested the crossroads of our winding mountain road. Tootling past the occasional house, smoke curling languidly from the chimney, we wended our way up the final ascent. Eucalyptus trees waved their welcome. The waning sun hung on to their silhouettes for a precious last few minutes.

Patrick popped his thumb out of his mouth and leaned forward.

"I see our Christmas tree!" he observed. Straining to peer between branches, I could just make out the colorful glimmer through the far-off window of the house below. Safe in our carport above, we leaped out and scrambled down the terraced stone steps toward the big pink hillside homestead.

"Race ya!" Mike yelled. Mike, Pat and I tore up the porch steps and slammed our hands in quick succession upon the door. Then we plastered our faces against the window, leering through the glass at our brilliantly lit Christmas tree. Large red, green, yellow, orange and blue bulbs beamed back at us. Daddy unlocked the door and we all tumbled inside. Quickly we dispersed.

But before I could escape to my room, Mommy corralled me in the kitchen.

"Cathay, would you please start feeding Eric," she requested, "while I unload some things from the car?"

"What things?" I asked, mystified.

"Oh...just some groceries," she waved her hand vaguely.

Groceries?

I shrugged and pulled up a stool to meet seven-month old Eric's high chair. *Wait a minute...We didn't go to a grocery store....hmm....This bears investigating....*

Eric pounded his tray with his fat little hand and gurgled at me, breaking my reverie. I stuck the spoon inside the glass jar (with the baby on it that looked like Eric) and pulled out a glob of yellow pabulum. *Yuck...* Eric waved his arms excitedly.

"Ok, Eric – turkey, turkey, lurkey....yum!"

Straining my ears, I waited for the right sound from the living room. When I heard the front door open I jumped up and peeked around the corner. Mommy *was* carrying a bag...a *big* bag...but she slipped into her bedroom with it, just off the side of the living room. I ducked back into the kitchen and shoved another dollop into Eric. He grinned up at me, slapping his tray, goo sliding out of the corners of his mouth.

I bided my time. Later that evening, after we all finished our chili and Daddy holed up in the den, Mommy trundled Eric downstairs for bed. I saw my chance.

Without a sound I slipped from the kitchen to the adjacent bathroom. Its other door opened into Mommy and Daddy's room. I crept in and peered all around. The bed sat unadorned except for the blue chenille bedspread. The dressers and chair were bare of any bundles. No packages on the floor, either. Disappointed, I started to leave when I noticed the closet door slightly ajar. *Aha!*

I swung it open and looked up. There on the top shelf was the *Package!* The same green paper bag Mommy had carried! Quickly I shut the closet and turned the knob on the door leading to the living room. No one in sight, I darted out and discovered Mike emerging from the basement stairs.

"*Psst!* Mike!" I urged. "Come 'ere!"

Startled, he followed me, our paces quickening as we

reached the bedroom. Once inside, I motioned towards the closet, a finger to my lips. Opening the door, we stared up, stymied, at the forbidden goods just beyond our reach.

"I know!" I cried. "Let me stand in your hands – like this...." I demonstrated with my fingers folded and cupped. Mike gamely complied, a puzzled look on his face. One hand on his shoulder, I stepped in, almost throwing him off balance. With a swift tug I yanked that bag down. *Oh!* We fell upon it, greedy for treasure.

Into the depths I thrust my hands, pulling out...a Kewpie doll! Next to it lay a clear plastic box with the word "BUGHOUSE" in black letters across the side. ... *Oh!* Underneath sat a real Betsy-Wetsy! I snatched it up. Blue and white playsuit, a baby bottle taped to her hand so I could feed her real water and change her wet diaper! Mike suddenly pushed past my arm and grabbed something.

"Look at this!" he whispered triumphantly. A knobby brown football gleamed in his hands.

"WHAT'S GOING ON IN HERE?!"

A voice I had never heard before boomed through the stillness. We wheeled around and froze. It was Mommy! Sparks flew from her eyes. My jaw dropped. I swallowed. The words disappeared from my brain. I stared up at her in silence. The air hung heavy between us.

"Those were special gifts I bought for the Hausermans," Mommy finally stated.

"H-Hausermans??" I stammered. *Our cousins?!*

"Hausermans?!" Mike exclaimed in dismay.

"Yes," she continued. "The dolls are for Susie and Mary and the football is for Danny."

"Oh...," we murmured in unison, crestfallen.

"And you are NOT to ever, ever go through my closet again!" she warned. "Do you hear?!"

I stared at the rug. "Yes, Mommy."

"There will be no dessert for you tomorrow. I'm very disappointed in you. Now go get ready for bed."

I could feel her eyes boring into my back as Mike and I trudged out into the living room. In silence we crept, single-file, down the basement stairs. At the bottom we stopped, not daring to look at each other. Finally I reached back, grabbed his hand, and pulled him across the hall to my room.

Once inside, I plastered myself against the door, facing Mike. His eyes looked ready to jump out of his skin.

"Why did you do that? Why did you *do* that?!"

"I don't know," I faltered.

"Now maybe Santa won't come!" he hissed.

I thought quickly. "Listen, Mike. We can't let Mommy think we're so bad. Because, because....we just can't!" I cried, horrified at the memory of those eyes.

"Now what?!"

"Ok, ok...," I stalled. "I know. We write her a letter, and tell her our side."

I sat down at my desk and ripped out a page of tablet paper.

Dear Mommy, I wrote. Mike leaned over my shoulder, breathing on my neck.

We are very sorry for what we have done. I was just coming out of the bathroom when I walked past your closet. I just happened to see something sticking out of your closet door. I reached to push it back, but it fell down. Mike came in and we wondered what it was. We are very sorry and we will never do it again.

Love,

Cathay and ...

"Ok – now you sign it," I thrust the pencil towards Mike. He grabbed it, and with teeth gritted, laboriously scribbled his name: *Mike Gunn.*

"There!" I declared. Slipping back up the stairs, we snuck through the living room and cautiously turned the knob of the bedroom door. I set the letter in the middle of the big blue sea of chenille. Tiptoeing back out the door, I sought out Mommy in the kitchen. She stood at the sink washing dishes. I stopped. Mike hovered just behind me. I cleared my throat.

"Mommy?"

She turned around.

"Um…there's something for you on your bed," I mumbled. "It's from Mike and me."

She nodded solemnly. "Thank you."

We waited an agonizing minute or two outside her door in the living room until she came back out. Quietly she shut the door behind her. We leaped up from the couch. She reached out for us. We hugged in silence. I peered up out of the corner of my eye. I could see a tiny smile tug at the edge of her mouth.

"All right. Off to bed now," she murmured.

Christmas Eve must be the slowest day of the year…

At long last the sun began to set as we sat down to our traditional homemade potato soup. We slurped it down in gathering excitement.

"Bedtime early tonight!" Mommy sang out.

Off to the living room with jammies on, we gathered 'round the tree for Daddy's reading of the First Christmas. At story's end, Mommy drew our eyes over to the side table decorated with greens. She pointed out the empty manger in our Nativity scene of ceramic figures.

"Tomorrow morning there'll be a new baby Jesus in there," she remarked. I knew she would sneak a tiny doll inside.

Mike leaned towards me. "That better not be *all* there is!" he whispered out of the side of his mouth.

"Hush!" I warned him, not wanting to be reminded of our indiscretion.

Closing the book, Daddy sprang up, rubbed his hands gleefully and gleamed, "So! Shall we build a big fire tonight?"

A forceful chorus of "No's" leapt back at him.

"We don't want Santa to burn!" cried Timmy.

"Are you *sure* you don't want a nice cozy fire to warm you up?" Daddy grinned.

"DaddEE!" I entreated. "Stop it!"

Quickly Mommy rounded us up and herded us down the stairs.

Teeth brushed, under the covers with lights out, I could hear last minute reminders wafting out of the boys' room.

"Daddy, remember, no fire in the fireplace tonight!" Timmy and Pat called out in unison. Julie, next to me in our double bed, echoed their plea. Mike and I alone remained silent. I lay in the dark, saying a little prayer that I had not caused irrevocable damage to our Christmas.

"Wake up, wake up, Cathay!" Julie landed with a *bam!* on top of me. "It's Christmas morning!"

"*Huh!*" Instantly I jerked up in bed. So it was! Just then our door burst open; Mike and Pat tumbled in.

"Christmas! Christmas! Christmas!" Patrick pattered, then disappeared up the stairs.

I needed no further invitation.

Julie scrambled ahead, but Mike stopped me on the stairs.

"Cathay!" he whispered. "Last night I heard *reindeer*

hoofs on the roof!" He gleamed at me in wonder.

"You did?!" I stared in disbelief.

"Yeah," he nodded. "And I heard *sleigh* bells!" His eyes shone.

"Oh... That's really neat, Mike," I said, still not too sure. "Well – c'mon!"

Upstairs, Mommy and Daddy had already been called into action. Timmy ripped through the packages, paper flying, as the grownups tried to orchestrate some sequence, but quickly gave up. In the midst of the fray, Eric crept towards the discarded wrapping and waved it up and down.

Julie squealed, "Cathay! Look what I got!" She thrust out a brand-new Kewpie doll: unmistakable smiling face with the spit curl on top of its pointed head.

"And look what you got!" she cried, pointing to a Betsy-Wetsy in a blue and white playsuit. ....*Huh?*...

I stole a glance at Mike. He howled in delight.

"Cathay!" he crowed. "Look!" Between his two raised hands he held a knobby brown football.

Wow! We got the exact same things that Mommy gave to the Hausermans! That's amazing!

Just then Mommy's voice rose above the din. "Who left the front door open?"

I turned, just in time to catch Patrick skipping up the porch steps and into the living room.

"Look, Mommy!" he exulted. "It works!" Between his hands he cradled a long, clear plastic box. Inside lay one of his favorite pals, a slimy brown salamander from our woods. As he drew nearer I could make out the big black letters emblazoned across the side: "BUGHOUSE."
Heyyy.....

My jaw dropped. I glanced over at Mike. He guffawed over his next present, totally oblivious.

I looked up at Mommy. She raised her eyebrows at me, tapped her finger against her lips, and smiled.

"Good for you, Patrick!"

The Big Five!
Michael, Patrick, Cathay and Julie
Timothy

Cathay (second row, third from wall)

Sacred Passage

"A new school! Why do we need a new school?" Mike exclaimed. A first grader, Mike had already been to three kindergartens, including our present public school. I knew how he felt. Mommy and Daddy, flanking Patrick, our current kindergartner, hunched over the coffee table breaking the news.

"We're not moving again, are we?" I ventured, suspicious. After attending three different third grades last year, I was none too keen to start over again in the middle of a school year.

Daddy shook his head and leaned forward. "It's going to be an adventure!"

"Yes," enthused Mommy. "They have hot lunches every day with *real* white cloth tablecloths!"

"Well, honey," smiled Daddy, "I think that's just for special events with the parents. But, yes-s," he continued, "I have it on good authority that the hot lunches in the dining room are excellent."

"And," Mommy added, "the uniforms are *very* nice."

I glanced from one glowing face to another. I didn't get it. My school was fine. My best friend Carol was there. I rode a school bus. Why would we want to switch?

Saturday found us tootling along together, all eight of us packed inside the Pontiac station wagon, over the Golden Gate Bridge. Daddy wore his army officer uniform. ("But you're not going to work today, Daddy!" "We want to make a good impression, don't we?" he had replied with a wink.) Mommy and the rest of us had struggled into our Sunday best on what *should* have been a play day. But part of me tingled with a kind of curiosity. *Why was this school so special?*

"It's too bad the babysitter cancelled," Mommy mused. Julie and Timmy, now four and three, as well as baby Eric, had become the accidental tourists. Suddenly she wheeled around in her seat and eyed us one by one with a steady, knowing gaze.

"I want each of you," she said slowly and deliberately, "to be on your best behavior. Because we want to be proud of you. And you should be proud of your brothers and sisters, as well. So let's do that for each other. All right?"

We nodded back at her. I stared out the window, watching the sailboats dart past between the orange-red railings of the bridge.

Daddy began his instruction of "nun" etiquette. "Now whenever one of these nuns speaks to you, you reply with 'Yes, Mother,' or 'No, Mother."

"Not '*Sister*'?!" I queried, mystified.

"Nope. Not with this order."

"And – oh, Walt," exclaimed Mommy. "We forgot about the curtseying."

"Oh, ho!" he chuckled. "You will learn some terrific social skills."

Mike and I exchanged puzzled glances.

"Yes," Mommy enthused. "The girls curtsey and the boys bow."

"When?!" I exclaimed in dismay.

"Why -" she raised her eyebrows at Daddy. He pursed his lips and frowned.

"Whenever you see a nun, I guess," he finished triumphantly.

Slowly, almost painfully we puttered up the cement-covered hills of Pacific Heights. At last the wagon nosed straight at the curb, into an empty, slanted pocket. It felt like the car was going to tip over on its side!

"*Errumph!* Daddy!" I grunted. "The door's too heavy! I can't get it open!" Feeling almost dizzy, I wobbled out of the opened car door onto the steep curbside.

"Wow!" cried Patrick. "There's steps in the sidewalk!" Situated halfway up the hill, we stared both backwards and forwards at the endless train of steps carved into the cement. It looked like a roller coaster!

Huffing and puffing at the top of the hill, we gazed in awe at the three mansions before us: the white columned palace in the middle, flanked by two red brick estates – one dark and brooding, the other clean and pristine.

"That's not a school!" I protested.

"Sure it is!" Daddy's eyes twinkled.

The central mansion's filigreed arched door swung open.

"Good morning!" A squat, shapeless creature greeted us. "Won't you come in?"

Instinct reminded me this was indeed a nun. However, her black habit bore little resemblance to that of my parochial school in Maryland – or in Menlo Park. This one sported a circular cape covering the bodice of her long black robe, secured by a single row of very tiny black buttons down the center. A large silver cross hung from a black cord around her neck. Beneath a translucent black veil I could see a snug white bonnet clinging to the shape of her head – like underwear I wasn't supposed to see. A scant few gray hairs peeked slyly out at the nape of her neck. (In the months to come I would find myself surreptitiously straining to catch sight of these rebels on many an unwitting nun.) A three-inch pleated border stuck out from the cap, lining the face like a white picket fence. *(How can they see what's to the right or left of them?!)* The requisite beads hung from her waist.

She ushered us through the immense marble foyer and into the reception room on the left. I gazed up at the far-off intricately carved ceiling, the gilt-framed paintings and the antique gas fireplace. Our host gestured towards the richly upholstered loveseats and wing-backed chairs.

"Reverend Mother will see you shortly." She bowed her head and disappeared.

I tapped my toe on the Oriental rug while eyeing the rest of the family sitting stiff and still on their chosen seats. Somewhere a clock chimed, long and melodious. Suddenly a whirlwind of black forms bustled into the room.

"Dr. and Mrs. Gunn! Welcome!" A tiny, wizened-faced nun beamed and offered her hand. Two taller nuns, like bookends, bowed and smiled. I leaped from my chair, yanked my skirt outward on each side and stumbled forward in a kind of curtsey. One of them smothered a chuckle and nodded at me. I could feel the heat rising from my chest.

"You must be our new fourth grader," she smiled.

"Er – yes, Ss-uh, Mother," I mumbled.

We were introduced all around. Mother Mardel, who had eyed me knowingly, was the "Mistress General"

263

of the girls' elementary school. Mother Carroll, the "Mistress General" of the boys' school, took keen interest in quizzing Mike and Pat. Julie and Timmy must've been awed into submission by the strange creatures because they sat motionless at Daddy's sides, Julie staring at the floor, Timmy at the ceiling. Mommy jiggled Eric on her lap while attempting to answer questions.

It was all over in a few minutes, Reverend Mother graciously offering to admit Mike and Pat at half-tuition, along with myself. I carefully extricated my crossed feet and rose, following the grown-ups' cue. As Mommy and Daddy shook hands with Reverend Mother, Timmy leaped off the loveseat, hand at his forehead, and saluted.

"G'bye, Gen'rul!" he chirped with a sunny smile.

All three nuns tittered.

"Why, we have a nursery school for you!" Reverend Mother exclaimed. "And your good little sister, too. Dear Lord, let's take them all!"

As we stumbled down the hill to our car, Mommy and Daddy marveled at the good fortune of the failed babysitter. Suddenly, five of us were going to this new prestigious school for the price of two!

All I cared about, however, was me. Sunday evening I twisted this way and that before Mommy's full-length mirror, practicing my curtsey. *Did the left foot go behind the right foot — or the right foot behind the left?* I bit my lip and kicked the mirror. A pouting face scowled back at me.

"Time to hit the sack!" Daddy's voice rumbled at the door. Just as well...

Brrriiinnnggg...

Oh! I sat up quickly, bemoaning my toss-turning night. My eyes burned, my skin tingled with pinpricks darting hither and thither across my face. *What's wrong with me?* I reached up my hand and froze. My skin rose in bumps like cottage cheese under my fingertips.

I flew to the bathroom mirror. There the most hideous face stared back at me. I couldn't believe it. My eyes were barely discernible between folds of swollen, overhanging skin. A mask of lumpy oatmeal seemed to have enveloped my face.

"Mommy!" I wailed.

No answer. I turned and ran down the hall, frantic. Outside the boys' room I bumped into Mommy bustling towards me.

"What's the matter?" she queried.

"Look at me! I'm a freak! A monster!"

Mommy bit her lip and sighed. Then she smiled and hustled me back into the bathroom.

"It's poison oak!" I cried. "What am I going to do?!"

"We'll put a nice cold cloth on it and some calamine lotion," she soothed.

I drew back. "No! Then I'll have big pink blobs all over, too!"

The house already in an uproar, Daddy soon appeared to assess the situation.

"Nno-o…no…" he mused, craning his big face on either side of mine. "You've just got an emotional reaction. It'll go away on its own."

"I don't care what it is – I want it gone!" I howled.

Much to my dismay, I soon found myself crammed into our sports Fiat, Daddy and I up front, Mike, Pat and Timmy snug in the backseat, with Julie squeezed into the storage pocket behind it. She clutched her peanut butter toast without eating it, crying. Mommy, balancing Eric on her hip, waved frantically goodbye, all smiles and twitters.

"Have a wonderful day!"

I stared out my window, careful not to let Daddy see me. Tears oozed, unbidden, down my craggy face, stinging my already ravaged skin.

I look like a monster. Like the Hunchback of Notre Dame. Nobody has seen me like I really am. All these new girls – they'll think this is what I really look like! They'll probably run away from me!

All too soon, we crossed the bridge, rounded the hills and slowed to a painful crawl in the "drop-off" zone before those imposing mansions. Suddenly I realized Daddy had no intention of parking.

"Aren't you coming in with us?!" I cried.

"Oh, no, I've got to go to work," he replied.

Julie started whimpering. Daddy shot me a stern look.

"Cathay – you take Julie and Timmy with you into the main school. Someone will tell you where to go. Boys..." he pointed to the dark-red brick building on the left, "...there's your school. Don't be late."

Reluctantly I shoved the door open and inched out. Daddy tooted his horn and waved at us before peeling back into traffic. Patrick skipped jauntily ahead of Mike, who dragged his feet as if they needed oiling. I swallowed hard, reached down for Julie and Timmy's hands, and trudged towards the great arched door. It was open.

Once inside, I stared at the ornate white columns and ceiling of the grand entranceway. Invisible voices echoed down from the vast hall beyond. A group of smaller girls rushed past me, almost tripping over Timmy on my right. I squeezed his hand, took a big breath and approached the large oak desk on my left.

"Um...I - we," I stumbled. "It's our first day. Is there – who – uh – where do we go?" I croaked.

The old nun's face crinkled into a smile. "Good morning. You must be the Gunn children."

I exhaled and nodded, relieved.

"You sit tight over there –," she indicated an intricately carved high-back bench, "and someone will come to claim you."

Julie practically sat in my lap, but I pushed her apart, not wanting to stand out any more than I already did.

Two women loomed ahead from down the hall, smiling knowingly. The younger one bent down towards Julie and took her hand.

"All right then, honey, here we go," she cooed. Julie slid reluctantly off the bench and Timmy leaped down to join her. Julie reached around and grabbed his hand.

"Oh, no, now, young man," the older matron chided. "You're to come with me." Extricating his hand, she led him firmly to the side. Timmy strained towards Julie, who gazed back helplessly, then hung her head and shuffled alongside her new teacher. Suddenly Tim broke away.

"Wait!" he cried.

I watched as the gray-haired, white-uniformed woman pulled him back.

"Now, now, dearie," she admonished. "You'll see your sister after school."

Leading him firmly away, she marched off out of sight. A high-pitched plaintive cry echoed from around the corner.

I swallowed. The empty hall looked larger than ever. Suddenly I wished Julie were back trying to get into my lap again. I squeezed my lids tight for a moment.

"Hi. You must be the new girl."

I snapped them open. A stocky girl with short blonde hair, blue eyes and a quizzical look gazed back at me.

"Oh!" I jumped up, my cheeks growing hot.

"I'm Tessie," she grinned. "I'm in your class. I'm to show you around."

Relieved, I followed her through the main hall, our shoes squeaking on the polished marble floor. Up ahead another girl about the same age bustled towards us with papers in her hands, on her own important "mission." She stopped short.

"Hey, Tessie! Who's the new girl?" she whispered loudly. "Is she a *first* grader?"

I stared at her. Tessie shook her head without looking at her, held up four fingers and kept on walking. *First grader indeed!* I was thankful Tessie didn't look at her, admiring her off-hand handling of the situation. I hurried closer to her.

Just outside a set of double golden doors she stooped in front of a tapestried bench. Much to my amazement, she grabbed the edge of the bench with both hands and lifted the entire seat up to reveal a hidden compartment.

Oh!

"We're going in the chapel," Tessie informed me. "But first we always put on a veil."

I peered inside. In what seemed a bottomless pit lay stacks of white lace veils, a headband stitched to each one. Following her lead, I carefully covered my head.

We peeked inside the heavy gold door. The entire room vibrated with a warm wooden glow.

"The stalls around the edges are for the nuns," she whispered. I gazed at the oak box enclosures along the walls.

"Who's that?" I stared at a life-size statue on the right of a young girl sitting in a pink robe and white veil, her eyes lowered. She was beautiful! A spindle lay in her lap, a basket of yarn at her feet, with a book spilled open on top of it. A distaff of thread stood on one side of her, a white lily on the other.

"Oh, that's Mater," murmured Tessie.

"Who?"

"Mary – Jesus' mother," she stated matter-of-factly. "We pray to her and she helps us."

"Oh." I could see I had a lot to learn.

"We go to Mass every first Friday of the month," she continued, "wearing our white uniforms for special dress days."

I glanced down. Suddenly I had an image of my red uniform jumper slowly draining of all color.

Next, she led me out a side door into a gated courtyard towards the "clean" red brick mansion.

"This is called the 'cortile,'" Tessie informed me. "And here is where you should come in tomorrow. *This* is the junior school. The middle building is for the senior school."

"Oh," I murmured, my head starting to spin. I clattered down a wooden staircase after her. Stumbling along an empty corridor at her heels, I wondered how I would ever find my way on my own.

"Here's the cloak room," she gestured.

Huh? I gazed helplessly into the wide, flat room at the end of the hall. Row upon row of colorful garments hung side by side on hooks.

Do I have to have a cloak too?! I don't think Mommy knew that!

"Um," I hesitated. "I don't – I mean – where do you get a cloak?" I squeaked.

Tessie stared blankly for a second; then giggled.

"No – a cloak *room*," she grinned. "It's for your jacket." She tugged at my navy coat.

I hid my face while I hurriedly fumbled my garment onto the proffered hook. I didn't need her to see my embarrassment on *top* of my poison oak! Or whatever it was.

Back up the stairs, Tessie ushered me into a formal wood-paneled room filled with row upon row of cranberry-jumpered students at their desks. A very tall, graceful young nun towered even higher on her own platform up front. Her dark eyes smiled down at me as Tessie curtseyed before her. I noticed Tessie didn't pull her skirt out to the sides, but simply dipped quickly down and up. I tried to imitate her. The young nun bade me wait. Then she picked up a stick with a round ball on the end and briskly tapped it against a steel plate on top of her desk. *Bong - bong - bong!* It resonated melodiously. Without warning, the entire roomful of girls rose.

"Good morning, Mother Eby!" they chorused. The students all curtseyed as one, with a few bobbing slightly out of sync.

"Good morning, girls!" she responded. "This is our new student, Cathay Gunn. She is in the Fourth Class." I smiled uncertainly.

"Tessie, please show her to her desk."

I sidled quickly into my row, thankful to no longer see all those curious eyes upon me. Another set of "bongs," and confusion ensued, with bodies darting into the aisles, reshuffling into some magical order. I glanced wildly about, trying to make sense of what was happening.

"We're going to *Primes*," the girl next to me whispered. "C'mon!" I gazed at her; her dark brown bob framed a pixie face. She was small, like me. "I'm Jane."

"We're getting in order," she mumbled under her breath. "I'm first –'cause I'm the shortest." She cocked her head and eyed me with a slow smile. "- Or maybe not…"

Minutes later we stood wearing white gloves before a pair of French doors in a grand white lobby. Sunlight poured in at the huge bay windows. The last of our footsteps echoed back at us. I stared up, up at yet another criss-cross, ornate ceiling.

The youngest, the First Class, stood prepared to enter. Two little Victorian-faced girls with long, matching banana curls stared back at me. *How did their hair get like that?!* They looked like they walked straight out of "Little Women."

I heard a *click* – Mother Eby had given a signal, clacking shut a small wooden box against the palm of her hand. One by one each group of girls, First through Fourth Class, entered the "Little Theatre." Thankful that Mother Eby had allowed Jane to go first, despite our heights, I followed my new friend up the steps of the polished wooden bleachers along the side.

A large mirrored wall expanded behind us. I stared down at the stage in front. Three nuns sat at three desks in the center. I recognized tiny Reverend Mother in the middle. Mother Mardel, the Mistress General, sat on the right. Mother Eby had joined them on the left.

One by one each class rose and reassembled on the floor according to height in a semicircle facing the stage. I surveyed the scene from the relative safety of the highest bleacher. Two or three girls wore pink ribbons, or sashes. These were stretched diagonally over the shoulder, across the chest and pinned at the waist with the ends hanging to the hem of the skirt. As each girl's name was called out, she curtseyed. I strained to hear. Another word followed, labeling her as "very good," or, occasionally, "good."

Jane leaned towards me and whispered, "If you've been really bad, you get…*"indifferent."* She spoke the dreaded label with a shudder. I feigned a look of dismay, which I sensed was the requisite response.

All too soon, Mother Eby announced, "The Fourth Class." *That's us!* With a click of her clacker we rose as one and I hurriedly wobbled down the steps after Jane. Down on the gleaming wooden floor I stared up at the triad of nuns in their official stateliness. Finally the names and curtseying stopped. As in a dream, I followed

Jane up the small steps on the right of the stage and crossed before Reverend Mother. She held out a card to me and smiled.

"Welcome, Cathay. Have a good week."

I curtseyed clumsily, took the card and tried to read it as I slowly followed Jane to the other side of the stage. *Trés bien,* it said. I looked up just as a girl standing at the bottom of the steps reached out for my card. *Huh? Oh.* Reluctantly I thrust it into her hand and scurried to catch up with Jane, already beginning the ascent up the bleachers.

"Medals for the week will now be presented," Mother Mardel announced. "This will be followed by the quarterly awarding of Ribbons, in recognition of good Conduct, Courtesy and Cooperation."

In a blur, names and words soon rose in a singsong harmony of sounds as I allowed the notes to billow about me, secure in the knowledge that I wouldn't be called to leave the comfort of my seat this time.

"Politeness: Barbara Carson; Order: Janet Mahoney; Christian Doctrine: Patty Rusek; English: Jane Gray; French: Kerry Williams; Mathematics: Leslie Cooley…

"C'mon, c'mon, c'mon! I wanna see what kind of jello there is!"

"Quit shoving!"

"Girls! That will be enough!" Mother Eby's voice rang out.

I stumbled forward in the traffic jam of the school's cafeteria. Mirrored angular columns separated rows of dark wooden tables with matching bentwood chairs. I slid my tray along the meal counter, staring at the brightly-lit offerings. *Spaghetti for lunch?!* I kept moving. A ruddy-faced matron smiled at me over a huge pot of steaming red soup. I faltered. I knew I didn't want soup. But what? I could feel the hordes behind me, breathing on my back. Suddenly, with relief I spotted a tray of sandwiches. *That's more like it!* I pawed through the neat, white packaged triangles. Egg salad, tuna, ham and cheese, peanut butter and jelly (*yuck!*)...*Isn't there anything else?!*

"What are you looking for, love?" the white-capped server queried.

"Baloney," I whispered.

"Lookin' right at you," she pointed.

I stared. "B-O-L-O-G-N-A," it stated. *They spelled it wrong! That can't be right...*

"C'mon," someone urged from behind. *Oh...*

I grabbed the sandwich and a carton of milk; then turned. I stared uncertainly at the sea of noisy eaters before me. They all talked at once and no one looked at me.

"Here, Cathay, you're assigned to Sherri's table," Mother Eby's voice broke through. I glanced up, grateful to see her smiling face.

After grace, she introduced me to the seven other girls there. Sherri, in my class, was the table "captain." The others all appeared to be younger. They glanced up, mumbled "hello," and returned to their conversations.

I couldn't help but stare at the thin, dark-haired little girl opposite me, Melody. She wasn't eating. Her black eyes gazed at me, unseeing. Unwittingly they grabbed me and drew me in as they widened with tears. She turned to Sherri at the head next to her and began murmuring. I strained to hear.

"...They said I have to go live with my Grandmother..."

Sherri cocked her head and whispered a question I couldn't hear. Their heads bent together in a sphere separate from the rest of the laughing, playful exchanges around them. Melody broke off and gazed once more resignedly in my direction. Her mouth slackened, her eyes seemed to extend back deep inside her head. I wanted to know, but didn't.

All of a sudden I wanted very much to rush home and see *my* Mommy and Daddy.

Honk, honk! Bbrroomm! Rumble, rumble...

A policeman blew his whistle while hordes of laughing, screaming girls darted this way and that between the curb and me.

Where, oh where are Julie and Timmy? And how will we find Mommy?

At last the crowded sidewalk thinned and I felt a tug on my skirt.

"Julie!"

Just then the familiar red and white station wagon pulled up and the man with the whistle led us to the auto. Suddenly it was the most beautiful car I had ever seen! Mommy blazed that giant smile as we clambered in.

There stood Timmy in the third seat already, jumping up and down.

"I went home!" he crowed. "I went home!"

I stared. "Timmy's wearing play clothes!"

"Yes," Mommy acknowledged. "He came home unexpectedly early. We all decided he wasn't quite ready yet. Next year," she smiled at him.

Julie quickly climbed over the seat to join him, their heads bent together in low murmurings.

Mommy inched forward to the boys' school. Seconds later, the door burst open and Mike and Pat bounded in. I turned to catch a glimpse of their excited faces and energetic babble, then wheeled back around in my seat next to Mommy and sleeping baby Eric. The air seemed to rush out of me like a balloon. My head sank back on the seat and I stared up at the gray, pebbled ceiling. My eyes closed.

"And how was *your* day, Cathay?" I heard Mommy say.

Voices, sounds and images rose up and fell, washing over me.

"My name is Tessie"...marble floors, *squeak, squeak*... "Is she a *first* grader?"...beautiful pink Mater...rainbow of "cloaks"...*bong, bong, bong*...girls rushing up/down, back and forth...white gloves...*clack, clack*...curtsey, curtsey...Reverend Mother's wrinkled smile...*très bien*... "Mathematics: Leslie Cooley"... "B-O-L-O-G-N-A"... Melody's black tunnel eyes... "Bonjour, Cathay!"...

At last I exhaled and opened my eyes.

"Fine," I murmured.

"Bless us, O Lord, and these Thy gifts
Which we are about to receive,
From Thy bounty,
Through Christ, our Lord. Amen."

Lunch at last! Relieved at getting through the second morning without any glaring mistakes, I was starved. I glanced up from my folded hands on the table to spy an empty chair directly across from me. I waited; I searched in vain for any stragglers aimed our way. The chair grew ominous. I peered over at Sherri. She munched away on her sandwich, oblivious. Finally I cleared my throat.

"Um, Sherri," I ventured.

"Huh?"

"Where's Melody?"

Sherri raised her eyebrows. "Gone," she said.

"Where?" My chest tightened.

Sherri shrugged. "To live with her grandmother, I guess."

I stared. Sherri sighed and returned to her tuna sandwich. Soon she chortled at a joke from little Emily, farther down the table.

On the chair before me swam the sudden image of that sad little face with the tunnel eyes. I swallowed. That was the last I ever heard of her.

"Class, please turn to page ninety-six in your readers. Did everyone finish reading…"

Mother McMonagle's voice grew fuzzy in my ears as I stared, unseeing, at the letters. My head felt prickly; the words before me jumped up and down on the page as if on their own trampoline. I glanced surreptitiously about at the girls around me. Already-familiar faces bent over their books…but their names seemed to be stubbornly hiding from me. *Why can't I remember anyone's name but Melody's?* I heard my breath suck in and out in quick little gasps. The room felt stuffy, the air pressing in on me. I couldn't seem to catch my breath. *What's wrong with me?!* Fighting the panicky feeling that threatened to overpower me, I gazed wildly about. Just then Mother McMonagle caught my glance and held it.

"Cathay, are you all right?"

I gulped. "No, Mother."

In a flash, she swooped down beside my desk. I could feel her slight black form leaning over me. I couldn't look at her.

"I can't breathe," I whispered. The air hung heavy with a roomful of silence.

"Why don't we go outside for some fresh air," she said gently. Murmuring quiet instructions to the class, Mother eased me out of my chair, slipped an arm across my back and led me firmly down the corridor. Once outside we sat on the cement steps of the entry.

I stared into the courtyard - the cortile - the silver monkey bars winking back at me. Mother said nothing but sat calmly next to me. Her black pointed shoes peeked out from under her skirts.

Why is she sitting on the step? She's a NUN! She's my TEACHER! Everybody else is inside. Shouldn't she be in there with the others?

Nothing moved in the courtyard. Gradually, as the minutes stretched on by, they seemed to add nice gray clouds of mist between all the brilliant pictures and sounds crammed into the last two days. I slowly exhaled to the bottom of my shoes. Mother McMonagle turned to me and smiled.

"Feel better now?"

I nodded.

"Ready to go back?"

"Yes, Mother," I whispered. Mutely I followed along side of her, sneaking a peek at the nicest nun in the whole wide world.

"Bonjour, mes enfants!"

"Bonjour, Mademoiselle Liliane," we responded in unison, leaping out of our chairs and curtseying. At last, it was Friday; my face was back to normal, and the butterflies had all but flown. Melody had become a distant memory.

"Attention, mes enfants! Comprenez-vous un 'spelling bee?'"

"Oui, Mademoiselle," we nodded uncertainly.

"Today we will have un 'bee Francais.'"

I swallowed. Last night in my room I had hunkered over my hand-copied list of French vocabulary, straining to memorize the elusive terms. Daddy had slipped in, reading over my shoulder. He frowned when he got to *le* and *la*, each on separate lines, and alone.

"Why are these here?" he asked.

"They mean 'the!'" I responded, surprised. He didn't like that, and made me re-write all the words with the "proper form of 'the' in front of each. I grumbled at his retreating back, but did it anyway. Now I was glad.

Quickly Mademoiselle jotted down *le*, *l'*, *la*, and *les* across the board. We stood next to our desks and waited our turn. Raising high a flashcard, she demanded, "Name zee article along with zee French word." One by one, girls spouted off as Mademoiselle Liliane flashed new cards before us.

"...Summer," she called out.

Oh, no, please get it – I don't know it! I prayed, my fingers crossed behind my back.

"L'été," announced Barbara with-the-curly-mop.

Whew...my turn...

"House."

"La maison," I declared. I smiled inside. *This isn't so bad...*

Gradually, the ranks thinned, as girls struggled and dropped, disappointed, to their seats. Barbara and I alone remained. Side by side, we stared up at the board.

"Winter," stated Mademoiselle.

Confidently Barbara replied, "Le hiver."

"I'm sorry, Barbara, but zat's incorrect."

Barbara inhaled sharply, eyes widened. Confused, she stared at the teacher.

"But I *know* -"

"I'm sorry, Barbara. Cathay?"

Suddenly I felt all eyes on me. I scrutinized the board, searching for some hidden meaning. I knew 'hiver' was right...I stared at *le...l'...la...* I hadn't a clue, but *le* was wrong, apparently. Whispers began to fill the silence behind me. All of a sudden, *l'* leaped out at me, demanding to be chosen. I knew not why, but I obeyed.

"Um...the second one...*l* –apos-apostrophy...hiver," I squeaked.

"Zat's right, Cathay. And zee 'h' is silent," Mademoiselle smiled. "L'hiver."

Without warning, the whole class erupted in cheers.

"The new girl won!"

"Hurray for the new girl!"

For a second my heart stopped. *Don't they know I just guessed?* I gazed around me. Their smiling faces sent a zing throughout my body. *But I guessed right...*

I grinned up at Mademoiselle Liliane. *I like this French. It's even better than pig-latin!*

"Medals for the week will now be presented..."

Today at my second Prîmes I sat poised and alert, hands covered and clasped in my lap.

'...Science: Sherri Smith..."

I clapped my white-gloved hands, enjoying the rhythmic *thud – thud* emanating from the soft cotton fabric. For a moment I gazed about the elegant 'ballroom.' *Cinderella could've danced here...*

The voice from the stage broke into my reverie.

"...and French: Cathay Gunn."

I jumped – and stared at Mother Mardel, who eyed me expectantly.

Jane nudged me, "Go on, Cathay! That's you!"

Carefully I descended the bleachers – all by myself this time – and floated, as though on water, across the 'ballroom' floor and onto the stage. Reverend Mother's eyes twinkled as she placed the medal over my head.

"Trés bien *encore*," she smiled.

I dipped in an easy, lilting curtsey.

"Tha – merci, Reverend Mother," I murmured shyly.

As I climbed back up the bleachers, I could feel my heart racing against my chest. Only this time I did not want to jump out of my skin. This time, a warm glow spread outward, filling my body with a tingle of sunshine. I spotted Tessie's pink ribbon in the sea of faces as I neared the top. At the same time I felt an imaginary satin sash singed across my own chest. *Someday...I might be a "Ribbon," too...*

I slipped in between Jane on my left and Barbara on my right. I had found my spot at last.

Julie

Pillow Talk

I hear Julie beside me in our double bed muttering to herself.

"Julie!" I whisper. "What are you doing?"

"I'm saying 'good night' to my 'Iddow Piddow," she chirps. "Good night, Fellie; see you in the morning, Pellie; and you, too, Sellie…and have a very good sleep, Tellie."

"Huh?" I roll over. "How many names does your pillow have?"

"Those aren't 'Iddow Piddow's names," she retorts. "'Iddow Piddow's name is 'Iddow Piddow," she enunciates patiently. "Those are the Corners' names. See?" She takes my hand and makes me feel them in the dark.

"This one's Fellie." I follow her lead along the silky edge to the next twisted point. The sharp end of a feather pricks my finger. "This one's Pellie. This is Sellie…and this…is Tellie!" she finishes.

Oh! Like the Blessed Trinity! Three Gods in One! …

But only there's four... My eyes droop.

I sigh. "Oh. Ok. Goodnight, Fellie, Pellie, Sellie, and Tellie."

"And 'Iddow Piddow!" she reminds me.

"And 'Iddow Piddow," I reply dutifully. "Now good night, Julie!"

"Good night."

Soon a repetitive grunt reverberates through the darkness, flowing into me with its ceaseless rhythm.

"UHNNH – uh...UHNNH - uh...UHNNH – uh..."

The head on the pillow next to me bounces in perfect time with the mantra that cycles through us both. My neck resonates in kind.

...But where she journeys I cannot follow, as Julie slips into her own private reverie...

...I'm on my own...

Sky High

*P*eter Pan! *It's finally here!*

Inside the cool theatre, I burrowed into the sagging seat, excited cacophony of voices bubbling around me. Mike and Pat whispered together on one side, Julie hugged my arm on the other.

"When's the movie starting?" she chirped.

I shrugged and returned to my reverie.

Now I'll get to see what Tinkerbell really looks like! Not just a fuzzy glow, like in the play on TV. Hmmm. Who should I be? Maybe Tinkerbell. She gets to fly with Peter Pan all the time!

The room slowly darkened. Voices squealed, buzzed, shushed. The sudden pinpoint of light that dazzled the screen seemed to reach out to me and zing my chest, sending sparks throughout my entire body. *It's starting!*

...Wendy is nice...she's an "old-fashioned" girl...maybe

283

*I'll be her... Tinkerbell talks in chimes, like a bell! But why
is she so mean to Wendy? I'D like to sew Peter's shadow back
on... Oh, let's fly! Let's fly! Up in the sky! The stars sparkle
like diamonds all around us! Me and Wendy and Peter Pan!
Yes! I'll be Wendy! ... She's such a good little mother, telling
stories to the Lost Boys... No, I'm already that....no, no....
not that... Who? Who shall I be? Tiger Lily! The Indian
maiden. She's so brave, so proud... She gets rescued by Peter!
Rescue ME! But she doesn't DO anything... I know! The
mermaids! Yes! I'll be one of them! Peter is laughing and
splashing with them; they have so much fun with him...they
swish so free through the lagoon...but Peter leaves them, and
they can't follow...if only they could splash through the air
with him... Tinkerbell is horrid to Wendy! I don't like her
at all! She tries to kill her! Oh! Wendy is brave... Fly home,
Wendy! Fly, Peter!*

The lights suddenly blazed on, blinding us with their
intrusion. Babble erupted all around me. It was over!
Riding the wave of human passage into the lobby, I
clutched onto my dream, unwilling to let it go...

And yet, just hours before, I could only guess at the
magical world ahead...

Peter Pan!

That morning I woke up with a jolt.

*Today's the day we're going to see "Peter Pan" at
the movies!* I bolted out of bed and pounded on the
bathroom door.

...Of course I had already seen the Playhouse
Production on TV – with "real" people – at least twice.
And I loved it.

"Hurry, Julie!" I cried, hopping from one foot to
another.

...But TV was black and white – and *this* was a

cartoon – and in COLOR!

The morning crawled by as I vainly attempted to speed the clock by slurping each mouthful of cereal in slow motion.

...On television a girl – Mary Martin – played Peter. On the one hand, I liked that – a girl getting to do a fun boy's part. On the other hand – it wasn't a *real* boy.

At long last, the hour arrived.

"Up to the car!" Mommy called.

A hodgepodge of children scrambled out onto the porch, down across the wild garden path and up the terraced stairway to the carport above. In quick succession doors opened and slammed as we tumbled inside the red and white Pontiac station wagon.

"Sound off!" signaled Mommy.

"One!" I declared, as the eldest.

"Two!" yelled Mike.

Pause. I glanced around, a double set of vinyl seats behind me. Julie and Timmy beamed from the last seat, waiting their turns. One-year old Eric bounced up and down in the middle next to Mike. But no Patrick.

"Where's Pat?" I exclaimed in dismay.

"In the mud! In the mud!" Timmy cried gleefully.

With an exasperated sigh I threw open the door and leaped out.

"I'll get him," I called back over my shoulder.

Sure enough, along the side of the house, situated on the slant of a hill, squatted a lone figure. Scrutinizing the muddy ooze that trickled from the woods above, Paddy "shushed" me as I approached.

"Don't get so close," he warned. "You'll scare him."

I stared, puzzled, at the murk, seeing nothing. Suddenly Pat's hand darted out into the rushes, then flashed back to expose a wiggling salamander in his grubby fist.

"There!" he remarked with satisfaction.

Impatient now, I blurted, "C'mon, Pat. We're going to the movies."

Pat studied his newfound friend, turning him this way and that to get a better look.

"You go," he commented. "I hafta take care of Brownie."

I could feel my chest tighten, my arms and legs prickling with heat. If Patrick didn't go, that meant Mommy had to stay home. If Mommy stayed home, there'd be no one to take us to see "Peter Pan."

"Pat," I began carefully, "You'll really like it."

"Naw. That's okay." He squinted closer at the tiny tail swishing in his hand.

I took a breath. "There's a big crocodile..."

Suddenly his head popped up.

"Yeah?" his eyes widened.

I nodded emphatically.

"Okay." With that, he set Brownie down on a rock, all but forgotten, and dutifully followed me up the path to the car.

...That was a close one! To think that I almost didn't get there!

Now outside the theatre, the sunlight stabbed me as I stood blinking on the sidewalk. I strained for signs of Mommy in the big red and white.

"There she is!" pointed Julie.

Inside the car, Mike and Pat chanted, "Following the leader, leader, leader, we're following the leader..." I gazed up at the wide blue expanse outside my window.

Come back, Peter...

Up the Tam Valley mountain the station wagon rumbled, twisting this way and that. With a sudden jolt,

Mommy peeled off the main road to the left. I craned my neck. "Alta Vista" the sign read.

"Where are we going?" cried Julie.

"It's the short-cut!" I whooped. I had always wanted to try it.

"Yes," agreed Mommy. "I thought I'd find out once and for all if Cathay was right."

The road steepened upward before leveling off and rounding the edge of the mountain, framing the grassy hillside. A lone ranch house popped into view. I leaned closer. A small girl with short dark hair skipped out of the doorway.

"That's Lynette!" I uttered, amazed.

A girl in my old fourth grade class, Lynette loved team sports. We never played together at school – but this was different. She lived quite close to me!

I stuck my head out the window and waved frenetically.

"Lynette! Lynette!"

She grinned and gestured for me to join her.

"Can I stay and play, Mommy?" I pleaded.

"Tomorrow," she replied. "It's getting late."

Back in the carport in our own forest alcove, I leapt out down the earthen steps towards the woods beyond.

"I'll be back for dinner!" I called over my shoulder. I didn't want to break the mood that "Peter Pan" had created for me, with mundane tasks such as setting the table, or changing baby Eric.

I trounced up the bumpy terrain above our big pink homestead. The trees waved invitingly.

"Peter!" I whispered. "Can you see me?"

All of a sudden a shot of adrenaline kick-started my feet and sent me charging forward. I raced to the top of the hill, weaving my way through a maze of branches and trunks. There at the crest overlooking Richardson

Bay I stopped. Slowly I raised my eyes to the sky.

"Peter!" I breathed. "Take me with you!" I filled my lungs with a great surge of air and took off like a shot. Down, down the road I roared, trees skimming past like darting deer. I raised my arms and stretched them forward, reaching up, up till I could slowly push the air down to my sides. My fingers cried out with joy as they splayed electrically outward. I was flying! The wind rose, billowed me up and whispered me forward as I sliced through the air with my wings. I was not Wendy; I was not Tiger Lily, or a mermaid. I was *me!*

"Hello, Peter!" I crowed. "I can feel you here! We are flying together!"

My feet skimmed the air just above the ground, propelling my body through the sky as I closed my eyes and floated. Every hair on my arms sang in the breeze. The woods nodded and parted on either side, ushering us forward. Eucalyptus wafted on the currents, tickling my nostrils. Peter was laughing now, urging me on.

"You're doing it!" I could hear him say. Together now we flew, like a bird and its shadow, clinging and guiding, as we glided through the air.

Clang! Clang! Clang! Clang!

Huh? A great bell jangled in the distance.

Is that the pirate ship?

No. It was Mommy's dinner bell. The spell was broken.

Tomorrow…

"We'll fly again tomorrow," I heard Peter promise.

I straightened my shoulders and marched up the pink porch steps, steeling myself for civilization.

Maybe Lynette might want to play Peter Pan…

Next morning after breakfast I set my cereal bowl in the sink and stole out the front door.

"Be back for lunch!" Mommy called out behind me.

Ah, freedom! My pace quickened. The sunshine glinted off the mountainside, pinpointing poppies and nasturtiums that dotted the landscape. At the bottom of our road I picked my way along the rocky edge of Alta Vista as it zigzagged steeply downward. It was farther than I remembered in the car – but it gave me a chance to explore.

Hmm...this must be Indian Island. Tiger Lily's tribe lives just beyond that bend... I wonder if the Chief is hiding behind those rocks, spying on the pirate ships...

At last I rounded a curve to confront the familiar ranch house of yesterday. No one was about. I approached the screen door and knocked. Peering inside, I leapt backwards as the door sprang open. Lynette appeared.

"Hey! You came back!"

"Can you play?"

Without a word she slipped outside, and with a toss of her head, motioned for me to follow. A basketball hoop protruded from the side of the house. Grabbing a ball from the ground, she immediately lunged at the basket. I stood still. Suddenly I wasn't so sure I wanted to be there.

"C'mon! Let's play one on one!" she urged.

"Umm...Okay..." Hesitantly I stepped forward. Without warning she thrust the ball my way. I jerked towards it but it slipped to the ground beyond my grasp. Lynette eyed me with a twist of her mouth.

"What's a matter? Can't you play?"

"Um...yes...no...could we do something else?" I squeaked.

She heaved a sigh. "How 'bout tether ball?"

I relaxed, "Sure." I followed her out to the top of the grassy hill. Down below I could see the winding road hugging the mountain. I glanced up just in time to duck the yellow target zooming my way.

"Whoa," I laughed uncertainly and socked it back on the rebound.

Suddenly Lynette stopped.

"Gotta go to the bathroom. Be right back." She turned on her heel and dashed back down to the house.

I was alone. Slowly I twirled, gazing at the massive sky around me. I could see for miles in almost any direction! Eyes open, I lifted my face up high to meet the warm rays filtering past the scattered cotton balls. I could hear the breeze rustling the tall grasses below. A blue jay broke the silent skies above. All of a sudden I raised my arms over my head and signaled back and forth.

"Hello, Peter!" I whispered. "Are you having fun up there?"

Just then the screen door slammed behind me. I jumped; and immediately shot my arms back down to my sides.

"Hey!" Lynette called, sauntering towards me. "Hey!" Closer now, she grimaced, eyes crinkled, mouth twisted to the side. "Who are you talking to?"

"No one."

Hands on her hips, she cocked her head and raised her eyebrows.

"Yes you were!" she crooned. "I saw you!"

I swallowed. My cheeks flamed, heat rising from my chest and spreading upward.

"I was just...I was just scratching my head."

Without warning she leaned over and slapped her knee, chortling wildly. Lynette waved her finger at me and hopped back and forth on her red tennis shoes.

"Cathay has an imaginary friend!" she guffawed.

I stared at her. The sea of blue cracked around us.

In a flash, a shimmering plume of fairy dust plummeted from the sky. It faded to nothingness as it sank like a stone into my heart and embedded itself there. Peter Pan was gone, locked up forever inside, never to return to the outside world.

I bent forward, reached for the tetherball, and socked it back to her.

Easter Rising

Easter morning dawned bright and fresh over our home in the woods. The evening before, I managed to catch a glimpse of the gorgeous chocolate bunnies that Tom Merrill, our old family friend and handyman, had given Mom. All smiles, with a bashful gaze, he had presented them on the porch steps after completing his day's work on the new basement bedroom. Nothing gave him more pleasure than to grace our family with gifts. Mommy accepted, pleased, knowing we were the "adopted children" he had never been fortunate enough to have. One glance was all *I* got, though, before she whisked them away.

"You want to be surprised on Easter morning, don't you?" she laughed.

However, Easter morning slammed me with an unwanted surprise. Scrambling out of bed, I scampered upstairs to view the great "Easter Bunny" offerings. Lined up before the fireplace sat six baskets boasting rainbow hues of sweet delight. But something jarred my vision. I blinked. A muddy-looking hole gaped in the midst of several colorful displays. I rushed forward. What used to be a large chocolate bunny in three of the baskets was now a soggy brown mess....complete with teeth marks.

"Katie!" I screamed.

Our little black curly-haired dog cowered under the coffee table. With one swift kick that found its mark, I sent the culprit flying across the rug. I charged after her out the front door and down into the garden.

"Mommy!" I wailed.

But there was nothing for it. The chocolates were ruined. Stomping back inside, I got Mom to help me hide the evidence before the rest of the children descended upon us.

"Don't tell Tom Merrill!" Mommy whispered under her breath.

The younger children popped goodies in their mouths and bandied about in their ignorance, satisfied with their booty...

"Time for Mass!" called Mommy.

We assembled in the living room, our best attire receiving the last minute inspection. Julie and I preened beneath our matching Easter bonnets. Mike, Pat and Timmy sported clip-on bow ties with their starched white shirts. Even eleven-month-old Eric looked dapper in his sailor suit. Daddy threw open the door, "Let's go!" and strode off in the lead.

A moment later, he stopped short. "WHAT?!" he roared.

We tumbled over each other down the porch steps, anxious to see. There, lying in the dirt next to the newly planted petunias lay Katie, panting, eyes glassy, mouth salivating. Next to her lay the remnants of the snail poison Daddy had sprinkled on the turf the evening before. We had been warned…

"Who let Katie out of the house?!" he thundered.

I gasped. With a swift turn I ducked under his arm. Julie and the boys began to cry.

"No time for this now," he said tersely. "Into the car with you. We'll take Katie with us."

He lifted her up, and with Mommy's help, laid her on a towel in the back of the station wagon. I sat next to her, my hand on her head, tears streaming. *How could we possibly drive to the City and leave her in the car while we go to Mass?!* But Daddy's rule reigned.

Out of the car and into St. Dominic's, we stared straight ahead, surreptitiously wiping an eye. The priest droned on and on. White lilies crowding the altar mocked us with their serenity.

At long last, we raced to the car, hands trembling, as we peered into the back. Katie's pants were weaker now, her eyes unseeing.

Daddy drove faster this time, to the Presidio Army Post Pharmacy. Being a physician has its privileges. He disappeared inside, only to reappear several agonizing minutes later with a vial and a syringe. I stared, eyes widened, as he stuck that needle into Katie's side.

"Now we'll just have to wait and see," he told us.

It was a long, silent ride home over the bridge. At last we parked under the trees and leaped out. Daddy threw open the tailgate and peered in at Katie. Not a whisper of movement could be seen.

My heart in my throat, I quavered, "Is she going to be okay?"

Daddy's hand settled on my shoulder. "I'm sorry, everyone. Katie didn't make it."

I stood there, rooted to the ground. My whole body burst into tiny sparks of light, zinging into each other. A chorus of sobs erupted around me.

"No-oo, Daddy!"

"We'll put her in the dugout for now, and bury her tomorrow," Daddy murmured.

"Wait!" I cried.

I dashed into the house and retrieved my favorite flannel nightgown with the orange and black figures strewn across it. It was too small now, but I hadn't been able to part with it – until now.

The shroud bunched under my arm, Daddy and I led the solemn procession down the steep steps along the side of the house. We hunched into the dugout basement beneath. With floors, walls and low ceiling all made of dirt, the space had just room enough to stand (if you were nine.) We couched Katie into the cardboard box Mom had provided and wedged it into a cubbyhole. With shaking hands, I folded the flannel nightgown around that helpless little body – so still!

Once everyone else had stolen away, I slumped on a slope beside her and whispered in her unheeding ear.

"I'm so sorry, Katie. I was so mean to you. And now I've *killed* you!" I sobbed.

At last I crept out. *Some Easter this turned out to be!*

Back in the house, the family had gathered in the kitchen, eager to put their minds elsewhere. With great effort, I threw myself into the frenzy of the big Easter dinner preparation. Already the succulent smell of baked ham wafted through the air….

Dinner behind us, dessert on the way, I couldn't stand

it any longer. *I must say goodbye to Katie!* Sneaking out the basement door, I hurried down the side steps, two at a time. I just had to see that sweet little dog once more!

Bursting through the doorway, I collapsed next to the still form in the box. The dam broke.

"Oh, Katie, Katie! How can you leave me?!" I wailed. "Oh, God, why did you take our little dog away from us?! She's never *really* done anything wrong! She didn't mean to eat our bunnies!" My tears dotted the flannel; my hand stroked her curly head.

All of a sudden a vibration touched my skin. My hand froze. Glancing down, I saw the minute rise and fall of the fabric. I leaped backwards.

"She's alive!" I yelled.

Hysterical now, I staggered back up the steps, babbling between chortles of relief and joy. In a tumble the family spilled out onto the porch. Mike and Pat clamored to see. As one we swooped back down for the grand revelation.

Inside the dugout, Daddy bent over the box, testing with his hand, then straightened. A slow smile spread across his face.

"We have our Easter Rising," he declared.

It was the best gift of all.

Hijinx

Mommy at last found us swimming lessons. With much trepidation, swimsuits in hand, Mike, Pat and I climbed out of the car after her. We joined the throngs of parents and children who milled about the parking lot of Tamalpais High.

Confusion ensued, as we bumbled through group after motley group before settling in the proper line. I stared up, up at the huge clock tower above me. I had never seen such a clock! *This is a HIGH school!* And *way* too big. I felt myself shrinking and disappearing into the anonymous masses...

Brrr! A shower BEFORE swimming?! I stumbled out of the locker room and into the sunshine, dripping wet. Resigned, I squatted at the edge and dutifully dropped first one leg, then the other as I hopped into the pool...

Afterwards, while dressing, a furtive movement at the next locker caught my eye. The thin, dark-haired girl

beside me slipped out a box of Good 'n' Plenty and a
package of M & M's. My eyes popped.

"Hi, I'm Marcie," she said. "Want some?"

I nodded. "Where did you get those?"

"Safeway – it's across the street a-ways. Right next
to Santa's Toys. That's a neat-o toy store. We could
go together right now and get more, if you want. My
brother's class is after mine, and I have to wait."

Oh, heaven! Since we had gotten out early for the first
day, I knew Mommy wouldn't get there for another half
hour. Marcie lent me a dime, and a secret treasure trove
opened before us.

After that, I persuaded Mommy she should pick us
up a little later so we could "swim some more." Visions
of root beer barrels and Jujy Fruits propelled me through
the jittery moments on the drive to Tam High. (Lessons
were okay, but the jitters beforehand were not.) Some
days I let Mike and Pat join me, and some days I didn't.

But Friday none of us could go. Mommy arrived
early. Mike pounded on the girls' locker room door.

"Cathay! Mommy's already here! Hurry!"

I sputtered in the shower in dismay. *Darn!* Wrapped
in my towel, I fumbled through my locker for
underwear. A giggle from the open doorway stopped me
in my tracks. There stood Julie, pushed in from behind
by gleeful Timmy.

"Stop it!" she retorted. Her big eyes then swept the
room in awe. "What are you doing, Cathay?"

"I'm getting dressed, Julie! And YOU, Timmy, are not
supposed to be in here!"

Just then Patrick swooped in from behind and
snagged Tim by the shirttail. "Hurry, Cathay!" The three
of them vanished.

I stumbled down the cement steps, my soggy bundle
in tow. *Why didn't she come later?* The Pontiac station

wagon sat a-ways up along the curb. Just then a foot slipped from view as Pat slammed the rear door shut. My legs balked at any need to rush. I dragged myself forward.

But, *horrors!* The old Red & White chugged to life; then slowly lumbered away from the curb! My feet quickened.

"Wait!" Frantically I waved my arm. But the car sped up and disappeared from view.

My eyes searched the empty horizon in disbelief. *What happened?! Why did they leave me?* I stood glued to the ground, hot tears burning down my cheeks; then shuffled back to the steps and sagged.

I scanned the street back and forth, like a ping-pong match. Only a few stragglers lounged about the parking lot now. I could feel the vastness of the building behind me. I didn't dare look at the clock tower. Like that first day, I had shrunken to a colorless speck, hidden against a mammoth landscape…

At last, a miniature model down the road morphed into the old familiar Red & White. Wheeling into a giant "U," it rumbled to a halt. The right rear door swung open. I grabbed my bundle and tore towards it.

Clambering inside, I glared into the uproar around me. Julie and Timmy cheered, while Mike managed to spurt out between guffaws the following scenario:

"All right; everybody ready?" Mommy had sung out from the front seat. "Sound off!"

Mike had then leaned over to his friend John, next to him in the third seat. "Say 'ONE!'" he whispered in his ear.

"What?"

"Say… 'ONE!'" he emphasized. *"Loud!"*

"Oh…ONE!"

"Two!" Mike crowed.

"Three!" hollered Pat.

"Four!"

"Five!"

"And Eric makes six," Mommy had finished. "Okay, here we go…" The engine had started and they were off…

Masses of giggles from the third seat had at last disintegrated as Mike twisted towards the front.

"Mommy! Cathay's not here! We left her at the pool!"

"Oh, you stop that teasing, Mike!"

"Well, she's not here!"

"Now, Mike, that's enough."

At that, John's head had popped up, his eyes round. "Really, Mrs. Gunn! She's *really* not HERE!"

Boy, did Mike have it coming.

Heidi

Ding-a ling-a-lingg! The jangle sliced through the darkness surrounding my bed. A guttural voice swam in and out of my head...

"Mrs. Gunn, please help me. I can't stay heehr any mohr." German Heidi... 'Heidi Hamman-Eggs,' as we called her - our brand-new, once-a-week 'mother's helper.'

"It's bad heehr," her voice pleads. "I called my brudder-in-law to come get me. Can I stay at yohr house?"

My eyes popped open. I strained to hear. Nothing. *Was I dreaming?* I drifted back into the folds of shadow, fear lurking around the edges, not wanting to fall back into that dream... *brother...and 'law?'* The LAW? ... *The police??... Are they coming for Heidi...?*

Morning. I plodded up the basement steps behind Mike, ready for cereal. "Slowpoke!" I teased.

We stopped short. There in the kitchen doorway stood Heidi-with-the-wiry-curls, a duffle bag in each hand. I stared.

"Good mohr-ning." She cocked her head and smiled at us.

Just then Mommy breezed in. "I have a surprise for you!" she sang. "How would you like to have Heidi move in with us?"

Mike and I exchanged glances. *Heidi's going to LIVE with us?! Just like my dream!*

"Did the police come to her house?" I blurted. "The 'Law'?"

"What?" Mommy's forehead wrinkled. "N-noo. Maybe you mean her brother-in-law? He came to see her at the other family's house. But she likes taking care of our family much better. So Daddy picked her up this morning and brought her here. She's all ours now."

"*Ja.* I'll take your six anytime," nodded Heidi.

Lunchtime. Eric's voice wafted up the stairs as Mommy settled him for a nap. Heidi scraped the crumbs off the table from our grilled cheese sandwiches. Under my lids I eyed her thick arms in the white peasant blouse....her calico jumper...*Just like the 'Costumes of the World' page in the encyclopedia!* (One of my favorites.)

"I haf some toys of mine I brought vid me from Gehrmany," chatted Heidi. "Vait right heehr." She disappeared a moment.

"Now," she said. Heidi squeezed in-between Pat and Julie at the table. "Let me show you someting." Timmy gurgled his milk. Out of a canvas bag she lifted a drawstring pouch. "Heehr's a puzzle my mudder gafe me ven I vas a little girl." She pulled out blocks with nonsensical bits of pictures on them. A partial face here, a chimney there... Timmy began stacking them up.

"But if you look carefully at each block," she continued, "you can make a whole picture, just by fitting

dem next to each udder in the right ohrder." Soon,
with her help, we created a farm scene with ducks and
cows, and little children pulling each other in a wooden
wagon.

"Ooohh," whispered Julie.

"But there's still bits of picture on the other sides of
the blocks," I mused.

"Oh, *ja,*" confirmed Heidi. "Dat's to make a new
picture." I grabbed a block and flipped it over. Patrick
leaned in and flipped another.

"Hey!" cried Mike. "It's a donkey cart!" Heidi
laughed and shifted aside so we could take over.

I glanced up. "Did you ever live on a farm, Heidi?"

"Oh, *ja,*' she chuckled. "Alvays. I just left dere two
veeks ago." Heidi stroked the blocks with her fingertip.
"Vee raised chickens and cows and goats. Ven I vas
very little I collected duh eggs every mohrning before
breakfast, vile my brodder Volffie milked the cows."

"*Voolffie?*" Pat's eyes grew round.

"Ja," Heidi nodded. "It vas still dahrk out. Only after
vee finished our chohrs could vee haf breakfast."

"What else did you do?"

"Ah," reflected Heidi. "Ven I grew bigger, I
slaughtered duh chickens for our dinner."

"You DID?!" Mike's eyes bugged out.

"All by yourself?" I squeaked.

"Oh, *ja.*"

"*How?!*" Mike and I screeched at once.

"Oh, I just clucked at her – 'heehr, chick' – as I got
closer – den grabbed her by duh neck like dis –" Heidi
shot her muscular arm up in the air – "and swung her –
very quick – in a circle." She twirled her fist.

My mouth fell open.

"Then what!" demanded Mike.

"I laid her across duh block, swung duh axe, and

chopped her head off."

"Oh!" All five of us stared at her.

"But duh funny ting vas," Heidi mused, "duh chicken jumped right up and ran in circles around duh yard, until it finally fell over on its side."

"Without its head?" I whispered.

"Vidout its head."

We soaked that up for awhile.

"And dat," concluded Heidi, "is how vee get our dinner in Gehrmany." Her eyes crinkled.

No one moved.

"Vell. Time to verk." Heidi pushed back from the table, filled up a bucket of suds and climbed atop the kitchen counter. With grand, sweeping motions, she swiped the windows with her rag, while a quiet hum slipped out of her mouth. We watched in silence.

So. Mommy finally got her household savior…and WE got our very own chicken butcher!

Tam Valley Sleuths

Down the woodsy mountaintop I skip, my house disappearing behind me as I wrap my way 'round the winding country road. The lazy drone of a "buzz-saw" echoes in the air. Alongside me, the sun glints off the golden hillside, gently rising. My nine-year-old footsteps hasten down a gravel driveway to the gray clapboard house beyond.

I knock on the door. A moment. A face appears, the door jerked open. Tight, blonde braids frame a round, blue-eyed detective.

"Are you ready to go exploring?" I whisper.

"Yes! Let's go!" Carol darts out the door; the path blazes before us. The dusty road leads onward as we wind down the hill, full of expectation.

"I'll be Nancy," Carol postulates.

A pause. "O.K... I'll be George."

"Not Bess?"

"No," I frown. *Too much of a 'fraidy cat.* If I can't be Nancy Drew, her tomboy chum will do.

We sink lower in our shoes, approaching "suspicious territory" as we veer off down the steep hillside. Without warning we surprise a gaggle of comical creatures trotting tipsily through the dried grass, absurd crowns on their heads.

"Quail," remarks Carol.

"Oh! California's bird!" I reply. "I know that!" *Imagine! Right here!*

A cloud of cattails waves idly in the breeze. Hmm. That bears inspecting. *Prickly.*

"I wonder if anyone eats these?" I mutter.

Onward we trudge, searching out bigger prey. The tall trees beckon up ahead; branches nod and sway knowingly in our direction. We pick up our pace, and spy a spot of sunlight shimmering off a half-hidden board amidst the brush in the distance.

"Look!" I exclaim. "It's an abandoned building!"

Trampling the golden grass beneath our feet, we head down to the slyly concealed construction, still in progress.

"Maybe someone's inside!" Carol whispers.

We stop cold, our ears on alert. No hammering. Boldly we approach, more sure of ourselves. Carolyn Keene would be proud. Stooping just in case, we enter the shack. The warm fragrance of sawdust suffuses my nostrils. I savor the aroma.

"Fresh evidence!" I exult.

We hasten forward. Two rooms, three...sawdust on the floor, cans of paint in the corner...end of evidence. Disappointed, we retrace our steps.

"Nah," I grumble. "Nothing here."

Outside, the sunlight dances across the leaves beyond.

"Let's explore the woods!"

"Yes," responds Carol. "That's why we came here."

Our pulses quickening, we hurry through the underbrush, anxious for the thrill of the unknown, waiting just around the corner. Long, languid boughs of an old sycamore tree beckon lazily. Eager for adventure, we bolt into a run. Closer, now, it reaches for us, soft in its verdant blanket of moss. We *ooh* and *ahh* as our hands caress the velvety covering. Suddenly I swing my leg up and over the tantalizing bough.

"Let's go!" I cry.

We shimmy along the horizontal surface, grasping at branches just beyond to pull ourselves farther forward

over the leafy abyss. The view expands as we catch
the woods opening before us. Through the eucalyptus
ahead, a clearing is born. Our ears tune in. *Thud, thud,
thud.* A hammer pounds; a house crops up between the
rustling trees. Higher, now, we scramble, for a clearer,
bird's eye view. Two small figures pop in and out of
eyesight. Low laughter peals forth.

Carol's voice escalates, "Boys!"

"Shh!" I whisper. "Let's spy on them!"

We slink down; our elongated bodies merge as one
with the green moss covering. My heart pumps faster;
pulse magnified in my ear, my arm resting beneath it.

The older boy whoops and dashes for an old tire
swing. He slithers within, increasing its motion.
Younger brother darts behind it and gives a quick shove,
upsetting the load. With a cry of glee, he races away. A
shriek of outrage follows, commencing the pursuit.

Carol and I exchange satisfied glances and settle
down to our latest surreptitious adventure.

TreeHouse Blues

THE FAR EAST... and POINTS INBETWEEN
August 1960

An Army vacation for three: at last
I get some undivided attention!

Chronicles of the Orient
Part I

"Wake up, Cathay! Today's the day we're going to Japan!" Mommy's early morning words echoed back to me now in the dark of night.

It had been a long day. I lay stretched out along the front seat of our Pontiac station wagon, my head underneath the giant steering wheel. Parking lot lights zeroed in on me through the windshield. If I twisted my neck a bit, I could see Daddy's socks flapping against the driver's window, pinned at the top by the rolled-up glass. I smiled in the dark, watching them flutter like some silly birds caught by the tail. Mommy and Daddy lay in the back, with the seats folded down to make a "bed."

Travis Air Force Base was "housing" us for the night.

Army life had its advantages. We could travel for FREE to anywhere in the world, Daddy had told me. As the lucky first-born, I got to share this vacation with Mommy and Daddy alone – without the five tag-alongs trailing behind.

But so far, the first day on the waiting list hadn't produced a flight.

The next day dawned bright and stuffy on this August morn. I peeled myself off the vinyl seatback and peered over the edge. Daddy groaned, motionless, under Mommy's prodding fingers.

"How many more hours today, Daddy?"

Much to my dismay, he soon traded places with me. Daddy turned the car around and headed back homeward to Mill Valley…"supposedly" to get some change-of-clothes to tide us over. (Our bags were already checked.) But I greatly feared, once there, they would decide to forget the trip altogether.

Eventually docked in the carport, I refused to disembark. I figured as long as I stayed put, technically, I hadn't returned home yet, and Mommy and Daddy would *have* to get back in and drive away once more.

Knock, knock, knock. Knuckles rapped on the glass. Two faces peered at me between flattened hands. Mike and Pat.

"Go 'way!" I growled. "I'm not here!"

Their eyes widened. Instantly they both twirled around, leaping up and down as they hooted and jeered with pointing fingers. I snapped my lids shut and snorted, my teeth gritted together. "I'm going to Japan, I'm going to Japan," I muttered to myself. *All those beautiful, shiny kimonos everywhere…*

Once back "safe" at the airport, I could breathe a sigh of relief. Now all we had to do was wait. And wait…

Two days later, the nights in the parking lot were
losing their mystique. The days spent traipsing through
terminals of bustling people, staring out at giant
airplanes that lumbered like elephants, began to get old.

"Will it be today, Daddy?" I whined.

But Daddy gazed past me, over my head; his
eyebrows flew up, head cocked. I wheeled around.
Down the wide corridor a small copper-haired figure,
flanked by her parents, gaped at me. "I know her!" she
cried, finger pointed.

Ellen Dolson. She was a whole grade younger than
me at school. But at that moment I was very glad to see
her. Soon our parents were swapping military stories
of airport life on hold. Ellen and I slipped off into the
adjacent bookstore, where we discovered a whole new
world together: comic books.

Rack upon circular rack held more titles than we ever
knew existed. Not just Superman, but Super*boy* and
Super*girl*; as well as Green Lantern, Porky Pig, Donald
Duck, and Mickey. But the most "otherworldly" and
intriguing was Young Love. Teenage characters with
"big" emotions. We fell upon the treasure, flipping
through the choices before settling into some serious
reading. Ellen and I promptly sat down on the floor,
cross-legged, and wafted into new worlds. Now we
SAILED through the airport wait!

Soon, unceremoniously chased away by the clerk, we
learned to bide our time before returning. One by one,
we sidled in, snuck a comic while the clerk's back was
turned, and strolled casually to separate locations. From
now on we read standing up.

The next day the Dolsons got their wish, and flew off
to Hawaii. *Our* name came up soon after.

But not for Japan. Daddy had taken a cue from Mr.
Dolson. As long as we had to wait for a flight to the

Orient, why not wait in Hawaii?

Once through the winding tunnel and onto the plane,
a swirl of butterflies fluttered inside me. I sidled into
our row and snagged the seat by the window. With
Mommy's help, I cinched the big silver buckle over my
lap and settled back for my racecar ride through the sky.
Will it be faster than a roller coaster?! Much to my dismay,
the airplane seemed not to move at all! *How can we be
going so fast if we can't even feel it?!* Severely disappointed,
I tried to distract myself with the upcoming meal. It
worked. *TV dinners!* (We never got TV dinners at home!)

I want to make this perfectly clear. *No one* met us at
the airport with flowered leis. (I never got one the whole
time we were there!) Daddy said it was because we were
on a *military* plane. *Humph!* It didn't feel like Hawaii at
all.

After ten hours on an airplane that didn't move (but
still made me throw up!) I was grumpy. Already after
midnight at home, the air here felt hot and sticky. Still,
we immediately drove to visit Daddy's friends, the
Lopianos.

Lush jungle greenery overran the patio outside the
low-roofed home. I sat on the flagstones, my head
bobbing like a basketball, while four brown, barefoot
children raced in and out through the sliding door.
Staccato shrieks sliced through the thick air straight
into my ears. I stared through the glass at the four
seated adults noiselessly moving their lips at each other.
Glasses swirled in their hands. Mosquitoes buzzed in my
ear, dive-bombing at my bare arms and legs. I nodded
uncontrollably. *Sleep…I want to sleep…*

Whoosh! The shower sprayed onto my head. We had already romped on the beach this morning...The Dolsons were there! *Ellen and I... racing each other into the waves...* I shook my head under the drizzle. *"White caps,"* she called them. *Funny name.* I rubbed the water from my eyes. *Like little bonnets. Crumpling on the beach...* I stared down at my feet; black specks oozed outward in watery arcs from my splayed toes. *Black sand it had!* I rubbed the suds on my head. *Mommy said this bathroom was for our "wing" of the hotel...* I closed my eyes and let the warm rivulets trail down my cheek. *WING? Do they have birds here?* I opened my eyes. *Like parrots! They would look beautiful in the Lopianos' jungle-yard! Bright colors...* I bent my head down. *Blue-green... and hot pink! Like my new muumuu!* I curled my foot on the wet tile. *I can't wait to try it on!*

With two hands I reached up and tugged hard at the faucet...and turned it off. I pulled back the shower curtain...and stared at the towel rack opposite. Empty. *Oh, no.* My gaze traveled down to the wooden bench beneath it. No towel there. No clothes. No underwear. Not even my discarded wet bathing suit. *Mommy must've taken it away...* I pictured the long hallway with the gray carpet beyond the bathroom door. An endless row of doors on either side between our room...and me. Not our doors. *Other people's doors!* Water trickled from my wet hair onto my already slick back. Drips from the faucet echoed onto the tile. I shivered, hugging my goose-bumped flesh. *What do I do?!* My eyes began to burn. I swallowed. A tear slipped out, followed by another...

Click. The door opened. *Somebody's coming in here!* I slammed the curtain shut and stood stock-still.

"Cathay?" *Mommy!*
"Here's your towel…and your muumuu!"

Flop, flop, flop, flop. I struggled to keep up with
Daddy's long strides, my thongs snapping back against
my heels. The slits of my new muumuu flapped
pleasantly against my bare legs. We hastened down the
sunny sidewalk, past flower stalls and clothing shops to
make the last scheduled brunch at the restaurant.

Outside the glass door Daddy stopped. He turned to
Mommy.

"You have no *shoes,* my sweet!"

I followed his gaze. Sure enough, under Mommy's
brown and white-flowered muumuu with the great
puffy sleeves…she was barefoot.

"Mommy!"

She simply threw back her head and laughed, a high
tinkly sound. "We're in Hawaii, darling – remember?"

Daddy and I exchanged glances. He grinned at
me as he pushed open the door. A man in a pink and
green flowered shirt strolled towards us, nodding and
smiling. That is, until he caught sight of Mommy's feet!
Eyebrows raised, his smile slowly faded.

"I'm so sorry, madam, but you must wear shoes in the
restaurant." He pointed to the sign above the doorway:
'No shoes, no shirt, no service.' *Uh, oh.* We all looked at
Mommy.

"I'll hustle back to the hotel," offered Daddy, "and
grab your shoes while you sit down."

"I'm sorry, sir," replied the waiter. "But I can't seat
anyone without shoes."

"Heavens!" Daddy started. Mommy interrupted him.

"Don't be silly, dear," she said with a smile. "I'll run

back and get them. You two sit down."

The waiter bowed to her and led us to a little table by the window. I stared out, watching the muumuus flow by. I thought about her shoes. This morning while I lay in bed I eyed her in front of the long closet mirror. Hands fluttered from her neck to her hips as she admired that new muumuu with the giant white flowers. *(Though why would anyone choose the color brown?)* Still, she looked very pretty. But...something was not right. As my eyes traveled down to the hem, I spied her black high-heels glaring out. I hadn't seen a single person wearing high-heels with a muumuu. I wondered if they were the only shoes she had brought.

Tinkle, tinkle. The restaurant door opened and Mommy stepped in. She glided towards us, nodding and smiling at all who glanced her way. She flowed like a true Hawaiian...not the *click clack* gait of high-heels. Just before she slid into her chair, I caught a glimpse of those telltale feet. No high-heels! Something like sandals seemed to be there...but not quite. I peeked under the tablecloth. They had no bottoms! I popped my head back up, eyes wide. She grinned impishly at us, tapping her finger against her lips. Down I ducked for a second peek. Something shiny and gold wrapped around her big toe, ran along both sides of her foot and tied behind her heel in a bow. I surfaced and stared at her.

"Ribbon," she said. "I stopped at the florist on the corner."

The Big Island! We're on the Big Island! "For five days of the Army's R and R," Mommy remarked mysteriously. Once out of the noisy, miniature plane, we bumped along in an open-air bus through a tunnel of jungle foliage. It rose on either side of us – so close I could almost reach out and snatch off one of those strange butterfly flowers. Orchids.

Those flowers were everywhere! Even on the food! We arrived in the nick of time for the army's 'welcome buffet dinner,' and the biggest, orangest fish I had ever seen! Orchids *surrounded* it! I wondered if people ate them. (I didn't see anybody who did, though.)

We got our very own cabin – with our *own* bathroom this time.

The next morning the sun beat down on the back of my neck as I tossed my ponytail from side to side, enjoying my own air conditioning. My new puka shell necklace swung back and forth in matching rhythm.

"Poi? Try poi?" the brown lady pressed with a smile. Hawaiian women on the beach beat the strange, gloppy batter with pestles.

"Do they cook it?" I whispered to Mommy.

"I don't know," she murmured. I stared up at her. Normally Mommy had an answer for everything.

"Just watch," she said.

A little girl behind the table reached up for a bowl. She stuck her hand right inside of it, scooped out a handful, and jabbed it straight into her mouth. *What manners!* I watched, fascinated, waiting for the reprimand that would surely come her way. Instead, the Hawaiian woman beside her settled on a stool with her own bowl; then she reached her hand in and rapidly shoved a fistful of glop into her own mouth!

Daddy prodded me forward from behind. "Go on, Cathay," he urged. "Try it."

Reluctantly I accepted a small bowl from the server.

"I need a spoon!" I whispered behind my hand. Daddy spied a tiny wooden paddle, like an ice cream spoon, and handed it to me. I stirred the thick goo and tried to pretend it was pudding. I opened my mouth and poked the spoon inside. *Uwwaah!*

317

My mouth threatened to glue itself together; the back of my throat did calisthenics in its efforts to reject the goo. Quickly I stumbled behind the luau shack and spat it out in the sand.

Later that night we savored a *real* feast – with meat roasted on sticks over fire, mixed with pineapple and other strange fruits. Flames danced on lamps stuck in the sand, while everyone settled on picnic benches for the hula dancers! Men wearing flowers strummed guitars on the stage and sang. Soon girls in real grass skirts and leis glided out, rolling their hands and hips like ocean waves to tell a story. Firelight flickered across their faces as I drowsed happily against Mommy's shoulder. NOW I was in Hawaii!

'Movie time!' We shuffled forward as the line inched its way towards the wooden Army theatre in the still-muggy evening. A poster's gigantic volcano leered at me beside the entrance.

Once settled on our folding chairs, Mommy bent towards my ear. The room darkened.

"This is a true story,' she whispered, eyes round. "It happened a long, long time ago."

I stared at the screen in the pitch-black room. 'Last Days of Pompeii,' it flashed. *Where's Pompeii…*

…Brown children without any shoes chase each other, laughing, squealing. Flat dirt houses sprawl on a barren mountainside. The sky grows dark. It thunders. Mothers in long robes call frantically for their children…Suddenly the sky fills with red. Everybody on the mountain screams… Red rivers ooze and glow, undulating down the mountainside. The sky rumbles and roars, much louder than the screams! Running… running. The iridescent ooze that at first seemed sluggish, rolls faster and faster… People running seem smaller and smaller as the great red rivers snake over them… Now closer and closer to us it comes… *Who has the camera? Why don't they run, too?! Don't they see it?! Can't they get away? It will roll right over them, too!* Soon the sky grows darker… All is quiet…no voices…not a sound…nothing moves. A child's sandal lays half-covered in dark red goop. Then…in the gray light of dawn…everything has turned to stone. All is still.

The lights brightened. I blinked in their sudden garishness. I stared, motionless, at the white screen while chairs scraped against the cement floor around us.

"Ready to go, Cathay?" Mommy's voice sounded far-off. I nodded and followed her out.

"What happened to the man with the camera?" I blurted.

"What man? What camera?" Mommy stared blankly.

I felt irritated. "You know. In the movie!"

"What do you mean?" she queried. "There were no cameras back then!"

Now I stared. "Then how did they make that movie?!"

"Ohhh…no, no!" Mommy shook her head, smiling. "It wasn't really happening. That was just a movie!"

I wasn't so sure. "You said it was a true story!" *So which was right?!*

"Yes, but that happened hundreds of years ago," explained Mommy. "This movie they made just recently to tell a story about it."

"Ohh." I still wondered…

Daddy interrupted, "Aren't you glad you learned about volcanoes?" His eyes twinkled. "Because one erupted right here on the Big Island last week."

"It did?!"

"Yes, indeed – and tomorrow we're taking a special hike across it," he grinned.

I was sure he was joking – till he shook me awake next morning before the sun was up. Sure enough, we soon huddled in the waning darkness at the volcano tour bus stop.

I gazed around. Only grownups. They all talked to each other. Someone told Mommy I didn't have the right shoes. I stared down at my thongs. 'Go-aheads,' they call them in Hawaii. Or 'zoris.' *I guess if you walk on a volcano, they just might 'go-ahead' without you.*

"We'll be walking over *two* miles," the lady told her. *Should we go back?* Too late. The driver hustled us onto the bus.

I stared out the window. I thought about the movie last night. This didn't sound like much fun to me.

The tour guide's voice droned on. "Just last week, Pele, the goddess of fire…"

A week ago we were already in Hawaii! We could've even been in it! I glowered at the tour guide. *How can we walk on a volcano that's just erupted?! Won't it burn us?* The tour guide must've read my mind. He said, "There's nothing to worry about. Everything's fairly cooled down now, and hardened." Then I thought about telling everyone back home I walked on a volcano. *Mike and Pat… hmmm… Maybe this won't be so bad…*

The bus finally rumbled to a stop. I climbed down and surveyed the "moonscape." Nothing but barren "roadways," crisscrossed like great rumpled ribbons, dusty black. But more fine-grained than asphalt.

We began the hike up the gentle incline. There were no trees in sight. *The ground looks like swirled icing on a giant black birthday cake!* Though still early morning, the sun coaxed the sweat right out of me. I fixed my eyes on my thongs as I walked. Lots of lumps, like things buried under the covers, sprang up hard in my path, causing my feet to jerk sideways in those 'go-aheads.'

Up ahead I spied *smoke!* People near it jabbered
excitedly. My chest tightened. I grabbed Daddy's hand.
"Look, Daddy! It's erupting!"
The tour guide glanced back at me and *laughed!*
"No, young lady," he called out. "Those are just steam
vents. Letting off excess heat." *Oh.*

Daddy and I trudged up close and peered down into
the gaping maw. A huge cloud of warm steam billowed
up. *But wait! There's something red...*

"There's fire under there!" I jerked Daddy's hand and
pointed. "Way down there! I see it!"

"Feel the ground!" someone shouted. I bent down.
My hand tingled with the sudden heat. *Yes!* We really
were on a volcano!

We trekked by two more steam holes before we finally
reached the waiting bus.

We never did get to the *top* of the volcano. Perhaps
that was just as well.

Back on the bus, I sat in my seat and cradled two
odd-shaped lumps of lava, snatched from the ground.
I turned them over and over in my hands. Very light
they were! Filled with tiny air holes. I glanced over at
my certificate of achievement for "crossing the goddess
Pele's fire," and smiled.

Together they would make indisputable proof of my
daring accomplishment.

Chronicles of the Orient
Part II

Japan! We're really in Japan! Nine days after leaving
California, we finally touched down at Tachikawa Air
Force Base.

Gray. Steamy. Blah. I gazed out the taxi window through
bleary eyes, as the heavy mist enshrouded the city.

At last in Tokyo, I studied the spare surroundings in
Gajokenko Inn. Only a low table and fat cushions filled
our small room.

"No beds!" I whispered behind my hand. "Where do
we sleep?"

"Wait and see," Mommy whispered back.

A man in shiny blue "pajamas" (!) soon seated us on
the cushions around the table. We were eating dinner
on the *floor* of our hotel room! The waiter nodded
and smiled – so many times! – as he served us watery

soup. *He put a raw egg in it!* And *raw* fish! I yanked on Mommy's dress.

"I can't eat this!" I pleaded. Mommy glowered at me.

"You can *try* it." I glared back at her till finally the waiter produced 'an American hamburger.' I smiled up at him, relieved.

"Time for bed," announced Mommy. I flattened against the wall while the same 'waiter' dragged the table into a corner and eased back a sliding rice-paper door. From behind it he tossed several bamboo mats. On top of these he laid three flat pads. We were sleeping on the *floor!* I stared up at Mommy. She shot me a warning glance. I decided not to say anything.

In the middle of the night I woke up in the dark. Rhythmical chirping sounds filtered in through the window. *Like birds and crickets together.* 'Cicadas,' Daddy had said earlier. When my eyes adjusted to the moonlight, the mat alongside my mattress appeared to quiver. I raised my head. Tiny winged creatures *covered* the mat! I reached over and shook the next sleeper.

"Daddy!" I whispered. "There's *bugs* all over the floor!"

He groaned, muttered something, and rolled over. Mommy's voice wafted over him.

"They're just tiny little moths," she mumbled. "Close your eyes and go back to sleep."

I squeezed my lids tight and hung on to the sound of the cicadas. Soon their music lifted me up and away as I drifted off to a safer landscape.

Splash! Just as we darted from the Tokyo taxi and ducked under the adjacent awning the heavens opened above us. Our first morning in Japan, and it poured down buckets.

"Just in time!" shouted Daddy. He had suggested we

wait out the impending storm shopping at the Army PX.

Rows and rows of metal shelves, laden with all kinds of merchandise, stretched before us. *Where to start?!* I skipped ahead, searching out the dolls I *knew* had to be there. I had seen pictures of dazzling Japanese dolls dressed in elaborate kimonos. *Funny they all had white painted faces, though.* "Geishas," Mommy called them. *I* needed one.

At last I spied my quarry. Multicolored and elegant, each stood apart from the others in her own glass case. They were huge! And so were the numbers on the price tags. So many zeroes!

"Mommy! This one says 6000 yen! How much is that?" Even translated to dollars, it was way too much money. Disappointed, I turned away and idly slid my finger along the edge of the metal shelves, my eyes intermittently sneaking back for a peek.

But what's that? Stuck between two huge glass geisha cases peered a small cloth 'little girl' doll. Her flat face with embroidered features sat on top of her cylinder body wrapped in a red-flowered kimono. I snatched her up and cradled her in the crook of my arm. *Julie would like that,* I decided, and Mommy agreed. Happily I handed her over to join our growing mound of merchandise.

Men and women crowded the store now, as we waited in line to complete our purchases. I meandered in and out of the queue, weaving between people until Mommy called me back. I glanced around.

"Where's Daddy?"

"We're all finished. He's just taken the packages to the post office across the street."

I peered through the opened doorway. Sheets of rain splashed before us, obstructing any view of the disappearing Daddy.

"Where?!" I cried. *How does he know where it is?* The

gray outlines of buildings through the watery curtain grew strange and ominous. I ducked back inside. Once more we roamed the store, up and down the aisles to bide our time.

All of a sudden, I didn't care anymore. My stomach growled. People seemed to push and shove. *Why is everyone in a hurry?*

"Mommy, I have to go to the bathroom."

She seized my hand and strode through the maze of warm bodies shopping out of the rain. "Let's go," she said.

How does she know where to go? We marched past rows and rows of shelves till she stopped before a Japanese man in a black suit.

"Where is the ladies' room?" asked Mommy.

The man pointed and giggled. "Radies' toi-*r*ette is to the *r*eft. Don't go to the *l*ight. That's the gen*ter*men's toi-*r*ette." He bowed low and giggled again.

Mommy thanked him and pressed forward. *Was he speaking Japanese...?...No...*

I spied the door with the silhouette of a little girl and scurried inside. Two cubicles popped into view.

Quickly I slammed the stall door behind me and turned around. My breath stopped. There was nothing there! Wheeling back out again I grabbed Mommy before she could enter the next stall.

There's no toilet!" I whispered fiercely.

"What do you mean?"

"There's just...there's just a *hole* in the floor!"

Mommy's eyebrow flew up. It didn't look like she knew the answer.

"What am I to do?" I wailed. "Now I really have to go!"

Without a word she followed me back in. Sure enough, no toilet seemed to be *anywhere* in the small bathroom. Only drains; one for each of the two stalls.

"Just squat down," Mommy said.

"What?!"

"They do things differently here. You need to squat over the hole."

I still didn't believe her. *Why is she telling me this?*

"See?" she pointed. "Here's toilet paper." Sure enough, on the stall wall sat a wooden shelf with a box of wax paper-ish squares.

"*That's* not toilet paper!" I snorted.

"It's *their* kind of toilet paper," she said shortly. "Please hurry. I don't want Daddy to miss us. I have to go, too."

Suddenly she was gone, abandoning me to my wooden cell, the stainless steel drain glowing up at me from the cement floor.

Darn! Darn! Darn! Stupid old Japan! Why did we come here?! At last I removed my shoes and underpants, and squatted. *I'm never telling Mike and Pat...never, never, never...*

Back out in the store once more, Mommy grabbed my hand. Her eyes bugged out, her skin ashen. "We have to find Daddy," she murmured.

Again we wandered, searching through the sea of anonymous faces for that old familiar dimpled grin. *Where is he?!*

"I *have* to sit down," muttered Mommy. I glanced up at her. Her face looked like chalk, her hand felt clammy. I swallowed. *Daddy's lost and Mommy's getting sick?!* I gazed around at all the tall bodies bustling about us, paying no heed. We kept pushing through the packed store.

At last Mommy spied a crate in an alcove beside an elevator. With a grateful cry, she sped forward with me in tow. The two of us collapsed onto the box. Mommy smiled wanly at me, patting my hand.

"The baby needs rest, too," she said. I stared at her tummy. I had forgotten there was a baby in there. It didn't look very big...

Without warning, a cry broke out. We glanced up.

"No, no, no, no!" A man in rolled-up sleeves and a black cap hustled towards us, crossing his arms back and forth. "Up, up!" he cried.

Reluctantly I hopped down from the box, following Mommy's lead. The man hoisted the crate on his shoulder and stomped away. Mommy and I stared at each other; then silently ventured back into the crowded store once more...

"Daddy!"

A shimmering mirage of army green glistened its way through the open doorway. Dripping wet but grinning, Daddy's face lit up as he threw a soggy arm around each of us.

"Shall we go?"

Sunshine! I hopped alongside Mommy and Daddy down the busy Tokyo sidewalk on our first day of touring. But sunshine quickly translated to *hot* and sticky. My sundress clung to my back, sweat oozing downward in ticklish rivulets.

I glanced around at all the people bustling past. *Where are all the kimonos?* Men wore black pants and white shirts, sleeves rolled up. Only old women shuffled by in true Japanese dress. But all in *black* kimonos, with 'pillows' attached to their backs. *Is that in case they fall over backwards? Or to be more comfortable when they sit on the floor?* I contemplated this as I hiked up the steps of the bus.

Out my window I spied an old woman scuffling through the crowd. She stopped short, threw her kimono high above her knees, and squatted over the curb. A thin stream trickled downward between her bent legs. Dropping her kimono, she ambled on again.

"Mommy!" I whispered.

Mommy cleared her throat. "Well," she began, "I guess she really had to go!"

On the bullet train (so fast!) men swayed at the end of long straps from the ceiling, while reading newspapers with writing that looked like ladders. Boys and girls crowded on in huge clumps, grinning and chattering like birds in a language I couldn't understand. I stared, wishing I could. I studied them... Girls wore sailor blouses and navy skirts; boys copied the men, but with shorts.

Their haircuts were all the same! Boys and girls. Long, straight bangs and hair cropped short just at the top of the ears. They looked so cute! *I* wanted to look like that! I stared at one little girl who eyed me, then turned abruptly away. *Oh!* Her head was shaved *bald* in the back! *Why?!* She looked so cute in front...*all* of them were shaved bald in back! Like someone had set a bowl on each head, and wherever that bowl ended, the hair was sheared to complete the simple shape of the sleek, black bowl. I sneaked peeks at their bare skulls, alternately fascinated and repelled.

The first week we paraded on and off of trains and buses, trooping behind tour guides past Shinto shrines and Buddhas, surrounded by gold, candles, and incense burning.

The biggest Buddha of all (in Kamakura) towered over us, black as ash. *Was he made out of lava?* A giant pimple stuck out of his forehead. Next to him sat a huge pile of thick, black rope set on its own special throne inside a well. "Human hair," the tour guide told us, "cut and braided from the heads of the ancient women." As we all trudged by it for a closer look, my hand cramped terribly. I did so want to reach out and *feel* that hair rope!

At week's end, our long white bus lumbered into the dusty outskirts of Tokyo. On foot we joined the queue snaking its way downhill, round and round a tall red-roofed house on top of another, fatter, red-roofed house that sat on yet *another* red-roofed house! Dizzy with the spiraling, I craned my neck up at Mommy.

"Why do they have so many roofs on one house?"

"It's called a pagoda," answered Mommy.

"It looks like a wedding cake!"

Far below in the courtyard our tour guide had gathered his flock around a fountain directly beneath the glaring sun. One by one a straggle of elders in faded kimonos and pajamas (!) shuffled their way through the crowd. Each in turn dipped the same metal ladle into the pool of water, and slurped noisily. The sun beat down on my dark head as I watched. The water sparkled invitingly. My tongue expanding against the roof of my mouth, I quickened my pace.

"C'mon, Mommy!"

By the time we reached the courtyard level, I could almost taste that refreshing remedy. But everyone else just stood there while the tour guide rambled on...

"This 'elixir of life' has supported the people through several dynasties, and continues to do so today..."

I edged forward till Mommy's hand squeezed my shoulder in warning.

"But I'm *thirsty!*" I retorted in a loud whisper.

"However," the tour guide raised his voice. "If any of *you* were to drink from this communal cup, no doubt you would become mortally ill and *die.*"

I froze.

"The villagers here, on the other hand, over generations appear to have developed an immunity to their fellow neighbors' diseases transmitted in the water."

I turned and scrutinized the last retreating drinker, yearning to have that certain something I knew he had that we didn't.

"A bath?! Why do we have to take a bath in the *afternoon?"*

After another dizzying journey on the bullet train, we had arrived in Kyoto. Wrapped in a towel, I padded after Mommy and Daddy down the corridor of our hotel.

"Wait and see," Mommy lilted.

I entered the 'Family Bath' first…and stopped short. This was not like any bathroom *I* had ever seen! The wrap-around white-tiled walls and floor stretched on for ages! Reflections of light bounced off all surfaces. The sound of rushing water echoed about. At one end, water splashed from wall fixtures like fountains in a park. It cascaded into troughs of tile. Soap cakes, wooden buckets, and thick-bristled scrub brushes sat on a built-in bench. *Are those for the maids to scrub the floor?*

All three of us stopped and stared for a moment. Then Mommy took charge.

"First, you get the soap wet, rub it all over, and scrub yourself with the scrub brush."

But what about the *bath?"* I protested.

"That comes later," she said. "Next, you take the wooden bucket, scoop it full of water from the fountain, and throw it over yourself to rinse off."

Tentatively I followed her cue. The scrub brush tickled! I traded it in for the wooden bucket. *Whoa!* It grew heavy with the water rapidly splashing into it. Stopping at half-full, I heaved it up and overturned it onto myself. *Ooh!* Pleasantly warm at first, I swiftly grew cold while waiting for the next bucket to fill.

"I'm ready!"

"*Now* we get in the bath!" smiled Mommy.

"But where's the bathtub?!"

I followed her gaze down the glistening room. At the far end I spied Daddy's bodiless head, eyes closed... suspended in wafts of steam on the *floor! Huh?* I scurried across the slippery tiles towards the floating head. I gazed down.

"It's a *swimming* pool!" I burst out.

Daddy's eyes fluttered open. He looked funny without his glasses. "Hop in," he grinned. I thrust my big toe into the water; then yanked it out.

"It's *boiling!*"

Take your time," advised Mommy. I watched as she slowly slipped in, the water swallowing her whole! All except her head. *Whoa! This is NOT like a bathtub!*

Carefully this time, I eased myself in, bit by bit, watching the angry red color creep up my legs as the water devoured them.

"I'm gonna be sunburned!" I gasped. Soon, though, as the water crept closer to my chin, I wedged into a comforting nook.

My breath slipped out in a huge sigh. My body began to grow bigger and bigger, until it seemed to fill the entire bath. I peered sideways. My arms floated on the surface of the water! I couldn't even feel them! I turned my head, water lapping against my cheek.

Mommy and Daddy lay smiling, eyes closed. *Ahhh...*

It's morning?! We slept through dinner!

The last I remembered, my pillow loomed up at me

as my heated, rubberized body sank onto a real bed after the bath. Mommy said all three of us napped till morning. Instead of dinner, luncheon awaited us.

We sat at a white-clothed table in the middle of the hotel dining room. Our waiter pushed my chair in for me. Another handed me a menu, all in English! A third one poured us all glasses of ice water. Each bowed low before he disappeared.

So much food! And American, too! Since Mommy said this was *dinner,* I ordered roast beef and potatoes. No more rice for me. (Daddy had had steamed rice for *breakfast* – with milk on it, like cereal. Luckily for me, they also had Rice Krispies.) Lots of little dishes arrived, too. One had carrots. Another had something dark green. I turned to ask Daddy a question – when a hand reached from the other side of me and took my plate away!

"Stop!" I cried. Mommy tugged my plate back, in the nick of time.

"Not yet," she smiled. I glowered at the waiter. He stepped back – and stopped right behind me. I peered over my shoulder. Two…three…four…*five* waiters stood there in a row against the wall, watching us! Whenever one of us paused, or set a fork down for a second, a black-suited waiter leapt forward to whisk away a dish, whether we were finished, or not! Nervously, I pulled my plate closer and held onto it with my right hand, my fork clutched tightly in the left. They hovered like flies, buzzing for the leftovers. I wanted to *swat* the next hand that sneaked onto the table!

Dessert time!

"Ice cleam," bowed the waiter. "Choc-rate ah lime?"

"Lime," I decided. *Mmm…I never had lime ice cream before!*

The waiter set a small silver dish before me. To my surprise, it was not green. The ice cream looked tan.

"Oh – they didn't use food coloring, like we do, to

make it green," offered Mommy.

I stuck my spoon into the icy goo and raised it to my lips. Then I sucked the mound right off – and *froze*. Inside my mouth exploding shards of rot rushed against my palate. I spat into my napkin and grabbed my water glass. Thankfully, the hovering waiter had refilled it.

"That's not lime!" I gasped. "It's something – something *nasty!*"

Mommy and Daddy stared at me – till Daddy suddenly guffawed.

"Rum!" he chortled. "Not lime! Rum!"

I decided after that I must *read* everything. *Don't listen to what they say. You must see it written down.* Only trouble was, it was usually in Japanese. And my three Japanese words, 'yes,' 'thank you,' and 'goodbye,' which I knew only verbally, didn't suffice.

Two days later we journeyed into Hakoni National Park, and settled in at the Fujiya Hotel. Eagerly we set out for a 'Mt. Fuji' hike – to see our hotel's namesake.

Wending our way through the hotel's lush garden, I spied an arched stone bridge up ahead. Lured on, I sped forward.

"This way!" I cried, and hopped from slab to chiseled slab along the path before it. I grasped the ancient stone rail and pulled myself up the vertical-leaning slats to the top of the curvaceous bridge. *Umphh!* It was high! I gazed down at Mommy and Daddy, two strolling midgets. *I'm King-of-the-Mountain!*

After twisting myself backwards, hand over hand I began my descent. *Whoa! ...Now that was fun!*

"Save some energy for mountain climbing!" called Mommy.

Just ahead I spied our first marker. Gratified to see an English sign, I read it aloud to Mommy and Daddy.

"'Mt. Fuji hike – 2.4 miles.'"

So! We really *were* going to climb Mt. Fuji! A *real* mountain! *Good thing I wore my sneakers this time!* Racing ahead, I stalled impatiently at every turn in the trail for Mommy and Daddy to catch up. Soon several hikers trooped behind us, like the Pied Piper. The winding path slowly steepened its ascent. I wondered if Daddy had brought his camera. We would need proof that we had scaled a famous mountain! *Will there be flags at the top?* I remembered in a movie seeing someone stick a flag in the ground when the mountain climbers reached the peak. *We didn't bring one! Maybe the people behind us did...*

Suddenly I felt light-headed. I began panting as the trail snaked upward through the fragile-looking trees. I knew we must be close. Tiny purple flowers graced the occasional clearing. *There should be snow, covering the top...any minute now...*

"Hurry!" I called to Mommy and Daddy, leading the pack below.

"Slow down!" replied Mommy. "We're almost there!"

I paused just long enough to grasp Daddy's outstretched hand, and pulled him along with me the last few twisty turns.

"This is it!" someone cried.

We halted near a large plaque: 'Mt. Fujiyama view point.' I hopped up and down.

"We climbed the mountain!"

I whirled about, gazing at the gathering climbers struggling to catch their breath. "But where's the snow?!"

Mommy took me by the shoulders, twirled me halfway around and pointed. *"There,"* she said.

I stared. Way off in the distance, directly before

me, rose a humungous mountain with a glistening, snowcapped peak.

That's Mt. Fuji," declared Mommy.

"Not *here?*" I squeaked.

"No."

"*Oh!*"

We all gazed in silence as a monstrous white cloud billowed across the sky...and swallowed it up.

"What do you think?" queried Mommy.

I scrutinized the little girl in the mirror from every angle. She stared solemnly back at me, tugging at the belt of her new kimono. Tiny pink and aqua flowers skittered across the silky fabric. So cool and slippery against my skin! Too bad it didn't have a real obi, though. Just a narrow sash, like a little girl's dress. Mommy had wrapped it twice around, and tucked the ties in the back.

"I like it."

My eyes trailed down to the ends of the full kimono sleeves. They practically grazed the ground! And they even had hidden openings – like deep pockets. (I hadn't known that!) I stuffed a Kleenex inside each one. Then I studied my reflection once more. Maybe now they wouldn't all stare at me so much. (When I had asked why, Mommy said it was probably because my hair was lighter than theirs. Somehow, I didn't think *that* was the reason.) I glanced down at my feet – clothed in genuine Japanese toe socks. I could even wear my thongs with them! I bowed to myself with a giggle. Now I was a real Japanese girl!

"Ready!" I crowed, and followed Mommy and Daddy out the door and down the hall for breakfast.

Flip, flop, flip, flop. I padded across the lobby floor, the slinky fabric whispering against my legs. Low voices mingled with the echoes of the garden fountain. The desk clerk bowed to us, smiling. I straightened up tall as I walked past. *I don't care if they look at me now!*

Just then I *sensed* a thundercloud hurtling towards me across the lobby. I glanced up to see an old woman bearing down on me, the corners of her mouth angled at the ground. Her jet-black eyes locked fiercely onto mine.

"No, no, no!" she shrieked, her arms thrust out to grab me. I reached for Mommy's hand – too late. The creature lunged forward and clawed at my belt, all the while spewing loudly in Japanese. She seized each side of my loosened kimono and threw it wide open, exposing my scrawny body to the world. Her voice continued its nonsensical tirade as I shrank inside my violated skin. All the spotlights of the world burrowed into me in this public display. Then, just as suddenly, her hands slapped shut my precious kimono, cinched the belt, and snapped back to her sides as she stormed out.

I couldn't move. From somewhere Mommy's voice murmured in tandem with that of the lobby clerk. I clung to Daddy's hand, and waited for her to return.

"It's all right," she soothed, leaning down before me. "She just wanted to tell you your kimono was wrapped the wrong way."

"What do you mean?" I whimpered.

"Left side over right means you are a single lady," explained Mommy. "You had it wrapped right over left – which would mean that you are married!"

I didn't care what it meant. I wanted that kimono OFF. I no longer wanted to be a Japanese girl.

Our last night in Japan... Thank goodness! I couldn't wait to leave. I stared out the taxicab window as we zigzagged through the outskirts of Tokyo. We had been invited to dinner at the home of Daddy's new friends, Mr. and Mrs. Miwaka. Mommy had persuaded me to put my new kimono back on for the occasion. I swallowed, and fingered the hem down the front as we approached the house, making sure the *left* side covered the right.

"Wehcome to ah home!" Mr. Miwaka bowed low at the door. As we stepped inside, Mrs. Miwaka appeared from behind, dressed in a white brocade kimono. I tugged at my own.

"Ah! Pletty! Pletty!" she exclaimed, taking my two hands in her own. I stiffened – then took a breath – and gazed back into her laughing eyes. She bowed low, and after a moment, I tried the same. We followed them through the foyer.

"Excuse me," uttered Mommy, "may we please use the bathroom?"

Our two hosts exchanged glances. Mrs. Miwaka murmured, "excuse, pwease – I go to kitchen." Mr. Miwaka smiled and bowed to Mommy. "Yes, yes. Fahwow me."

I hurried down the hall after them. Mr. Mikawa opened a door, bowed low and murmured, "I wih bring towehs," then disappeared. We stepped inside the doorway – and gasped. *Uh oh!* The all-tiled room looked just like the 'Family Bath' at the Kyoto Inn! And *no* toilet.

"Mommy!" I whispered.

"I know, I know!"

We stepped back out the doorway and peered up and down the deserted hall. At last Mr. Mikawa reappeared, balancing a stack of snowy towels.

"So saahly, so saahly," he rushed, shaking his head.

"No – we-we're sorry," faltered Mommy. "I meant – the *toilet*. Not the bath."

"Ahh!" beamed Mr. Miwaka. "Light this way!"

…This time the door opened onto what we really needed – and a 'Western' one, at that!

Back out in the hallway, I wandered along the white carpet, fingering the edge of my kimono. I gazed at the delicate watercolors along the walls. Such simple, sparing strokes – *why, they look just like the crooked trees on our Mt. Fuji hike!* I spied the writing along the sides. *Like little pictures…* I knew only one character in Japanese. When we first met, Daddy's friend showed me how to draw one. I stepped up and studied each character more closely… *There it is! 'Spring!' I can read it! I can read Japanese!* I burst into the living room, eager to share the news.

I stopped. Empty. Uncertain, I stood in the middle of the sparse room and listened. Animated grownup voices rose and fell just around the corner. I hesitated. Instead, I tiptoed over to the big picture window and gazed out over the city.

We were *high*! From the top of a gently rolling hill the house's view dipped down to the valley below. One by one I watched lights twinkle on; the graceful shapes of scattered homes nestled against a pink and blue sky.

I glanced down. All along the windowsill a troop of wooden dolls stood in gradually decreasing size. Each one was 'dressed' in a fancy painted kimono. I knelt before them and quietly spoke for them.

"My name is Keiko," the 'big sister doll' whispered. In my hand she bowed before me. "These are my sisters, and we are going for a walk." Then, against the beautiful water-colored city, Keiko and her sisters strolled up and down the roadway…

"Why, heh-ro!" a voice broke in.

I wheeled around to see a smiling young woman I hadn't met before. *She* was dressed in a kimono, too – sky blue.

"Oh!" I startled, caught in the act.

"*My* name is Keiko!" she laughed.

I knew then she must be the Mikawas' 'college daughter.' Sudden heat flamed in my cheeks. I quickly re-set the wooden doll back on the sill.

"You know," she began, "these daahs wuh given to me by my oba-san...my grandmotheh."

"I'm – sorry," I murmured, biting my lip.

"No, no. Pwease. You ah wehcome to pway with them."

Out of the corner of my eye I watched her. Keiko glowed like a Japanese geisha doll. *So pretty!* Then she knelt beside me and showed me how the dolls actually fitted inside each other! We worked together opening and closing the halves. When we had finished, the big sister doll had swallowed them all up! I studied the lone, heavy doll a moment and shook my head.

"No," I decided. "Then nobody can see how beautiful they all are." One by one we laid them out again.

"I think you'uh wight," agreed Keiko. "And this way they can aah see each otheh." I smiled up at her.

She raised her eyebrows a moment; then stood up. "I have something foh you."

She took my hand and led me into a tiny room.

On top of a desk sat a row of egg-shaped men in red-and-black painted kimonos, each one slightly smaller than the next. Keiko reached over and picked them up all at once! They were glued to a black wooden base.

"Foh you," she smiled. "To wemembeh us by."

I cradled the fat egg-men in my hands. Each face sported a finely stroked beard and puffy pink cheeks. Their wispy black hair looked nearly bald on top. I laughed, and pictured Daddy in a red kimono, making funny faces at me. Then I gazed up at her, searching for one of my three Japanese words.

"Arigato," I whispered. "Thank you."

"Fasten your seatbelts and place your seatbacks in the upright position."

I stared out the airplane window at the cement runway; then reached for my satchel under the seat. Carefully I extracted a cloth-wrapped package. Opening the fabric, I lifted up my final good-bye gift from Keiko. Two concentric brass circles in red and black sat upright on a stand. My magical 40-year calendar! I spun the smaller circle against the one underneath. By lining up the numbers and names, I could see any month at once between 1961 and *2000!* Two Japanese characters scrolled across the middle. I rubbed them with my finger, feeling the willowy shapes. *I wonder what they mean…*

I wrapped it back up again, my head filled with years of twirling it, and remembering Japan.

The plane's engine growled into a low, steady roar. I gazed out the window as we lifted off, suddenly light and motionless above a slowly descending landscape. Tiny figures on the ground disappeared as I strained for one last grasp on that ancient world.

I grazed my lips against the glass.
Sayonara.

MILL VALLEY/SAN FRANCISCO REDUX 1960 – 1961

Cathay, Julie, Timmy, Pat and Mike

Dad's stint in the Army will end December 1960. As a civilian, he will work at Franklin Hospital on Divisadero and Duboce Streets in San Francisco. Here he completes a second Residency in Oncology (a new field!) as our family of eight, going on nine, indulges in the stability of living in the same house for a grand total of three years. What a relief for Mom!

Meanwhile, the challenges of "Big Family Life," along with my growing self-awareness and search for where I fit in, continue to spiral.

Twirling

Saturday. I push off from the breakfast room table and wander into the living room. I gaze. Vacant, and unnaturally still. No one about; just uninterrupted space on the Oriental rug.

All of a sudden the room calls to me in a mesmerizing circular motion. "Spin," it whispers. "SPIN!"

Without warning, my arms shoot out like wings, my foot swings to the right and I *SPIN*. Colors blur as they merge and undulate around me. Faster now, I whirl like a top; the air tugging at me in a last-ditch effort to slow me down – but then – gives up and lets me – *GO!*

The world is gone, now; I'm aloft in a tight spiral that throws off anything that dares to touch me. Shall I stop now? - *No, no! Not yet! Not yet! Put it off: that high point – so delicious and alluring…just ahead…* Faster, faster… and… *NOW!*

Whoaaa… Drunkenly I stumble to a halt as I force myself to break through my cocoon of motion to reach that evaporated world. But it's just a tease, for the room continues to rotate around me. It bends and tilts as I joyfully stagger from one foot to another, while my stomach flip-flops with delight. Oh! The pinnacle of pleasure!

At last my footfalls become grounded with the real room once again.

Just then I spy a familiar brown head as it flits past the breakfast room doorway.

"Mike! Mike!" I shriek. "I have something to show you!"

…Soon Patrick joins us, and my 'ode to joy' surrounds us all.

Pat and Timmy

Upstaged by the Kindergarten
Don Juan

*Mother Eby is so beautiful...*I leaned my chin on my
hand and gazed up at the nun in charge of afterschool
study hall. *She looks so young.* I outlined her full, black
eyebrows in my mind over her dark brown eyes. Tall
and willowy, with her smooth, olive skin and gentle
smile, she didn't look like other nuns.

Mother Eby caught me staring at her. "Your father
should be here soon," she smiled. "It's almost five
o'clock."

Five o'clock! Instantly my gut churned with that
familiar wobble. *Would Daddy show up in time?* Too
many times, now, I'd been the last one. I glanced
surreptitiously around me. Mary Anderton hadn't left
yet. *Good.* She usually stayed till the bitter end, as well.
Up front, the little Wong sisters tarried. They, too, stayed
till 5PM.

I watched tiny Cathy flit about, chattering to Mother Eby *(I wish I could do that!)* while her calmer, older sister Christy slowly *gallumped* her way down the aisle in her heavy metal braces and arm poles. I liked watching them because they were so different from each other, one brown-haired and one black, a firefly and a turtle.

Suddenly Mary sprang up and stuffed her books into her bookbag. I glanced at the door. There, indeed, stood her aunt, ready and waiting. Moments later, Mr. Wong stuck his head in, and briskly claimed his brood.

That left me...and the ticking clock overhead. *Oh, please! I don't want to stand out. Not in THAT way...*I watched the long, black hand as it jumped erratically to the next black dot – already on the right side of the twelve.

Soon, a young teacher herded in Julie and Timmy from the kindergarten/nursery afterschool care.

"Is Dr. Gunn here yet?" she queried. I could feel the heat scorch my cheeks.

"You may leave them with me," replied Mother Eby. I searched her face. Did she frown the tiniest bit?

Julie scurried towards me and climbed into the adjacent chair. Timmy leaped up and down at the front of the room, chirping, "Hi, Cathay! Hi, Cathay!"

"Sshh! Timmy!" I whispered out to him. "This is STUDY Hall!" *Where IS Daddy?!*

Timmy wandered up and down the rows, slapping each wooden desk with a loud *smack* as he passed. Cringing, I eyed Mother Eby between half-closed lids. Her bonnet frame obscured her face as she stood on tiptoe in the sunlight and eased the great windows shut with her long, raised pole. *What does she think of him?!*

Without warning, the very first day of this school year flashed before me...

❧

...Three o'clock dismissal...*Fifth grade is fun!* I raced
out through the courtyard with Barbara and Cindy; only
to be caught short by Mother Mardel.

"Walk!" she admonished. As I guiltily glanced back,
she crooked her finger at me.

"Cathay, I need to speak with your mother."

I stiffened, and waited for the axe.

"Mrs. Korwin is having difficulty with Timothy."

My eyes flew up. *Timmy?* The cheery-faced tyke
with the head hard-as-rocks? I guessed it was, anyway,
because as long as I could remember, he kept flinging
himself off of things; that's why Mommy called him
'Timber.' Yet he always had a smile on his face beneath
the constant egg on his forehead. *What did he do?!*

I held down the fort in the station wagon while
Mommy hastened out to confer with the Mistress General.

Back in the car, she sighed. "What happened?" I burst out.

"Well," paused Mommy. "It seems Timmy hugs all
the little girls and knocks them down, making them cry."

"Timber!" I blurted. "Why do you do that?!"

Timmy glanced off to the side, seeing something we
couldn't see.

"Because," he piped, "I just lub them so much I
want to *squeeeeze* them!" He scrunched his eyes tight
and wrapped his arms around himself, quivering with
intensity.

I eyeballed him. "You're gonna get into so much
trouble, Timber!" *And I will be SO embarrassed!*

Mommy reached out and took his hand. "Try to be
more gentle, sweetie. You're so strong, you might hurt
them." He shrugged, and climbed into the third seat.

"Mommy," I moaned. "They're gonna send him home for ANOTHER year!"

Somehow, he must've learned to control himself, because no more scolds from school were forthcoming.

Or *were* they?

...Maybe I was right!

But Mother Eby simply set her pole down and smiled at us.

"Well," she began. "Why don't all three of you come with me while I shut the windows upstairs?"

I pattered after her with Julie in tow. No need to ask Timmy; he danced ahead of all of us.

Instead of the stairs, to my surprise, Mother led us to the little elevator used only by the teachers and nuns. After twisting the knob of the outer door open, she tugged the crisscross scissor-gate to the side.

"We're going in the *elubator!*" whispered Timmy loudly.

"Yes, Timmy – just this one time," said Mother. We crowded in and I gazed around.

Mother Eby stood against the gate opposite me, beautiful, like Mary...like Mater. *I bet no one else in my class has ridden in the elevator with her!* Julie, ever silent, clung to my hand. With nowhere to go, Timmy stood still and held onto the wooden ledge along the sides. Then with a jerk, the elevator pushed upward.

Out on the next floor, we tagged after Mother.

The classrooms shone oddly with all the empty desks standing upright at attention. *How different it sounds now!* Mother leaned into the waning rays of light, wielding her great pole. For a moment, she stood frozen in time. *Like a statue...*

Timmy raced past me towards the blackboard. Grabbing a piece of chalk in his fat little fist, he dragged it across the surface.

"No, Timmy!" I cried, and swooped down on him. I peeked over my shoulder at the window, but Mother Eby had already slipped out to the next classroom.

"Woo, woo!" crowed Timmy, as he ducked under my arm and scrambled after her.

At last I had him corralled by the elevator. Julie whispered into his ear while Mother approached from down the hall. Timmy danced up and down and bubbled, "We're ready, Mother! We're ready!"

Once more we climbed into the little cage.

I relaxed. *Not much he can do in here!* I smiled at Mother; then lowered my eyes.

Timmy's voice broke through the silence.

"Mother," he bubbled, "Do you wear pajamas when you go to bed at night?"

The tiny space snapped into glaring light. His words seemed to crash into shrinking walls and bounce all around us. *Timmy!* I peered sideways at his sunny face. Never, *ever* do you ask a nun personal questions! Never do you even *think* them! *What will she say? What will she do? What will she think of us?!* Mother Eby, looming taller than ever in her jet-black robes, simply giggled inside her cupped hand. Her eyes twinkled down at him.

"Well, do you?" he persisted.

"Timmy!" I hissed, and jerked his arm. I didn't *dare* look at her this time. *If she answers, I will die!* My eyes clenched, I willed myself far away – far away from Timmy, far away from Mother Eby...

Mother simply giggled again.

"Ow!" Julie cried. I opened my eyes and peered down at her. I had squeezed her hand till it turned red. "Oh - sorry, Julie," I mumbled.

347

After eons of resounding silence (*ISN'T she going to say anything?*) the elevator landed with a *thud*. Mother tugged open the gate and turned the knob.

Up ahead crouched Daddy, arms out, grinning. As Timmy tumbled towards him, we all trooped out into fresh air once more.

The Red Petticoat

Birthday present in hand, I stared up at the massive revolving door before me. The cool, moist fog seeped through my white cardigan. I shivered. I could feel the scratchy texture of my red tulle petticoat against my legs. It made my (almost) new party dress flare out – like a ballerina's! Cherry red, with white daisy rickrack sprinkled with *real* diamonds (well, *they looked like it!*) - the hand-me-down dress from "the cousins" was *supposed* to be my Christmas dress. But I had persuaded Mom to let me wear it to the birthday party at the Big Fancy Club in San Francisco.

Twisting backward, I waved goodbye to Mom in the waiting car. Off she rumbled.

"Hey!"

I glanced up; then bounced on my heels as I awaited the fast-approaching figure on the sidewalk. Barbara-with-the-curly-bob.

"Hi!" Barbara breathed, out of breath. Banana-curl Candy appeared right behind her.

"Hi!" I grinned.

Candy pointed to the door. "What are you waiting for?"

I hesitated. "Umm…' I stalled. "How do you do it?"

Impishly wrinkling her nose at me, Barbara reached past us and shoved against the glass with her shoulder. "Like this!"

Ohh… We whirled ourselves through the circular glass cage until, one by one, we popped out at last. *Wheee!*

A wood-paneled lobby spread before us. Smiling
knowingly, a tall blonde with upswept hair greeted us
with a clipboard.

"Good afternoon, girls! Are you here for Nancy's party?"
We nodded in unison.

"Follow me!" We trailed after her, entering the
monstrous dining room on the left.

I stared. An endlessly long table draped with white
linen flowed down the middle of the room. Girls in
party dresses of chiffon and lace pattered back and forth,
choosing which massive chair to sit in. Windows all
along the left poured opaque sunlight into the center.
I cranked my neck back as I gazed up, up at the great
vaulted ceiling. Not one, but *three* chandeliers graced
the regal table: gold with crystal droplets dangling
from each tiny lamp. Why, it was grand as a palace!
Voices echoed in the vast room, giggles and shrieks
intermingling in delightful patterns. Nancy, I could see,
sat tall as a queen in her white starched dress at the head
of the table. Her blonde head bobbed happily with every
greeting.

A bell tinkled. "Lunch – is *served!*" A deep voice rang out.

Uh oh – my eyes darted this way and that. Quickly
I slipped into a vacant seat beside Barbara, fluffing my
skirt and letting my petticoat flounce around me. Waiters
dressed in black and white held high their trays as they
processed into the room.

"Club sandwiches!" someone crowed. "We're having
club sandwiches!"

I glanced sideways at Barbara. She looked as pleased as
the voice down the table sounded. I leaned towards her.

"Barbara," I whispered. "What's a 'Club Sandwich'?"
She raised her eyebrows. "Don't you know?"
I shook my head.

"It's like a 'BLT', but with turkey, too."

"Ohh..." *What's 'B-L-T'...*

I stared at the perfectly cut white triangles, their insides piled impossibly high. Through the center of each one a curly-headed red, yellow, or blue toothpick waved gaily. Oh, so fancy! Next, the waiter set a tall, green bottle of Coca-Cola beside each plate. No one had to share! I *liked* this fancy club!

Before long, waiters began whisking the glass plates away – *uh, oh!* – before I had half-finished.

"The cake! The cake!" Sheryl piped up, followed by a chorus of echoes. Before a beaming Nancy the waiter placed the largest cake I had ever seen! White, with swoops and swirls and pink roses everywhere. Quickly I crammed the last triangle into my mouth just as my plate disappeared before me...

Pleasantly stuffed, I sank back as the lady with the clipboard announced, "It's time for swimming. Girls, please follow me."

Swimming! I had forgotten all about that. I glanced up at the girls clambering out of their heavy chairs. *Oh, no!* I scurried down the long hallway after them.

"Barbara!" I grabbed her arm. "I forgot my bathing suit!"

She stopped cold. "Forgot your bathing suit?!"

I nodded, hot tears threatening to escape. We wheeled around a corner, alone, and plastered ourselves against the wall.

"Well...well...," she searched.

I swallowed. "I guess I could...just watch..."

Suddenly her eyes widened. "I know! Why don't you just wear your underwear!"

"Are you crazy?!" *Have everyone see me swimming in my....underwear?!*

"C'mon," she urged. "Once you're in the water, no one will really see you...your suit, I mean...*uh*, your

351

'not-suit'"…She laughed and gave me that wrinkle-nose, sparkle-eyed look. "Oh, you know what I mean!"

I laughed – somewhat reluctantly. But she clapped her arm around my back and nuzzled her chin against my cap sleeve. "C'mon, Cathay!"

And won me over…almost.

"But what about a bathing cap?"

Barbara frowned. This was an absolute requirement. Before I knew it, she marched me over to the information desk and cooed, "Excuse me, Ma'am, but is there an extra bathing cap for my friend here who forgot one?" The tall blonde with the upswept hair peered down at me over her half glasses.

"You didn't bring a bathing cap?"

"Uh…no," I said faintly.

Her eyes closed; her lips pursed together. I wanted to punch Barbara for asking her!

"Well," she began. "I can lend you one. But *be sure* to return it before you leave." She smiled widely, head tilted sideways, her eyes boring into me.

"DON'T…forget!"

"Uh, yes, Ma'am. Thank you, Ma'am." *Whew!* We took off like a shot.

"Good thing you didn't tell her about my *bathing suit!*" I whispered, skipping back down the hall.

Five minutes later we emerged from the dressing room, my party clothes off, bathing cap on, and a towel tucked up tight around me.

Inside the pool area all the other girls had already jumped in. Hollow voices echoed among the splashes. I hesitated, clinging to the edge of my towel.

"C'mon, Cathay," Barbara muttered. "Just do it quick!"

Sucking in air, I counted, "One - two – three!" With a single jerk I tore that towel off and leaped over the side.

"Oooh!" I shrieked. I was in! I bobbed up and down to stop the chill, careful to keep my shoulders covered.

Swish! Splash! Tall Cindy lunged towards me. Suddenly she stood up, eyes widened.

"Huh!'

I swirled my arms back and forth in front of me, foaming up the water.

"Hey!" she cried. "Is that a *white* bathing suit, or..." She squinted, head forward; then her mouth fell open. Quickly I paddled behind Barbara.

"She forgot her suit," I heard Barbara mumble. I splashed her. "*Hey!*"

"Oh," Cindy tried hard not to laugh. I glowered.

"It's okay; we'll protect you," she declared. The two of them proceeded to swim around me in circles. I splashed; they splashed back, amid shrieks of laughter. I grinned at their teasing faces, basking in the special 'club' of our own.

All too soon, the whistle blew. "Everybody out!" Lickety-split, I leaped out of the pool and grabbed the towel.

"No running!" a voice yelled behind me while I dashed along the wet cement into the dressing room. Feeling triumphant, I managed to peel off the wet undershirt and underpants before slipping into the shower just as the rest of the girls burst in.

Minutes later, after drying off with the towel, I realized the folly of our plan. *No* underpants! Back over my head went the special red dress; up over my legs slipped my prize petticoat. I glanced covertly around the dressing room; sure *someone* had noticed my lack of underpants. But everyone else seemed busy struggling into their own party clothes over their still-damp bodies. I sat down on the end of the bench – *wet!* I stifled an exclamation and leaned over, careful to keep my bottom covered. My white anklets twisted sideways, refusing to budge as I tore at them with fumbling fingers. *Stupid socks!* Finally I managed to buckle up my Mary Janes. *How can anybody get shoes and socks on when the floor is soaking wet?!*

I straightened up, thoroughly disgruntled now. My bottom itched terribly from sitting on top of that tulle netting. Quickly I stuffed my sopping underwear into an empty locker, left the towel and cap on the bench, and hurried out of the now-vacant dressing room. *Mom better be out there!*

Sure enough, Mom was there, massaging her bulging belly. But something was wrong. The lady-with-the-clipboard seemed to be spitting words at her while Mom, meanwhile, scanned the room. She caught my eye and gestured frantically for me to hurry up.

"...*And* I was told that she did *not* have a bathing suit," the woman was saying, "...which she did not tell *me*..."

With a sigh of relief, Mom grabbed my hand, uttered: "I'm so sorry," over her shoulder and yanked my arm towards the door.

"Where *were* you?!" she hissed between her teeth. "You're the last one out!"

I couldn't tell her right then about trying to keep my bottom covered – so no one would see. Maybe *that* slowed me down. Anyway, the story was much too long, and I had abandoned my wet underwear, besides. *Not* a good time.

"We *have* to get back to the car!" she continued. "We're parked in a tow-away zone – and it's four o'clock *right now!*"

Up the cement mountain we trudged, Mom pulling, me scurrying to keep up. "C'mon, c'mon!" she urged.

The icy air chilled my wet head. My tulle petticoat bounced against my tender skin, the cruel wind wickedly curling up under my dress. *Oh, when will we get to the car?!*

Mom stopped short. She dropped my hand with a gasp. I gazed up and down the block. Not a parked car in sight (but plenty of parking spaces.)

"Well, where's the car?" I cried, confused. Slowly Mom turned and fixed her eyes on me. A strange, deep voice slipped out of her mouth.

"The car...has been...TOWED."

Vrroomm, rrroomm.... I could hear the sounds of traffic zooming by as I stared back at her, uncomprehending. My thoughts swirled. *Well...so...but where's the car...* Mom stood stock-still. The traffic sounds expanded like monstrous bubbles gone berserk, enveloping me. The street rose up before me, mammoth and menacing. Cars whizzed by, uncaring. I swallowed, waiting for Mom's next move.

At last her hand began massaging her enormous tummy.

"Let's go," she muttered, tight-lipped. Back down that hill we marched, my patent leather shoes barely holding their own against the magnetic pull downward. We whirled ourselves once more through the revolving glass door.

I slipped into an over-stuffed chair facing *away* from the reception desk (I didn't want Blondie-with-the-clipboard to see me!) while Mom set off in search of a payphone. Grateful for the soft cushion, I carefully raised the tulle petticoat up *above* my bottom this time. (I could hide against the circular back of the chair.) In and out of the revolving glass door ladies in fine hats ventured, their voices tinkling.

At last Mom hurried over, her pinched face relaxing into a small smile: "Daddy's going to meet us at the place where it's towed."

Minutes later we hiked up the steep steps of a Big
City Bus. Once again, I sat on that tulle and hung on
to the silver bar before me (wishing I could stand up
instead!) But on second thought, I wasn't so sure I could
balance on that jiggety floor and not show my bottom if
I fell.

After a second bus ride, we arrived at a windowless
building full of old cars and greasy-overalled men.
Stale cigarette smoke hung in the air. I hid behind Mom
while she talked to the man dangling a cigarette from
his mouth. His gruff voice grated against my ears.
Following his dismissive thumb, we settled ourselves
against the wall on folding metal chairs.

I sighed. I was sure by now I had little criss-cross
patterns all over my bottom, maybe even permanent
ones. I tried swinging my legs. That seemed to make
it worse. I gazed up at Mom. Her face had pinched up
again. *C'mon, Daddy, c'mon...*

"Having a little adventure, are we?"

I wheeled around.

"Daddy!"

Mom jumped up and the two of them conferred in
low tones. Mom's fingers twisted in a little circle at her
side as she spoke. Dad's eyebrows flew up.

"What!" he cried.

With a great intake of breath, he drew himself up and
marched over to the man-with-the-cigarette. (Daddy
gleamed in his gold-buttoned Army officer uniform, his
hat perched staunchly on his head.)

"I am Captain Gunn and this is highway robbery!"
he boomed. "How dare you charge $100 to this poor
pregnant woman, ready to give birth any moment,
stopping briefly to pick up her child?! This is an outrage!"
bristled Daddy. "We absolutely will not pay it!"

Immediately the man-with-the-cigarette dropped his pen and fumbled with his papers,.

"Well, sir, uh...yes, sir," he stammered. "Uh, I believe we were, um, somewhat incorrect. The charge should be...uh...$20...Sir."

Daddy raised an eyebrow and nodded. He peeled off some bills from his wallet and handed them over; then he wheeled about and curled his finger at us.

"Let's go."

I leaped up, my hands against my skirt, and scurried after him. Gazing skyward, I snuck one hand inside his as the three of us rounded a corner. Just ahead glimmered the long-lost red and white Pontiac station wagon. I sidled into the back and crouched down. Quick as a wink, I whisked that petticoat off and tossed it into the third seat behind me.

For *good.*

The Schism

Turning ten can be a momentous occasion. It must've been, because Dad remarked that morning on the way to school: "Now that Cathay has two digits in her age, she acts like she has THREE." *Huh.* Whatever that meant, I knew it wasn't complimentary.

All I cared about was coming home. My school chum, Mildred, was spending the night. I could hardly wait for the end of the school day.

The bell tolled freedom; we fairly flew out the door of our distinguished Elementary, and into the little Fiat humming at the curb. Five little Gunns crammed inside; all of a sudden, the grossly crowded condition of our modest little "toy car" glared out at me.

Mildred, all arms and legs, managed to fold herself up, accordion-style, and hold her breath, wide-eyed at the novelty.

I'd already spent the night at her house – after being buzzed up by a uniformed lobby guard! An only child, living in a penthouse apartment with an elevator and a maid who made her bed every day (!) Mildred must've viewed my family of eight, going on nine, as a total zoo.

As one, we crowed Dad's familiar song:

"No more backfire, not for me! No-no-no -
backfire just means mis-er-eee!"

Dad, oblivious, warbled louder than any of us. Then he continued our repertoire with "Down by the Old Mill Stream," "School Days," and -

"When you wore a tulip,
A big yellow tulip,
And I wore a big, red rose – *ba-bum-ba-bum-bump!*

Your lips were sweeter than julep,
When you wore a tulip,
And I wore a big, red, rose."

I snuck a sideways glance at my friend. So far so
good. I began to relax and settle into the half-hour
homeward jaunt.

Up the winding hill we chugged, forging a path to -
"the top of the mountain!" I crowed, in rural Tamalpais
Valley. The Golden Gate Bridge had long since been
spanned. Mildred shrieked uncontrollably as we
careened around a curve.

"Hang on tight!" I chortled.

The trees waved their homespun greeting as we
whisked between them. Finally the car lurched to a halt,
and we all piled out. Mildred did a 360° turn, eyes wide
on the "forest" around us. I laughed, "C'mon!" and
pulled her along into the house in the midst of the wild
terrain.

Mom appeared, a babe on her hip, and a babe in her
belly. She sang out a radiant "hello," planted a kiss on
each face, and then settled into the arms of Dad for the
ritual homecoming embrace.

"Dinner at 6:00!" she chimed. In one's and two's, we
dispersed.

Tossing off our uniforms in my basement bedroom,
we switched to play-clothes: Mildred in creased white
shorts and collared blouse, I in my tee shirt and jeans.

"Mildred!" I exclaimed. "Let's go check out my
brothers' new rope swing!" I couldn't wait to show
her. Our teenage cousins, Jimmy and Billy, had built a
fabulous tree fort for Mike and Pat on their visit here.
They lassoed the branch above it for our swing.

I raced out the door with Mildred in tow, and flew up
the path to the eucalyptus grove. A wildflower bonanza

greeted us as I bounded through it. The golden rope dangled before me, ready and waiting.

"C'mon!" I shouted.

Without a backward glance, I scrambled up the rungs hammered into the tree trunk and onto the platform. Stretching out as far as I could, I grasped the old familiar rope, wrapped my legs around its tail, and hunched over the giant knot. With a kick I shoved off! *I'm flying!*

A huge spread of leaves lay beneath me, beckoning. I refused to obey. *Let the wind sing through my hair awhile as I sail through the sky!* The air felt clean and crisp as it whipped my skin. I glided with the pendulum.

At last I leaped. *Crunch!* With a roll, I tumbled into the leaves, arms and legs splayed. Laughing now, I sprang up.

"O.K! Now it's your turn!" My eyes glistened, my heart pounded. I was *alive!* I couldn't wait for my friend to share that same joy.

Mildred seemed to be in another time zone. She dragged her shoes over the dirt to the treehouse and stopped. She didn't move. Impatient, I prodded her from behind.

"C'mon! It's great!"

Slowly, as though in water, she pushed her way through the resisting air currents and planted a foot on the lowest rung of the ladder. One leg, then another, gradually bent in the middle. Up at last on the platform, she stared at the view below.

"*C'mon!*" I urged. The air stood still, waiting.

Suddenly she broke the spell.

"NO!"

Down the ladder she scrambled, tripped on a rock and staggered to her feet. Without a word, she bolted down the path to the stone steps, up to the road and out to "freedom." Open-mouthed, I lunged after her.

"Wait! Wait!" I yelled, sparks shooting throughout my

body. Through the trees I caught a glimpse of the lanky figure vanishing down the road.

My whole night's expectations disintegrated before my eyes. This was not happening! Faster I flew, till I caught up with her, faltering out of breath near the rambling ranch house down around the corner.

"Mildred, come back!" I cried. She wheeled to face me. Her bottom lip loomed farther and farther out, her eyebrows slanting downward like shades over her eyes.

"I'm never going back," she glowered. "You get your Dad to take me home."

I couldn't believe it. What had I done wrong?! Just then, Teddy, the rotund neighbor collie waddled over to me. I sank to the ground and flung my arms around his neck, my face buried in his fur.

"Oh, Teddy! Teddy!" I sobbed. "My birthday's ruined!"

I pleaded, I wept, but her heart remained of stone. Mildred's rampage continued.

"You expect me to be just like your brothers! Well, I'm not!"

At long last, an inkling of light forced its way through a crack in my brain. Mildred-of-the-Penthouse-Apartment didn't belong in the woods. With quick back-stepping murmurs, I promised we could play whatever games she wished.

"We can stay inside in my room, if you want!" I implored.

Slowly, she softened. With huge sighs, we shuffled toward each other. I reached out. Her hand in mine, back up the winding country road I led my delicate city friend.

Mike and Pat

Quarantine

*M*ike has been sick for seven days.

I tried not to think about that as I shuffled through the leaves and across the road to Mrs. O'Bannon's house. My piano teacher… I loved to watch her long fingers as she demonstrated the notes for me on her piano. *Better to picture this instead...* The trees before me fell away as I slipped into that reverie. Her red-gold hair cascading across her shoulder as she flexed and unflexed those fingers on the keys…

I had arrived. Mrs. O'Bannon greeted me at the door.

"Good afternoon, Cathay! Come in!" I murmured my hello and slunk past her into the sparse living room.

"How's your brother now?" she chirped. "Back in school?"

"Um, not yet," I mumbled. *Did she have to bring it up?*

"Ah. Soon, then," she smiled; then swooped up her baby from the rug and set him in the playpen, so as not to disturb our lesson.

"You be a good boy, Bryan," she cooed. *He looks like a little Mike,* I mused. Abruptly I turned and approached the piano. I sidled onto the bench and waited...

At first I could not understand why Mike was allowed to stay home from school. *Was he pretending?* Then Mom moved the *new* new baby downstairs into Heidi's room – too soon, I thought – and let Mike sleep upstairs with Mom and Dad in their bed. He stayed there day and night. *Why does he get to do that?* When I had the flu I still slept in my own bed.

"We don't want any of you catching it," Mom had remarked.

We were on strict orders NOT to go in.

I waved goodbye to Mrs. O'Bannon on her stoop at the end of our lesson.

"Remember to practice hard for our recital," she called out. I nodded and trudged homeward through the trees across the road.

Back in the house, I hurried to the piano and flipped the pages of my music book. Hands raised, I checked the fingering and struck the notes.

"Oh, no, no!" Mom scurried out from the kitchen and shook her head at me. "Michael has just fallen asleep. No playing now." Those new furrows on her brow deepened further.

I let my fingers crash down on the keys and glowered up at her.

"THAT was uncalled for." Mom's eyes burned. I stared at the keys.

"Sorry."

That night Dad lined us up in the living room and, one by one, swiped the back of our throats with a cotton swab on the end of a long stick. All but Mike's, that is.

"Ahhhhhh... *ACKKK!*" The back of my throat flip-flopped forward of its own accord.

"Why are you doing this?"

"Tomorrow morning I will take these with me to the hospital," Dad replied, "and check to see that none of you are getting sick." *Hmmm… He never did that before…*

After everyone else had scattered, I hung back till the den door creaked closed. On impulse I followed Dad in and shut the door behind me. He glanced up from his desk, head cocked.

"Dad," I began, "what's wrong with him?"

Dad's lips pursed; then he shut his book, turned towards me and met my gaze.

"Mike has scarlet fever."

I stared. People died of scarlet fever. I knew that. On "Wagon Train" they certainly did. I remembered all the wooden crosses sticking out of the freshly dug graves as the wagon train rumbled away. I twisted the hem of my shirt between my fingers.

"Will…will he get better?" I croaked. Dad scanned my face a moment; then smiled.

"Of course he will."

I stood for a while in silence, waiting for some feeling of reassurance to settle over me… but it didn't come. At last I nodded and backed out through the glass door.

I stalled in the living room until he seemed engrossed once more in his medical journal. Then on tiptoe I approached the forbidden door and turned the knob. Holding my breath, I whispered in.

The room felt heavy and stifling. I stopped at the foot of the bed and listened. The clock on the dresser ticked. I gazed at the lump under the covers in the middle of that big bed. So tiny he looked! I crept closer. *He doesn't move at all!* So still his frame lay…like there was no life left. I bent down across the mattress and stared into his face. *So white!* A vein throbbed on his temple. My hand shaking, I put a finger on Mike's cheek. *So hot!* His lids

flew open. His watery gaze seemed aimed at my eyes –
but did not quite reach across the distance to meet them.

"Mike!" I whispered. "It's me!" His eyes shifted
slightly but could not grab mine. I stared harder. A
trickle of icy liquid threaded through my veins. I froze.

"Mike!" I tried once more. No response. Time stood
still while I forced my own eyes to stretch larger and
larger in order to reach his. But Mike's eyes had sunken
in their sockets and would not reach back. I eased away.

Slowly, then, his pajama'd figure receded deeper and
deeper into the mattress until he appeared a long way
off. I sensed his body fly back in space farther away from
me, untouchable, unreachable.

At last I took a step back and saw my arm rotate
languidly through the air as it swam in slow motion
towards the door. Then I turned back one last time and
gazed at my brother – who was not my brother – before
floating back out of the room.

I stumbled downstairs and sat, motionless, on my
own bed.

I did not sleep that night.

The next morning I hiked back up the stairs, two at
a time. Striding through the living room, I snatched at
the "forbidden" doorknob and thrust in my head. The
sun streamed in the window; the bed lay empty. I bolted
back out.

"Where's Mike?!" I shrieked. Silence. *Where IS
everyone?!* I raced through the house. Empty. *Is he dead?!
Did they take him outside to bury him?!* Pins and needles
pricked every part of me. I lunged towards the stairs.

Just then Heidi emerged cradling the baby; Eric
trailed her heels with a fistful of skirt, followed by Pat,
Julie and Timmy climbing close behind. She tilted her
head at me.

"Cat-ay," she said. "Come eat. Your mommy and

daddy haf taken Michael to da hospital."

I could not eat. Mike's empty chair stared back at me.

On that day, Sunday, I wandered from room to room and gazed; then dragged on to the next room. Normal baby cries, play chatter... bubbled up from different corners. Pat, Julie and Timmy prattled on in their silly games as if nothing was amiss. Eric demanded to be picked up, so Heidi juggled two babies. I did not want to be around any of them.

The woods! With sudden relief I yanked open the front door and bolted down the porch steps. I flung out my arms to embrace the sky.

But it did not embrace me back.

I trudged towards the tree house, intent on holing up in there. As it peeped into view, my feet faltered. *No. It's not right; it's Mike's; Mike should be there.*

It was not the answer. There was no answer. I slumped down on the bottom step of the porch and waited.

After dark Dad returned. But Mike and Mom did not.

Monday morning I did not know how I could go to school. The Fiat chugged over the bridge and up the San Francisco hills with Dad, only, warbling the ritual songs. Pat and Tim were unusually quiet. Julie, in the back pouch, whimpered as usual, but did not have her peanut butter toast this time, for us to complain about. No one had made it.

And no one had waved us goodbye.

At five o'clock Dad returned to pick us up from study hall. We raced outside ahead of him... only to spy the empty Fiat.

"Are they home already, Daddy?" squeaked Patrick.

"Not yet. Perhaps tomorrow!"

I didn't say a word. I waited the agonizing drive back till I could get Dad alone. As the others trooped through the front door I tugged on his sleeve.

"Why are they not coming home yet?" I whispered.

"The doctors needed to do lots of tests today," he said in a low tone. "We just have to wait and see."

Tuesday in study hall I caught myself drawing crosses in the margin of my composition book. Hurriedly I erased them. Dad appeared and we squeezed back into the Fiat. He told us that the doctors had started a new medicine on Mike. We might see him soon.

Once back in the carport I strained against the door of the Fiat as it ground to a halt. I spied a glimmer through the trees. Ignoring the gloom of dusk, we all scrambled down the long path and into the lighted house.

"Mommy!" Julie cried. There she stood. With a great sigh, Mom threw open her arms and gathered us in. My eyes traveled past her shoulder to her bedroom door.

"Is Mike home?"

She nodded. "You may go in for a minute." I crept inside her room to the foot of the bed. The entourage followed.

Mike was awake.

"How are you?" I murmured. He smiled wanly.

"Tired."

His hand fluttered with the barest of waves as his eyes rotated and took us all in. I sighed all the way down to my toes.

Mike was coming back to us after all.

Bonnie Moreaux

Dancing on air

"What are you doing?!"

I stop in mid-spin, my head reeling, and try to focus on Mom's frowning face. Mike and Pat instantly throw themselves down on the rug, giggling with infectious glee.

"We're just spinning around, Mom." I watch her eyebrows raise...then lower.

"Well," she says, "I have a better idea." She clutches the freshly laundered stack of diapers in her arms and disappears into her bedroom. "But I have to dress for it," she tosses over her shoulder.

Mystified, we sit cross-legged in front of the couch and wait.

She slips back, the more usual skirt exchanged for capris; her face glows with eagerness.

"What are we going to do?" I query.

Without a word, Mom plops down on the floor next to us. Mike and I exchange glances. *Mom's never sat on the living room floor before!*

"We're going to stand on our heads," she responds.

"What?!" Mike's eyes widen." How?"

"Watch."

She forms a triangle with her forearms on the rug, places her head between them, and slowly hoists her body up in the air – first folded in half; then her legs shoot up in the air like an erector set! *Whoa!* We all stare.

Pat pops his thumb out of his mouth. "How did you DO that, Mommy?"

She flips right side up again. "Easy," she says with an impish grin. "But I think first you'd better crawl the wall." *Huh?*

Soon all three of us line up crouched against the living room wall, our heads on the rug between our hands. I gaze through the upside-down coffee table legs ahead of me. With a grunt I heave my legs up over my head – *bam!* Feet slam against the wall, knees bent, legs quivering.

"Now walk your feet slowly up the wall till your legs are straight..." The wall feels solid, unyielding, and surprisingly supportive. *Oooh! I'm a bug crawling upside-down!* "Feel your balance..." *My face feels prickly...* "Now carefully push your feet a little ways away from the wall." *Wh-whoa!* My feet let go, my body quivers wildly, undulates – then, of their own accord, those same feet slap frantically back against home base. At last, with second and third chances - *I'm doing it!*

Soon Mike, Pat and I venture into the middle of the rug – without the safety net – and follow Mom's lead with the triangular base. My head wobbles into a position of comfort, then...one – two - THREE! I boost my lower half up – first resting my knees on my bent biceps till my body finds its center – then – slowly I unfold. I feel the wildness of the air on all sides of me, tugging at me. "Fall! Fall!" it hisses. I fight back till I'm nearly still, and ramrod straight. My whole body fills with electricity – it's connecting me to every radius of the room. The air is my friend now, holding me up on all sides in equal measure. *I'm a circus acrobat!*

Mike and Pat shriek as they tumble down on either side of me. I follow suit. Without a word Mom bends over and leaps onto her hands – not even her head touches the ground! She 'steps' *one…two…* with her palms, legs aimed for the ceiling, then pops upright again. She prances toward the new hi-fi and drops the needle.

"O.k.! Let's dance!" she cries.

Mike, Pat and I hug our knees as we watch.

"Yes, sir, that's my baby…"

This time Mom foregoes the triangular base, and positions her head between her parallel palms. Up she goes!

"…No sir, I don't mean maybe…"

Her legs, still as a statue for only a moment, suddenly separate and scissors open and closed, to the sides, then front and back, in syncopated time with the music.

"…*That's my baby na-oww!*"

…*She's dancing on her head to the music!*

Mike, Pat and I scramble back over upside down again. I can just barely hold my pose without toppling – but this time the notes in the air shoot vibrations right through me. In my mind, my legs cut rhythmical swaths through space as I hold…hold…

"*Yes, ma'am, we've decided, no ma'am, we can't hide it…*"

Without warning, a deep voice booms out of nowhere:

"Honey, I'm ho -"

...The front door slams shut.

I stare upside-down at Dad's army green cuffs floating under the edge of his oxford shoes. I can only imagine the big round "O" that must be plastered across his frozen face. With a shriek and a chortle, the circus collapses like dominos and we all clamber to our feet to greet him.

Holy Orders

Mike gripped the front seat ahead of him. Fingers rigid, he pleaded into Mom's hair, "I don't want to go. Please, please don't make me go!" I stared sideways at him; pity gave way to trepidation.

Today was Mike's First Holy Communion. No big deal. I'd been through that, three years before, and I loved it. Of course I got to wear a *beauteous* white chiffon dress and veil – like a bride! Mike wore his usual Sunday clothes (school pants and blazer.) The only new item was a tie. *Boring.*

But he had a problem. He could not swallow the Host. At the "dry run" in the chapel yesterday, he choked and coughed till finally Mother Carroll dashed in with a glass of water. (I know all this because I listened at Mom's door while Mike whined and whimpered the whole story. I stayed out of sight so I could hear all the details.) Today was the day, and now we were almost THERE.

"Why on earth don't they have a parking lot!" Dad grumbled, edging up the mountainous side street for the third time.

"Let us off in front, sweetheart," Mom suggested. "Then Mike won't be late, and the children won't have to walk. And you can relax."

"Yeah, Dad!" I piped up. "We'll save you a seat!"

One by one we clambered out of the station wagon, like clowns out of an impossibly small circus car. I jumped out first, followed by Patrick, who leaped up the sidewalk in the lead. Timmy and Julie climbed down next, trailed by Eric the toddler and Mom with the new baby. At the tail end, Mike reluctantly crawled out, aided by a firm prod from Dad. He stood rooted to the ground, his eyes glued to the taillights as the red-and-white Pontiac station wagon disappeared into the fog.

"Hurry, Michael!" Mom urged. With a sigh, he turned and dragged his feet along the walk. Mother Carroll, the boys' Mistress General, greeted us at the door. She smiled at Mike and gestured ahead.

"Mother Sullivan is waiting for you, Michael."

He threw Mom one last desperate glance; then trudged off, shoulders slumped. The rest of us trooped behind, our footsteps echoing throughout the grand marble Main Hall. I hurried forward to catch up with him.

"Mike!" I called. He stopped. I leaned in towards his ear.

"Does it get stuck on the roof of your mouth?" Mike peeped at me out of the corner of his eye, lips tightening. He nodded slightly, but continued walking.

"Work it with your tongue."

"I did!" he retorted.

"Make some spit in your mouth and squirt it up high. And keep pushing at the Host with your tongue." I could see his back stiffen. "But, whatever you do, DON'T let it touch your *teeth*." I shuddered at the forbidden sacrilege.

Instantly he turned on me. "I know that!" he hissed.

Then he whirled around, straightened his shoulders
and marched out into the 'Cortile' to join his waiting
class. I scurried up the hall after Mom and the gang and
into the burgeoning chapel. We spotted our family name
inscribed across the white satin ribbon that marked our
pew, and shuffled in.

Just then, a familiar face popped up from the aisle. *Dad!*
He genuflected and squeezed in beside Mom.

"Found the perfect spot!" he whispered with a grin.

At that moment the organ groaned with the opening
notes of "Holy God We Praise Thy Name." We all rose
and peered behind us while the First Communicants
filed in, hands folded, girls in white on one side, boys
on the other. I strained to catch a glimpse of Mike. Sure
enough, he was there; his face pale, his eyes huge. I
tried to smile at him as he passed but he didn't see
me; didn't see anybody. Impatient to get to the Main
Event, I distracted myself with wrapping my tongue
around those lovely long Latin responses. The songs
were the best. "Tantum ergo sacramentum..." I read and
rearranged the gold-edged holy cards in my missal.

At last, the novitiates rose and approached the altar
rail. I shifted back and forth, craning my neck, anxious to
follow his progress. For a moment, time stood still. *Will
he bolt suddenly out of fear and flee back down the aisle? What
will we do? Grab him as he sails by? Run after him? Will we
make him go back?*

He made it to the altar rail. *Will he faint before the
priest even gets to him? Will Mom run up and catch him?
Dad is in the way...she'll never get there in time...*

The priest was almost upon him! *Will he choke? Make
all kinds of noises? Clutch his throat? Dad's a doctor... Will
he run up and do something? What?*

The priest stopped before Mike. I felt Mom stiffen. I
squeezed the pew before me. We all froze.

Father raised the Host. I heard the privately-murmured words in my head. *Corpus Christi. . . Amen.* Mike lifted his head. I held my breath.

Just then, out of the corner of my eye, a dark shadow rose from the left side of the chapel. It flitted past the other boys and stopped right behind Mike. Mother Carroll. Her hand rose past her filmy veil, cradling a tiny white cup. It disappeared over his shoulder. She paused behind him till he had finished; then retreated to her station with the emptied cup. An audible sigh escaped Mom's lips. He had done it.

Afterwards, we all celebrated with hot cocoa and pastries in the ornate reception room opposite the chapel.

"You did it! You did it!" I exulted, clapping Mike's back.

"Did you see Mother Carroll?" he whispered. His eyes darted right and left.

"Yeah – wasn't that great?" I exclaimed. "She saved the day!"

"Naw," purred Mike. I did it myself, before she even got there!"

"Really?"

"Yeah…"

At last the hubbub abated, and we moseyed out with the stragglers through the wrought-iron front door. I blinked in the sunshine, filtered through the last lingering wisps of fog.

"Where's the car, Dad?" I queried. "You said it was close!"

Dad jingled his keys with a twinkle in his eye. "Not far indeed!" Like a Pied Piper, he led us down the street, whistling. Sure enough, as we rounded the corner of one of the steepest streets in San Francisco (another one with steps in it), our perpendicularly-parked car sprang into view. The old red-and-white appeared to wink at us while leaning sideways in a battle against gravity.

"Whoa!" yelled Mike. "How are we going to get in?"

Entering on the high driver's side, we managed to keep our balance as we all stumbled into our seats.

"All set?" Dad called out.

"Hurry, Daddy!" chirped Pat. "Mike still has to open his presents!"

Dad turned the key. *Grr...grr...rrr...rrr...* Nothing. Dad tried again. *Grr...rrr...rrr...* Silence.

"Confound it!" he exclaimed. "The lights were on!"

We all stared at one another. *Now what?*

"Well, don't just sit there. Everybody out!"

We all scrambled to obey. I flung open the downside door; it bounced on its hinges. We trooped out onto the sidewalk, wondering what would happen next. Dad, I noticed, stayed hunched over the steering wheel. He rolled down the window.

"What are you going to do, Daddy?" I squeaked.

"You, Mike and Pat are going to push the car from behind while I steer it down the sidewalk."

"What!" cried Mom.

"The motor will eventually catch, and we can drive home."

"But, but..."

"Just DO it!"

"You need help!" she pleaded. "The children can't do it alone!"

By now the new baby had awoken, Eric began to wail and Julie clung, whimpering, to Mom's skirt. Timmy, however, hopped up and down and cheered, "Do it, Daddy, do it!" Pat looked scared, but resolute. Mike snarled, "Shut up, Timmy!" Mom gave him "The Look"; then marched to the corner and flagged down the first unsuspecting pedestrian...another First Communion parent.

After a brief dialogue with Dad, The Parent pushed

the car from behind, while Dad, up front, pushed and steered. Mom held us all at bay, refusing to let any of us help. We huddled together on the stair-stepped sidewalk, frozen with fear. Even Timmy no longer hopped.

"Don't, Dad, don't do it!" I sobbed. "There might be people on the sidewalk!"

Ever so slowly, the car lurched forward over the curb. The Parent gave one last heave and leaped down the street like a madman.

"I'll head them off!" he yelled.

Dad cranked the wheel and jumped in. The car's rear end looked HUGE as it turned to face us, red taillights glinting in the sun. Slowly at first, then faster the car gathered momentum. It glided silently down the roller-coaster hill. It did not look real! *Cars don't drive down sidewalks!* Faster! Now faster! My eyes burned, my jaw ached, my chest felt ready to burst! The car reached the bottom of the hill. But it kept going! Without slowing down, it crossed the street, leaped onto the next sidewalk, and *disappeared!*

"Mom!" I screamed. A cacophony of cries erupted around me. I wanted to fly down the hill, but felt myself rooted to the ground.

"Everybody just wait," ordered Mom. "Stay calm."

We stood, mostly in silence, and waited…a long, long time. We stared at the crest at the bottom of the hill…so empty now. No sounds emerged from the street. *Please, God…*

"Dad – dy…" Timmy sniffled.

Beep, beep! Beep, beep!

We jumped; and whirled around. Up at the corner behind us idled that old red-and-white Pontiac station wagon, a beaming face at the helm.

"Daddy!!"

"Well, what are you waiting for?!" he hollered.

377

Whooping and shrieking, we all tore up to the car and climbed aboard.

"How'd you do it, Dad, how'd you do it?" cried Mike.

"Well," Dad replied. "I just figured Mike got us some extra good grace today. Thanks, Mike."

"Oooooh," I crooned, rolling my eyes. Pat chortled, and Mike stuck his tongue out at both of us. Then he puffed up his chest and pointed his nose at the ceiling.

"I...*swallowed.*"

Before we could pummel him, Mom called out in her best authoritative voice,

"SOUND off!"

"One!" I sang.

"Two!" crowed Mike.

"Three!"

"Four!"

"Five!"

("Say 'six,' Eric!")

"Sikth!"

...And off we tootled.

Director at Large

*S*queak, squeak! *Squeak, squeak!*

I popped one eye open. Rays of sunshine poured through the window, laying wide stripes across my bed. *Mmmmm.* Summer vacation. Glorious. *But what's that sound?!* I rolled over on my side and gazed at baby Eric's crib.

Two years old now, he had been ousted from Heidi's room to make way for Mom's *new* baby. Quietly he turned the pages of his little cloth book. My chest tingled as I gazed at the back of his head. Now Eric was *my* baby.

But he was not squeaking.

I glanced at the window above my head. *Must be a bird on my windowsill!* No birds in sight. Still that tiny, incessant sound... Barely discernible, but definitely close by. *Squeak, squeak. Squeak, squeak.*

I raised myself on my elbow and scanned the clutter... Eric's toys tossed from the crib, my books strewn over the nightstand, and on the floor... *Oh!*

There, alongside my bed on the hardwood floor four tiny pink blobs pulsed and wriggled. I flung back the covers and leaned over the edge for a closer look. I gasped.

"Wat dat? Wat dat?" Eric pulled himself up and stretched out his hand over the railing.

"Eric, it's mice!" I cried, scrambling out of bed and crouching on all fours.

"Mine!" Eric shrieked. "Mine!"

I unfolded and bolted out into the hallway.

"Mom! Mom!" I accosted her hurrying out of the laundry room. "Come quick!" I grasped her arm and propelled her back into my room. She stopped short and stared, her mouth open.

"Oh, no, no, no!" Mom moaned, shaking her head. "That mouse in the trap last night was a *mother!*"

Suddenly it hit me. I *knew* why they were there, in *my* room. It was no accident.

"Mom!" I squealed, hopping up and down. "I can use them in my play! They can be the real, live mice that get turned into horses!"

I, a ten-year-old budding playwright, actor and director, had been rehearsing "Cinderella" for over a week. Casting was the hardest. When you only have your siblings to draw from, plus your loyal best friend, you take what you can get. With much wheedling and cajoling on my part, Mike and Pat had agreed to be the wicked stepmother and stepsister. (We would have to make do with just one of the latter, as Julie, "on stage," steadfastly refused to speak.) So I turned her into the footman and made bold four year-old Timmy the coachman. Good-natured Carol would play the Fairy Godmother as well as the Prince. I, of course, was Cinderella.

Mom glowered at me with pursed lips. "I don't think they're going to live that long – without their mother."

"But we could feed them – with my doll's baby bottle!" Mom shut her eyes and probably counted to ten. At last she opened them.

"Are *you* going to feed them?" she challenged.

I sucked in air, eyes widening. "Yes, yes!" I rushed. "I could sit with you and feed them while you're giving the *baby* a bottle!" Mom gave me that look.

"We'll see."

After breakfast, I settled myself, cross-legged, in a spot of sunshine on the clay tiles of the front porch. Four pink blobs wiggled in front of me, more frantic now, on a potholder in an old pie pan. I glanced up past the camellia bush, through the eucalyptus to our roofless carport above. My new stage. I smiled to myself. *Mmmm! And to think I've discovered real live mice to add to it all!*

I grasped one tiny, warm creature between my fingers. It kept moving! I held the bottle firmly and tried to insert it into the teensy mouth. This was harder than I thought! The mouth didn't open wide enough, and the squeaking intensified. Just then Mom appeared in the doorway behind me.

"How's it going?"

"Terrible! They should be *hungry.* Why don't they drink it?" I felt a lump forming in my throat. *This has to work! After all, they were born in my room!*

Mom watched awhile, sighed, and finally settled herself on the top step next to me.

"Let me try something."

She pried off the cap of my doll bottle and stuck a medicine eyedropper inside. I gaped as, one by one, she got each little mouse to open its miniscule mouth and take a few drops. I think she simply squeezed the bulb, because I didn't see any real sucking. After a few minutes, I patted her shoulder, "Thanks, Mom!" and leaped down the porch steps to check out the stage.

Out on the gravel carport I twirled, eyes closed, my arms outstretched to play with the breeze in the dappled sunlight. *Perfect!*

Later that day I hunched over the breakfast room table, needle and thread in hand, white sheet on my knees.

"I'm so glad Grandmamma left these scraps!" I exclaimed, eyeing the multi-patterned "patches" I had carefully cut from her rejects. I studied my costume: a hole for the head clipped out of the middle, long hand-stitches down either side, just as Grandmamma had taught me, with openings left for the arms. The patches truly gave it that "Cinderella" look, I decided.

Costuming the rest of the cast was not so easy.

That evening in my room, Mike scowled, outraged at my suggestion that he wear my dress.

"I'm *not* a girl! I'm *not* a girl!" he howled. "You can't make me!"

"But you *promised* you'd be in my play!" I pleaded.

"Yes, but not in a DRESS!" he retorted. Patrick stood behind him, trying hard not to suck his thumb, taking it all in.

Mom peeked around the door frame and flashed one of her giant smiles. "I think I have just the costume for you, Michael!" she trilled. From behind her back she whipped out a wad of blue velvet and gold lamé. "It's the perfect 'wicked stepparent' costume!"

I gawked as the folds of heavy fabric cascaded to the floor. "Where did you get that?!"

"Oh – I have my own costumes," she said with a sly smile.

Mike grimaced. "It's still a dress!"

"*Ahh!* BUT, it's a mean, nasty stepmother's dress!" continued Mom. "And while wearing this costume, you'll be able to say mean, nasty things to your sister!" she enthused.

I raised my eyebrows.

"Well – in the play," she added.

"Can I say anything I want?" His eyes lit up.

"You can say what a wicked *stepmother* would say."

"*Hmm.* Okay."

"Pat?" I held his gaze.

Patrick thought a moment. "Can a wicked stepsister put a frog on her head?"

"No!" I snapped.

"Then...no." Pat shut his eyes and lifted his chin.

"Hey!" I blustered. He eyed me, waiting.

"Umm...you can make Cinderella brush your hair," I wheedled.

Patrick guffawed. "I don't have any hair to brush!" I stared at the boys' butch haircuts. I hadn't quite solved that problem yet.

"Well...we'll have to make wigs out of yarn, or something," I mused.

"No *sirree*! Not on your life!" Mike roared.

"Okay, okay," I hastened. "No wigs. Hats! Hats! Mom – hats?"

Mom vanished without a word, soon to reappear with scarves, pillbox hats and berets. Half an hour later, clothing strewn across my bed, we had reached an agreement. Mike and Pat would allow me to drape scarves around their heads, underneath one tied like "an Indian headband," I told them – "I can pretend it's hair," I whispered to Mom - and I would give each of them half my dessert for a whole week. Mike would wear the fancy blue and gold dress, and Pat agreed to my flannel nightgown with his cowboy belt.

"Now if only they'd learn their lines," I sighed.

Next morning I bounded into the kitchen, eager to rehearse with my cast. *Only two more days!* Julie and Timmy looked up from their cereal bowls.

"Don't tell her," Julie whispered.

"You're not gonna be happy," warned Timmy, trying hard not to burst out with the news.

Uh oh. My stomach lurched. "What is it?"

Timmy opened his mouth, but Julie elbowed him into submission.

"Talk to Mommy," he uttered; then held his breath.

I wheeled around and marched into Mom and Dad's room. Empty.

"Where is she?" I demanded on my return.

Julie leaned forward over the table and whispered behind her hand, "Look in the dugout."

I stared a moment; then turned on my heel, clattered down the basement stairs, and out the side door to the steps along the house. The dugout basement lay just beyond. Before I could yank that door open, Mom suddenly slipped out.

"Mom!" I startled. "What's going on?"

Mom halted; then wrapped her arm around my shoulders and sat me down on the step next to her. "I'm afraid the mice didn't make it," she said.

"Make what?" I scrunched up my forehead.

"Life without their mother."

I stared. "You mean they're dead? All of them?"

Mom nodded.

"But you were feeding them!"

She sighed. "They needed to be fed many times a day. I have a *real* baby to feed. *Besides –*" her eyes glowed bright, "What was I doing? Raising baby mice so I could kill them later in the trap?!" Mom closed her eyes and shook her head.

I couldn't believe it. "You killed them! I only needed them two more days, and you killed them!" I yelled.

Mom just looked at me. I could feel the blood moving in my arms. My teeth ground together. I would *not* give them up.

"Where are they?" I demanded.

"In the dugout for now. We can bury them, if you like," she offered. I pushed roughly past her into the low ceiling'd dugout. She followed me in.

Blinking in the semidarkness, I waited impatiently. Dust assaulted my nostrils. Finally the familiar pie pan materialized before me. Sure enough, they were not moving. And nary a peep. Or squeak. But they still looked like mice.

"Well, I'm going to use them, anyway," I growled.

"Then you'd better do the play *today*."

I glared at her. "I can't! We need to rehearse! Carol's still in school this week! And we – we need an audience! Dad has to be here!"

I could feel my dream slipping away, but my mind reached out and grabbed it back. *Not without a fight.*

Amazingly, Mom said yes.

The next day and a half I spent feverishly drawing and coloring programs. If Mike and Pat saw their names "in print," maybe they'd be more cooperative.

Friday afternoon I attempted one last rehearsal. I was stumped. No matter how hard I tried, Mike and Pat could *not* remember their lines. Carol shook her head in disgust.

"Maybe we should forget it, Cathay."

"No, no!" I cried. "*I* know. Let's let them make it up. *You* know, Mike. Like playing house."

Mike twisted his mouth. "Huh?"

"You don't have to remember the words," I grew more excited, contemplating it. "Just say whatever you think of – that would be mean and bossy. Like Mom said. Tell me things to do for you. You, too, Pat."

"Oh, yeah!" Mike warmed to the idea. Pat studied me, chewing on his lip.

"Cinderella – go stand on your head!" Mike chortled.

"Eat dirt! Eat dirt!" Pat chimed in with delight.

Carol and I glowered and groaned.

Saturday morning finally arrived! I threw on my play clothes, patted Eric's head, and bolted up the stairs to breakfast.

Before long Carol joined me. We lugged the large

cardboard box out of the laundry room, through the side door, and up the stone steps to the carport. Our fireplace! (With Mom's help, I had hacked away a hole in the center and charcoaled it black and dusty inside.) Clapping our hands clean, we leapt like gazelles back down the steps for more. Soon the stage was set: two orange sleeping bags for beds, a cardboard "table" with my doll's tea set, a hair brush, and a letter, plus Mom's old broom. Our pink foursquare ball I nestled among some ivy for the pumpkin – soon-to-be – coach. *Now for the mice.*

Back in the dugout I stared at the shriveled nubbins in the pie plate. They had shrunk! No longer pink, they looked stiff and wrinkled. *How did that happen?!* They smelled like old blood. I managed to avoid running into Mom on my slow trek back up to the carport.

"Eww…" Carol spat, wrinkling her nose. "Get rid of them!"

"No!" I cried, shocked. "I worked hard to get these!"

She grimaced while I set them down carefully beside the "pumpkin."

"Next, the 'audience'!" I crowed. We dragged four folding chairs up the long trail from the laundry room and placed them in two rows at the edge of the gravel.

"We really only need three," Carol remembered. "My Mom can't come."

"What!" I stared at her. "Doesn't she want to see you in a *play?!*"

"She forgot she and my Dad have to go somewhere," she said, shrugging. "It's ok."

"Well," I mused. "We'll put Biggie Bear on the fourth chair. He's almost as big as a person. After all, it has to be like a real audience!"

Revolving slowly, I surveyed our handiwork. The woods surrounding our little set seemed to nod its approval. I smiled with satisfaction.

"Costume time!"

Half an hour later, the motley crew of scalawags fidgeted around me. For once, though, they were all giving me their attention! I felt like Mom. Mike actually looked a little nervous and tugged at his scarf. Pat sucked his thumb, twisting a corner of his nightgown. Julie gazed quietly up at me, her head cocked, wearing her green pedal pushers and bright green cardigan. Mom's beret threatened to fall off her head at any moment. I shoved it back. Timmy hopped up and down in Dad's long black sport coat, the sleeves rolled up. Dad's Army hat with the visor bounced on his head.

"Stopp!" I whispered. "It'll fall off!" Sensing a strain of rebellion, I slipped the dinner cowbell into Tim's hand. "You get to call the audience, Timmy. Ring the bell!"

At the prearranged signal, Mom, Dad, Heidi and the babies poured out of the house below and trudged up the steps to our theatre-in-the-trees. Sparks of electricity coursed through my veins. *It's happening! It's happening!*

Carol, her Fairy Godmother costume hidden under her "royal messenger" raincoat, passed out the programs. As the usher, I pointed out their seats; Mom and Dad in the front with the baby (asleep) on Mom's lap; and Heidi in the back row with a firm hold on Eric (who had discovered his neighbor, Biggie Bear.)

"Sit down, Eric!" I hissed.

"Oh, Cathay – let him sit with the bear if he wants to," Mom prodded, turning around slightly.

I frowned. "He's supposed to sit on Heidi's lap."

Heidi leaned forward and patted my arm. "Don't you vorry, Cat-ay. I vill vatch him."

I stepped back to the center of the "stage" and flung my arms out to the sides. *It's time!*

"Attention!" I commanded. "Our show is about to

begin! It is the story of Cinderella. Now you must know that her mother died when she was little, and her father – who she loved very much – " my eyes wandered over to Dad who was nodding and smiling, making a little round "O" with his mouth. " – DIED," I glared at him, wanting him to stop that, "after he married my wicked stepmother." Dad instantly clapped his hand over his mouth and raised his eyes to the sky.

"Oh, yes – and *I* am Cinderella." I wheeled about and flounced offstage to the group huddled behind the nearest trees.

"Ok," I whispered. "YOU, Timmy – and YOU, Julie – stay hiding behind these trees until Carol waves her wand at the pumpkin and the mice." They nodded mutely. Carol stood guard over them.

"Mike and Pat – let's go!"

I marched out across the gravel, snatched up the broom and swept around the fireplace. My whole body hummed inside. "La, la, la," I sang. Mike and Pat clambered into the orange sleeping bags. Soon giant snoring sounds emerged. Then more. *Sweep, sweep. Sweep, sweep.* Still they snored. I began sweeping around them and "accidentally" tripped over Mike's bag.

"Oh, dear! I'm sorry, Stepmother!" I squeaked.

Mike sat up, enraged. "Get off me!" he yelled. "Or I'll step on *you!*"

"Oh, right away, Stepmother! Would you like some breakfast?"

"Yes! Bring me Hot Chocolate and Liver!"

I stared. "Liver for breakfast, Stepmother?" Mike liked liver and knew I hated it.

"Yes, of course. And you must eat it, too!"

I growled under my breath, but smiled and curtsied.

At that moment Patrick sat up and shrilled, "it's time to feed the snakes, Cinderella! Please get the mice for the

snakes!" I froze; then started to stamp my foot – *but no!*
Cinderella wouldn't!

"But I can't do that, Stepsister – they're-they're-
they're running away in the garden. Here, I'll brush your
hair for you," I offered. Seizing the hairbrush from the
cardboard table, I lunged towards him with my arm.

"Stop! Stop!" he commanded. "I'm most beautifuller
enough already. *You* need a bath."

Mike leaped up. "Where's my liver, Cinderella?!"

I glanced from one to another. Quickly I grabbed
the tray from the table and set it precariously on top
of Mike's sleeping bag. "Here's your liver and hot
chocolate, Stepmother."

Mike grabbed the little plate and spoon and thrust it
towards me. "You first, Cinderella. You must have your
vitamins."

Resisting a glare, I pretended to eat a bite and smiled
brightly, chomping away.

Patrick leaped back and forth over his sleeping bag.
"Make my bed, Cinderella! Make my bed!"

"But-but you're on it!" I protested.

"Make it anyway!" he crowed, as I attempted to pull
an edge of it forward, without success.

"I think it's time for the mail!" I beseeched, nodding
over at the clump of trees. Carol strode out and pushed
an imaginary button in the air.

"Ding-dong!" she warbled.

Mike mimed opening the door. "I'm sorry, we don't
want any," he announced in a nasal voice.

Carol thrust her arm out with the envelope, "Letter
from his Royal Highness," and ran off again.

Mike tore open the envelope, the letter itself ripping
in two. "Oops!" he giggled.

Irked, I poked him while I reached for the letter. "*I'll*
read it for you, Stepmother."

"No!" he wrenched away from me. Holding the two halves together, he frowned at the gold crayon squiggles. "You are invited to a Big Ball," he proclaimed.

"A ball?" Patrick piped up. "Basketball?"

"No!" I muttered; then smiled. "Stepsister, it's a big fancy dress party. With dancing."

"Oh. Are we going?" Pat asked.

"Of course we're going. We're *all* going – right, Stepmother?" I raised my eyebrows at Mike. I could feel the play dangerously close to dissolution.

"Not *you*, Cinderella," he smirked at me. "You're ugly. 'Sides, you have patches." He pointed to my costume.

"Yeah – you stink!" Pat cried delightedly. "You can't come with us!"

I spun about and collapsed in front of the fireplace, my arms wrapped around my head. "Then go! Go without me!" I sobbed. Peeking over my elbow, I spied them frowning at me, rooted to the ground. "Leave!" I hissed. I sensed a whirlwind of bodies as they flew around me on their way off stage.

"Yah! Yah! We're going to the Ball!"

"Whoopie! Whoopie!" A smattering of applause and audible giggles rose from the chairs.

I sobbed louder, hoping Carol would hear. A crunch of gravel nearby alerted me. I breathed a sigh of relief.

"Godchild, look up."

I raised my head. There before me stood Carol, her blonde braids undone, flayed out in zigzag wisps. A gasp escaped from the audience. I knew it must be Mom. Over Carol floated a filmy white negligee. Mom's. Dad chuckled.

"Don't cry," chirped Carol. "You can go to the Ball, too. Here –" she tapped me on the head with her long brown stick, covered in gummy stars (the ones that still stuck to it.) Then she dropped a bag on the ground behind me. While holding one of Mom's old kitchen curtains in front of me, she fluttered it back and forth... back and forth...

Meanwhile I tore off the rags. Stripped to my undershirt, I reached in the bag and stepped into Mom's full, white petticoat. Lastly, I wriggled my feet into the clear, gold-strapped high-heels we had bought at the dime store. Rising up, I took a tentative step on the gravel and nearly tumbled over. Carol's arm flung out to save me and the curtain dropped.

"It's beautiful!" I crooned. "But how will I get there?"

"Oh," she said. "Do you have any mice? And maybe a pumpkin?"

"Yes, yes!" I cried. "Over in the garden!" I pointed frantically at the all-important pie pan, afraid to move.

"Abbra Cadabbra!" Carol sang out, waving her wand in circles over the pink ball and mice. Nothing happened. Carol and I exchanged glances. *Uh oh! I forgot to figure that part out!*

In an extra loud voice I called, "Oh! What beautiful white horses! And a lovely pink carriage!"

Carol waved her wand again. "And now a coachman and a footman will appear!" She turned around and eyed the trees. Yet she didn't need to, because at that moment Timmy and Julie raced out onto the stage.

But Timmy did not stop there. Oh, no – he leaped into the audience, hopped up and down and crowed, "Look at me, Mommy! Look at me! I'm in the play! I'm the Coachman! I'm the Coachman!" Following his lead, Julie, at first frozen in one spot on the stage, scurried after him and climbed up on Dad's lap. Everyone laughed. Then the audience, in slow motion, it seemed, got up one by one and bent over, patting Julie and Timmy. They paid not the slightest attention to the stage. Mom hoisted the whimpering baby onto her shoulder.

Then she began to make her way across the edge of the gravel towards the stone steps. My jaw dropped. *They act like it's over!*

"Stop!" I cried. "Where are you going?!"

Mom looked up, surprised. Dad continued chuckling with Timmy. Heidi led Eric around the back of the chairs.

"It's not over!"

"Oh – you did a wonderful job!" Mom cooed, gazing behind her at the grownups and attempting to clap her hands. In uneven chorus, they nodded and echoed, with a smattering of applause.

I looked at Carol; she half-smiled, shrugged, and jerked her head towards the porch. "Wanna play cards?"

Mike and Pat had already disappeared, their voices whooping and hollering from down by the ravine.

I gazed about at the costume-strewn carport. Suddenly, old ragged cardboard boxes, dirty rumpled sleeping bags, and upside-down play dishes crystallized into view. Hard brown lumps glared at me from the old pie tin. Programs lay upside-down under the deserted chairs. I sighed.

"Naw. Better clean this up."

From the Horse's Mouth

Carol couldn't come. She said she would, but at the
last minute, ducked out. Or so it seemed. I trudged up
Smith Road towards the mansion at the top of the hill. I
could see just the tip of the roof peeking out between the
wavering eucalyptus leaves. I would be careful to sidle
alongside the gate without being detected. I didn't know
if anyone could see me passing or not, but I wasn't about
to take chances.

Today I would venture into the Smith stables…alone.

Last time Carol and I even clambered up on top of
"Silly" – that's the name we dubbed the smoky-black
Shetland pony. *He's just the right size!* I mulled over the
week's previous adventure. With one foot up on the
second fence board, I could throw my leg in the air and
straddle him. Once we'd coaxed him over to the fence,
that is! I could feel his warm, solid girth firm beneath me
even now. My feet quickened up the asphalt.

Today my plan involved something better. A carrot.

I glanced now at the treat in my hand. I had slipped
it out of the fridge and under my shirt without Mom
noticing. I didn't want to bother with explanations of
where I was going and why I needed a carrot. After
all, it was my adventure, wasn't it? The hill stretched
invitingly before me.

Besides, I'd ridden plenty of times. Didn't I have my
Girl Scouts' horsemanship badge? Carol and I and Troop
89 had trotted countless times 'round and 'round the
rancher's corral at the bottom of Tam Valley. The first
time I stepped into the stirrup and heaved my leg up – I

couldn't get it high enough to swing over his back! *I'm too short!* My cheeks burned while I stared at the velvet tufts of hair inches away from me. But Mr. Johnson shortened the stirrup and let me stand in his tobacco-stained hands to reach it. Finally I could stretch high enough to step into that stirrup on my own – and swing that other leg right up and over! I *loved* the powerful muscles that undulated *life* under me as we walked circles around the corral. (Trotting hurt, though!)

Now I would duplicate that performance on "Billy's" stable mate: "Daisy," the chestnut mare.

The road leveled out before me as I crested the very top of the highest peak in Tamalpais Valley. (Besides Mt. Tam, of course.) *Our* road. I scurried past the massive gates of the Smith homestead on marshmallow toes...

There before me spread the hay-strewn ramble of barns and fences with the unmistakable earthy aroma that peaked my nostrils. My pace quickened.

My feet drawled to a halt before the center stable – the way they always did. Above the half-doorway a signpost stated: REX. The only nametag on the ranch. In the pasture beside it the king of horses eyed me with an unblinking stare. His brick red form gleamed majestically. I gazed up at that regal figure towering just behind the fence. *So huge!* I lingered a moment, uncertain, the carrot weighing heavily in my hand. But with sudden resolution, I whispered, "Bye, Rex," and wheeled around towards the stable on the end.

They're waiting for me! Up ahead Billy's ears barely poked up past the top of the corral. But Daisy's head ambled backwards and nodded as I raced towards them. With glee I scrambled over the fence rail and plopped to the ground. *Mmph.*

"How're ya doin', Beauties?" I breathed. I threw my arms around Billy's neck and felt the angel-soft down of his mane on the underside of my wrist. He stumbled backwards in a kind of two-step. Then I released him and approached the chestnut mare. Suddenly she loomed a lot larger than my last memory!

"C'mere, Daisy," I whispered. I've got something for you." In my hand I gripped the carrot, the 'golden treat.' I raised it up and waved it back and forth.

"C'mere, Girl," I clucked. Her ears twitched. I backed slowly towards the fence. She clopped closer, her liquid eyes glued to mine. *She's so beautiful!* The rough boards now pressing against my back, I shifted and stared for the first time at the carrot in my fist. *How do I hold it?* I remembered on *My Friend Flicka* seeing Ken offering his horse sugar cubes on top of his flattened palm. I opened my right hand and laid the prized carrot across my splayed fingers. The mare was close now, so close, I reached up and patted her taut neck. A spasm rippled through me. *She's so alive!* Daisy snorted. Her head bent down; her great horse lips opened as she swooped towards the carrot. The hairs tickled – and then – razor-sharp pain zinged through my hand and brain as an ambulance siren shrilled above me! *Uhh-AAHHHuhhhh…*

I jerked my hand back, the carrot tumbling in two to the ground. *No. No siren; that sound was ME!* I shut my mouth and stared at my shaking hand. An inch-long gash grazed the flesh of my ring finger. Dark red beads lined the tear, then leaked languidly into each other, like pancake batter in the pan. The hairs on my neck quivered, shooting light currents across my back. *Oh, no!*

I looked up at Daisy. She whinnied and grunted, shaking her head. *Why did she do that?!* Suddenly the barns, pastures and stables sharpened and elongated, glaring and pulsating. *Get away! Get away!* they groaned. I wheeled around and tore down the road.

The eucalyptus blurred and streaked away from me, those favorite trees of mine now hissing and whispering: *you should've known; you should've known…*

Up the porch steps I stumbled and shoved my shoulder against the great front door. I pushed my way through the warm currents of the living room begging me to stay and burst into the kitchen. Mom calmly turned from the sink. "Cath –"

Her eyes fell to my hand, already dripping blood down my wrist.

"I – I'm sorry – " My eyes burned and the dam broke.

I didn't *know* I'd get stitches; I didn't *know* the doctor would call the SPCA, who called *Mrs. Smith.* And I certainly didn't know she'd have to keep "Daisy" locked up ("quarantined?") for 14 days!! We found that out when Mom answered the phone that evening – and it was…MRS. SMITH. Hopping mad.

Mom hung up the receiver and said, "I think you should go for a visit tomorrow and apologize."

Once again, I scaled the road towards the top. S-l-o-w-l-y, this time. I stared at the cracked asphalt as it slipped backwards under my feet. *What am I going to say to her?!* I swallowed, forcing my knees to bend and unbend.

At last I stood before the massive black gate, the ramrod bars prison-perfect with their long, sharp angles. *Maybe it won't open!* But already my eye spied the traitorous buzzer so conveniently located in front of me. My body rigid, I thrust my finger into its belly.

Slowly, without a sound, the gate swung open.

I tiptoed across the threshold and up the pebbled path to the vast verandah above. The screen door opened.

Mrs. Smith was expecting me.

A long swath of charcoal tweed ended in a beaded grey

sweater. A matching cloud of curls hugged her head.

"How do you do?" she intoned. "I'm pleased to see you." She nodded towards a white wrought-iron table nearby. "Why don't we sit on the verandah, shall we?"

Her head disappeared through the doorway behind her for a moment.

"Sarah," she muffled, "you may bring the tea outside."

I tugged on the scalloped white chair and sat, careful to keep my bandaged right hand in my lap. Across from me Mrs. Smith peered over the tops of her wire-rimmed lenses. "Cathy, is it?"

"Cath-AY."

"Cath-ay, then. So. We finally meet…"

I tried to smile, but my throat thickened and jammed. I ducked my head.

"Have a cookie."

I reached across the table and plucked up a white powdered cookie from the proffered plate. Steam wafted in a sinuous curl from my freshly-poured tea. Into its magnetic pull I willingly fell. Still, I could feel the weight of her eyes pressing against me. I squeezed a half-moon lemon slice into my gold-rimmed cup – just like Mrs. Smith had done.

"You have many brothers and sisters, do you not?"

Oh! I should say something about why I'm here. Why isn't she talking about it?! I glanced sideways across the table – my eye fixed on the crystal glimmer of sugar cubes in a cut-glass bowl. *Why, just like in "My Friend Flicka" - Oh!* My breath caught.

"Dear -?"

I looked up. Mrs. Smith pointed a pair of silver tongs at me with a sugar cube grasped in their teeth. "Sugar?" she smiled. (Or was it a leer?) At last I exploded.

"I – I'm sorry I – " my voice rasped. *Say it! Say it!* My chest hammered.

"Yes, dear?" Her eyebrows arched.

"I'm-sorry-I-climbed-in-your-stables-and-got-bit-and-and-got-your-horse-locked-up-for-it." My mouth clamped shut. Just then an ant scurried over the curve of the table. I followed its progress as it headed for the sugar. In silence Mrs. Smith stirred her tea. *Clink, clink. Clink, clink.* I could hear a sudden breeze pick up the eucalyptus. At last she spoke.

"Well. Thank you for telling me." Without warning she leaned across the table. Her eyes bore into mine. "You like horses, do you?"

I nodded, unable to move.

She pulled back. "Well. You are a very lucky little girl, let me tell you. If you had climbed over into *Rex*'s corral, you surely would've been killed. He is a breeding stud, and he would've trampled you."

The air stopped. Sound traveled as if under water. I swallowed. My tongue held tight to the roof of my mouth and clung there. Rex's deep liquid eyes swirled into focus before me. Majestic, godly Rex. The carrot weighing heavily in my hand...my hesitation...

Mrs. Smith's voice droned on in rolling tumbles of syllables. Then...silence. I sipped my tea. At last I looked up. She peered quizzically at me.

"Oh, uh, I promise never, *never* to go near your stables again."

Finally she smiled. "Don't worry, dear. But just remember: any time you'd like to see the horses, you give me a call, and I'll have my man Jake show you around."

Carefully I folded my napkin and eased off the iron seat. "Thank you for the tea and cookies."

Mrs. Smith rose and walked me to the screen door. "Any time, dear. I'm an old woman, and am mostly here all by myself. Please come visit me again."

"I – I – thank you," I squeaked. I inched myself off the porch, her eyes burning into the back of my head. I knew I would not be back.

My feet stalled each step against their will, holding, holding, till, at last, beyond the gate, I gave them free rein. *Fly! Fly!* With a whoosh and a kiss, the breeze lifted them up and propelled me down the slope – to freedom...

...And yet, from behind, did I hear a whinny? I shivered. Gradually it receded in the distance...until I could hear it no more.

Cathay (left end)

Public Display

The full bloom of September's First Friday Mass still upon us, we processed down to lunch, more solemn than usual. I stared at the white dress-uniform in front of me – only worn on special occasions - and reached up to touch my own. I stroked the red piping that ran along the sailor collar – *like railroad tracks!* – and fingered the scarlet bow beneath it. The white fabric itself felt pebbly under my fingertips. Somehow, it marked something indefinably special.

Our line had now snaked around the corner near the lower school's lunchroom, when an unmistakable stench billowed towards us. Sure enough, up ahead lay the characteristic layer of sawdust coating the polished hardwood floor. No need to ask why… Soon the entire chorus of new sixth graders groaned as one…*eeeuuwww!* The line halted.

"Why did it have to happen right next to the dining room?!" someone whispered.

"Yeah – couldn't they wait till they got *past* it?"

"Who WAS it?!"

"Must've been a Lower Form."

"Yeah – *had* to be some little kid."

400

"I heard it was a first grader," the voice behind me mumbled.

"Really?" I turned around.

Leslie nodded knowingly. "Susan heard when she was in the bathroom that one of them threw up in line – all over the back of the girl in front of her!"

A huge intake of air imploded around us.

"Oh my gosh!"

"No!!"

Instinctively we each tried to distance ourselves from the student behind us – then giggled.

"Imagine the face of the girl in front of her," I whispered. "All of a sudden – *blahh!* – all over her back!" I thrust my chest out, eyes and mouth popping wide in terror. My snorts brought on infectious giggles. I rolled my eyes at Cindy in front who peered back at me in mock horror.

"All over her white uniform!" she hissed.

"Yeah – *both* of them!" I snickered.

We shuffled forward while attempting to stifle our glee behind cupped hands. Just then the line dominoed.

"Watch out! I'm coming at you!" Leslie whispered wickedly behind me.

"*Aaaah!*" someone screamed.

"Girls! That will be enough!" commanded Mother Deming, patrolling the ranks. She raised her clicker over her head and gave it one sharp clack. As one, we held our noses and marched with exaggerated high steps past the incriminating sawdust.

The smell lingered in the corridor throughout the afternoon, meandering into our basement classroom. *Can't we ever get away from it?!*

Finally, with the pealing of the dismissal bell, I snatched my jacket from the infected cloakroom and hastened up the stairs to fresh air outside. *Ahhh…*

"Mom! Mom!" I exclaimed as I lugged my rubber-strapped books into the station wagon at the curb. "You won't *believe* what happened at school today!"

"Hurry, Cathay," she interrupted. "We need to get home right away." Without pause she peeled back into traffic. I threw my head around. The car seemed too empty.

"Wait!" I cried. "Julie's not here yet."

"No... She's not," Mom frowned. "She's already home, sick."

A slow free-fall at the pit of my stomach spread upward.

"What... do you... mean?"

"Poor thing," sighed Mom, "she threw up at school right after Mass, and I had to come pick her up."

I set my jaw as I stared, unseeing, out the window. *It can't be Julie! It can't. Not my little sister!*

The vision of Cindy, Leslie and I, and all the others howling with hoarse laughter now rose up to haunt me.

"Julie..."

Back home, I peeked through the crack in our bedroom door. There she lay in the darkened room, knees curled up towards her chin under the blankets, the telltale soup pot next to her head.

So. It was true. Biting my lip, I tiptoed into the room. "Julie?" Her eyes, wide open and glassy, now snapped shut. *Is she mad at me? Does she know - ?*

I tried to imagine this new face and tiny figure on top of my previous vision. Immediately I banished it. *No!* Julie was too shy, too timid, to have something so public assault her.

"Does your tummy hurt?" I whispered. She nodded her head once, then turned to face the wall.

"Are – are you okay?" I faltered. No response. "What happened?" I had finally asked the dreaded question. Silence.

"You can tell *me,*" I coaxed. The tangled head rolled back and forth, then stopped. I shifted from one foot to another. At last I slunk out of the room.

I did not sleep well that night.

"Hey, Cathay!" Cindy clutched my sweater as we pushed through the double doors for recess. Shrill cries of freedom filled the air.

"What?" I twisted away.

"That girl on Friday who threw up was your SISTER!" Her eyes bugged out.

Two other girls turned suddenly with interest and stared at me. A ball bounced past and disappeared. Screams and laughter intermingled from across the playground.

"Who told you that?" I glared.

"Barbara did – " She nodded towards the curly-top in the foursquare box.

"How would *she* know?" I retorted, but with sinking heart, for I knew…

We both gazed towards Barbara, who peered over at us. Her eyes widened as she nodded solemnly back.

Cindy responded, "Her sister Joanie."

…Joanie was Julie's best friend.

By now, Leslie, Jane and Janet had joined the clutch surrounding us. *What am I, a magnet?!* My mind roared. *Go away!*

"Hey, Cathay, is that true?!" pounced Leslie.

"Oh, gosh!" echoed through the throng.

Julie's stricken face wavered before me. I took a step towards Cindy and bellowed, "NO! It was NOT my

403

sister! It was someone else who *looks* like her!" My mind
grabbed at passing straws. "*Lots* of them are small! It
could be *anybody!*" My throat tightened and I drew a
breath. Everyone glanced at Cindy, then at the ground,
and, one by one, slipped away. Only Cindy remained.
She gazed at me out of the corner of her eye, raised her
eyebrow, and slowly nodded.

"Okay..." she said.

That afternoon after school I discovered Julie propped
up on top of the flowered bedspread, picture book in
hand. I sank down next to her.

"Watcha reading?"

"*Mmph.*" She thrust out her lower lip at the page;
then flipped back the cover so I could see it.

"Ohhh. 'Peter Rabbit'."

"Mmhm."

"Can you read it?"

Julie turned her head and eyed me with scorn.

"'Course I can!"

I smiled. She was feeling better already.

"Do you know what happened at school today?" I
ventured. Julie studied her book.

"I told all my friends that it wasn't you who got sick.
That it must've been someone else."

Julie's eyes darted up to mine. "Why?"

I shrugged. "I don't know. I mean, it could've been
someone else, right? *Lots* of people get sick. All the time."

Julie squinted at me.

"I mean," I chewed my lip and mused. "It could've
even been Joanie – who knows?"

A smile snuck up along the corners of my sister's mouth.

"Yeah," she giggled. "It could even happen to Joanie."
With that, I grabbed her with my tickle-fingers. She
squealed, and we rolled over on the bed together, images
of poor Joanie washing away the ills of our day.

The next morning after school Mass, I spied Cindy and Barbara hustling into the doughnut line. I wormed in under the bar along the counter and tapped Cindy on the shoulder. I cleared my throat. "Hey."

"Oh, hi." She looked surprised.

"Um, I was wrong yesterday. About Julie." I studied her sleeve. "You were right."

She grinned. "I know. So what?"

Barbara peered over Cindy's shoulder. "Yeah. Is she okay?"

I let slip out a longggg stream of air...

"Yeah, she's fine," I said. I grinned. "She even stuck her tongue out at me."

Then we all grabbed our 'twistie' doughnuts and chased each other, laughing, towards our chosen table.

Julie (center)

405

Un-Blessed Trinity

"In the name of the Father, and of the Son, and of the Holy Ghost..."

The vast, vacuous voice boomed from the sky. I gazed all around at the endless crowd on the fields of Golden Gate Park. Today I had joined the Carson family for San Francisco's "largest ever" religious gathering, a rally for World Peace.

Our voices droned on in unison, reciting the familiar prayers of the rosary. Spread out on sprawling parkland in the fog, hundreds of bodies huddled over clenched fists. Blotches of color – reds, blues, tans – sprang up here and there on blankets in the cool October air.

I fingered the white plastic beads in my lap. *They glow in the dark!* My wandering eye met Barbara's – she appeared not to notice, but reverently murmured on without missing a beat. I darted a glance at Cindy – the other "outsider" to the Carson family – and her eyes danced back. I smothered a giggle. Tonight the three of us would be sharing an overnight! *Just like the Blessed Trinity!*

Back again in their elegant Victorian home in Pacific Heights, we settled around the Carson's formal family dinner table. I wallowed in the superior knowledge of "knowing" Barbara's brothers and sisters (even Anne, a grownup!) – having stayed there before, while Cindy had not. After all, Robert was in Patrick's class, and Joanie was Julie's best friend. For once, *I* could be the "old-timer" – and not the newcomer.

But after dark, the tables turned. In the midst of us all lounging around the family room with *Father Knows*

Best, my left ear pricked up. A furiously whispered buzz behind stiff palms passed back and forth between Cindy and Barbara. Then, on tiptoe, they slipped out of the room. *What...?* I unfolded and slunk past the TV in pursuit, only to glimpse a hand tugging the bathroom door closed behind them, the lock snapping shut. I stood still. The whispering beyond grew to a heated mixture of moans and queries. I took a breath.

"Barbara?"

Silence.

"Cindy?"

I waited. At long last the lock slid back and the door cracked open; then flew wide as Cindy and Barbara slunk past me.

"You can go in now," Cindy mumbled as the two of them hastened down the hall and into Barbara's bedroom. The door slammed shut.

I stared after them. *What happened to Cindy?* Her eyes were puffy, her jaw set. I crept down the hall; then wavered outside the door. Their voices grew louder now.

"...What am I going to do?" Cindy's voice quivered. "I've never, ever missed a single night!"

"Let's talk to my Mom," Barbara murmured. I strained, but could hear no more.

Suddenly, I knew. In a flash, that first time at Cindy's enveloped me. We had ridden the elevator together up the modern apartment building: Cindy, her tall, stylish mother, and I. Entering her (very own) bedroom, I found myself surrounded by crisp white shelves, walls and windowsills. No dolls, no stuffed animals, no artwork to soften the lines. Instead, realistic, plastic horses of all sizes and colors decked out the room. I marveled at the differences between us as I wandered past the stark 'pastures.' Cindy pointed out the type of each horse as I poked its hard surface.

"...And THIS one is an Arabian stallion – which my father gave me a long, long time ago. It's my very favorite."

"Oh." I wondered if she still had a father. I knew she and her mother lived alone in that tiny apartment; that was the only time she had ever mentioned him.

Just then my eyes had fallen upon an odd bunch of lumps half-hidden between her pillow and the wall. A faint, faded face peered up from the threadbare cloth.

"Oops!" Cindy snatched up the bundle and stuffed it under her pillow. "You weren't supposed to see that."

"Oh – I don't mind."

Yeah, well, it's kind of private. I've had him as long as I can remember. Just don't tell anybody."

"Okay..."

...So THAT'S what the fuss is about! She forgot to bring her special 'friend' (whatever it is.) She's never slept without it – and NOW it's not here... I stared at the shut door. *But... but I know about it. She KNOWS I do. Why are they hiding it from me? BARBARA probably didn't even know about it!*

I swallowed. Slowly I twisted the knob – then strolled in past them to the cot with my pajamas on top. I turned back to them – just as they hustled toward the door.

"Where are you going?" I blurted.

"Oh, uh, Cindy forgot something," Barbara halted. "We'll be right back."

I sank down on the cot and dangled my legs. *Was I supposed to be invisible?* The light overhead glared back at me. I got up and flicked it off, then sat back down in the dark. The close quiet of the room was broken only by the muffled voices beyond, urgently mingling with the deeper tones of Mrs. Carson...

Ding-dong!

"Goodness! Who's ringing at nine o'clock at night?!" bellowed Mr. Carson from the den.

I swung wide the bedroom door and stood at the top of the stairs. Far below, Cindy and Barbara raced towards the big oak door and yanked it open, accompanied by Mrs. Carson. They disappeared onto the porch. I slumped on the top step, chin in hand, and waited.

Moments later, Barbara and Cindy galloped up the stairs from below, Cindy clutching a precious bundle, Barbara clapping her on the back with a conspiratorial chuckle of delight. They drew up short upon seeing me; then Cindy ducked behind Barbara as the two of them stumbled past me up the last step.

"Oh, hi – be right back," Barbara called. I leaped to my feet after them and peered through her doorway.

...Just in time to see Cindy stash her bundle under the pillow of the twin bed she had claimed for the night. Barbara leaned over and whispered something in Cindy's ear. Cindy collapsed on the bed in fits of laughter.

I wondered if they even knew I was there. Slowly I pulled on my pajamas and crawled between the loosely laid covers of the cot.

"Lights out!" called Mrs. Carson.

Somehow, I didn't feel like whispering in the dark. I lay there and waited for their voices to fade.

I guess we weren't like the Blessed Trinity, after all.

Unholy Ghost Writer

Tongue between my teeth, I popped a fresh ink cartridge into my fountain pen. *Darn!* Hastily I soaked up the errant drops that had slipped onto the margin of my paper. *I wonder if Cindy will mind…*

Never till this year had I ducked into study hall before school. Never before had I missed morning Mass (and the hot chocolate and doughnuts!) to do homework instead. (Though we were often late for Mass, it was 'optional' – that is, unless you wanted *doughnuts* afterward!)

I glowered at the blank page before me. This time it was someone *else's* paper – and not mine! Now that we were in sixth grade, we had to write a weekly one-page composition for English class on any topic. Cindy had persuaded me to write a *second* composition each week in her name – because I was "the better writer." I would hand it over to her complete; she wouldn't even need to write her name on it (because the handwriting would have to match.) Of course I would disguise *my* handwriting - and she would turn it in.

This was the third one so far. I screwed my eyes tight and wrapped my foot around the leg of the chair. *How 'bout…horseback riding at Camp Winnamukka…* Once begun, the words poured onto the page as Cindy 'galloped down the dusty trail, hair flying in the wind…'

At last I tossed down the pen and slouched, my hand limp. With a glance at the clock, I scanned the completed story. *Hmm…I like this one* better *than the one I did last night…but this sounds more like Cindy than 'losing our dog down the ravine.'* Heaving a sigh down to my toes,

I slipped the paper into Cindy's desk. Then I scurried around to my own and waited.

I stared at that desktop, boring a hole with my eyes right between the lines of grain. *I do NOT want to do this...Why did I say yes? ...Because I didn't want her to stop liking me. She was starting to talk to Jane all the time, and not me. But now she's following me around instead ...because I'm writing her compositions!*

I stiffened, and held my breath. *But no more!* With a flourish I ripped off a half-piece of binder paper and snatched up my pen.

"Dear Cindy, (I wrote)

I'm sorry, but I can't write any more compositions for you. I've written three already and that's enough. From now on you need to write your own.

Your friend,

Cathay"

By now girls had begun trickling in. Mother Deming soon followed and heaved herself up to her platform desk. I threw open my desk and, under cover, finished folding the note. *No time to give it to her now... I'll pass it to her on the way to Prîmes...*

Library time! I surged forward at the head of the line through the dark double doors. Miss Mathé nodded and smiled at us as we filed past her desk. *Now I can finish "The Clue of the Velvet Mask"...*

Without warning Cindy jostled me from behind and shoved a crumpled note into my hand. I glanced over my shoulder as she marched off to the far corner table and plopped down. I pulled out the chair in front of me and wedged in, with just enough room to unfold the note in my lap.

411

"Dear Cathay,
I tore up your note. I don't ever want to be
your friend any more. You know I can't do those
compositions. You can, and you said you would do it for
me. Now you've changed your mind and I HATE YOU!!!
Your NOT friend,
Cindy"

Afraid to glance her way, I folded it up and stuck
it inside my book. I swallowed; then buried my face
between the pages of Nancy Drew. The words blurred
a moment. I gritted my teeth and slipped into the
Costume Party with Nancy, George, and Bess...

Up the back stairs in the tiny third floor classroom, I
leaned over my right-handed desk, my left elbow flailing
in the open air. *Why don't they make left-handed desks?!*
Carefully I copied the English diagram from the board.
With a sharp rap, the door to the right swung open and
Mother Deming burst in.

"Excuse me, Miss Knight," she muttered, "but I need
to see Cathay and Cindy immediately."

Cindy and I exchanged glances from across the room.
Did she know about our compositions? My head filled with
angry ants; my mouth sucked dry. Miss Knight raised an
eyebrow and cocked her head at us.

"You may go, girls."

With leaden feet, Cindy and I followed the nun out
onto the stairwell. She turned to face us on the cramped
landing, her back to the classroom door. The ruddy face
behind the rimless glasses bulged out of her bonnet.
Between her thumb and index finger she dangled an all-
too familiar fold of paper. Cindy's note.

My breath stopped. I didn't dare look at my cohort.

"This note," Mother boomed, "was discovered on

the floor of the library." (Cindy poked me from behind.) "I was *horrified* to see this from a Child of the Sacred Heart." *…Because we were passing notes??...Because I wrote compositions for Cindy?*

Mother Deming unfolded the note and thrust it before our eyes.

"What is *your* impression of this?"

I tried to re-read it, my brain frantically shutting down.

"Uh…that we shouldn't pass notes?"

Mother impatiently shook her head. Cindy remained silent.

Leaning into our faces, Mother Deming drew her thick finger along the offending line: 'I HATE YOU!!!' She eyed each of us without a word, waiting.

Through the ringing silence I could make out the English lesson's muffled murmurs behind the door, continuing as calming as before…

"Well?!"

I snapped back at attention.

"Is this what we teach here?!"

"N-no, Mother."

"No, Mother."

I turned to Cindy. "But-but…she didn't really *mean* 'HATE' – DID you, Cindy?" (Cindy shook her head, eyes down.) "It's just…an expression. It's just… something to say."

Mother Deming puffed up; her eyes flamed. "NO ONE should EVER 'use that expression.' I am so ashamed, and shocked. I want both of you to stay after school and write an essay on 'What it Means to be a Child of the Sacred Heart.' You may go back to class."

We turned toward the door and froze, while listening to the echo of her footsteps down the circular stairs. At last, silence.

413

Cindy rounded on me. "You idiot!" she hissed. "Why did you drop that note?!"

"Me?! *You're* the one that wrote 'I HATE YOU!!!' Now we're *both* in trouble for what *you* wrote!"

Our words hung in the air a moment, as we stood there and gazed at the floor.

"Are you going to write this essay for me?"

I bit my lip at her shoe…and shook my head. Then I heard a click. Cindy had turned the knob and without a word, the two of us trudged back into the classroom.

Back at morning Mass again with my sister and brothers, we managed to make it to school in time to earn hot cocoa and doughnuts. I no longer wrote compositions for Cindy.

Instead, she pattered happily after Jane.

The *New,*
New Baby

'*T*hree *days after Christmas, and Mom's baby* still *isn't here!'*
Now many months after that, I lay across my bed,
my diary clutched to my chest, as those long-past days
washed over me… ✍

I had hoped it might be born on *my* birthday
(December 3), but Mom had said that would be too early.
Then we all grew more and more nervous as Christmas
drew near – and *still* no baby. We certainly didn't want
Mom to miss Christmas! (Who would be Santa? I knew
Dad couldn't do it. He'd never remember where she'd
hidden all the presents!) Of course I, at the ripe old age
of ten, and the oldest of six then, knew the whole scoop
on that holiday.

'Anyway, Mom better have that baby sister *soon,'* I
had grumbled.

Of course I had known it was a girl. Didn't we already
have four boys in the family? With only one sister, it
just made sense that God would be on the side of equal
distribution. He and I had discussed this point every
night before I fell asleep. I knew he agreed with me.

That Saturday morning I had stumbled upstairs
from my basement bedroom into the kitchen. Heidi
leaned over the high chair and scrubbed Eric's oatmeal-
encrusted face. *That's funny. Mom usually does that.* But
she was not in sight.

"Cat-hay, your Mummy and Daddy just left for da
hospital. You're going to haf dat new baby brodder or
sister real soon!" she exulted.

"SISTER," I corrected her. She smiled knowingly. "Sister, den."

I feigned nonchalance as I slurped my bowl of Wheaties; then bolted out the basement door to freedom.

The eucalyptus trees waved and beckoned. Up the dirt path I skipped into the side woods. Slowly creeping up my spine, now faster, flew a menagerie of baby butterflies. I bent down, smiling at the nasturtiums at my feet.

"Today's the day," I whispered, "I get my own baby sister!"

Little Julie was all right, but at age five, she just didn't always cooperate in my more "sophisticated" role-playing games. And anyway, like I said, we were already outnumbered.

The hours dragged by. Later that afternoon Heidi had offered to wash my hair in the kitchen sink – a ritual Mom usually reserved for Dad, and sometimes Mike. *(Why does he get special treatment, anyway?)* Anything to distract my attention from the crawling hands of the clock.

Ah! The flash of waterfall cascaded over my down-turned head. Warm and comforting it flowed, like a continuous curtain.

Dingling - Ling! Heidi stopped and marched across the linoleum to the telephone on the wall.

"Hello?" she lilted. "Yes, Dr. Gunn! How's Mrs. Gunn?"

I held my breath.

"A boy! Dat's vunderful!" she exclaimed.

A cold, steel-edged finger slid down my spine. *A boy! There must be some mistake! I can't have another - BROTHER!* I stared, horrified, at the silver drain basket in the pink porcelain sink.

An hour later Dad had arrived home wreathed in smiles. "Grab your jackets! We're off to see your new baby brother!"

I gawked at him, incredulous. Missing my meaning

completely, he hustled us all out the door and into the station wagon.

I stared straight ahead on that half-hour drive. At last the car swung into the hospital parking lot. Lurching to a halt, Dad craned around and beamed, "Let's go!" I hunched myself down in the seat, determined to meld into the vinyl upholstery.

"I'm NOT going!"

Dad gazed quizzically at my stone-set face. Deciding not to fight it, he bundled the rest of the gang out.

"I'll tell Mom you said 'hi'."

I bowed my head and pouted, my jaw set. *They wouldn't understand. Babies, babies, babies. Always babies.*

Moments later I heard a muffled tap high above outside the car. Glancing up at the many rows of windows, I caught sight of a flutter from one several floors up. There stood Mom, smiling beatifically, waving at me. With one swift, exaggerated motion, I jerked my head around and refused to look at her. *It's all her fault! She needs to know that.*

Slowly, over the next few days I thawed a little. At Mom's homecoming, we had all gathered around Mom and Dad's big bed to watch her change the baby.

"Look at his little toes!" Patrick chortled. We all crouched closer for inspection. Just then a perfect arc of streamlined liquid pierced the air....and splashed poor Patrick right in the face! He squealed. The rest of us howled. That was the best moment so far.

Next to that, his name gave him a redeeming quality. "Peter Gunn," named after that detective TV Show Mom and Dad watched. *He'll be famous. I suppose that counts for something.*

Gradually, over the next few weeks, although I chose not to refer to him by name, I had begun to accept Peter into our household. I mean, after all, I had no choice. I forgave Mom.

But God and I had a falling-out.

Now, some ten months later, Peter has just begun to crawl. This afternoon each of us puttered at our own favorite pastime. Up and down the stairs Mike and Pat crouched over their strategically placed toy soldiers. Dad poured over his medical journals in his favorite chair in the den, while Julie sprawled on the couch, buried in her picture books. Eric sat on the kitchen floor, happily banging on pots and pans, totally oblivious to my need to read the comics. Mom, balancing a monumental pile of laundry, strode past me and into her bedroom.

All of a sudden she let out a shriek. "Walt!"

I marveled as a part of me noted I'd never seen Dad move so fast. (Usually he took about five minutes before he complied with her requests.) I darted after him.

There was nothing to be seen. But Mom, her face white, pointed to a gaping hole in the floor where the heater grating should be. Four-and-a-half-year old Timmy had pried it up with his usual curiosity and tossed it aside.

"Peter!" Mom cried. "He's slipped down there!"

With a dash, Dad raced down the basement steps to the furnace room, his entourage in tow. There stood a monstrous blue metal air cylinder right next to the furnace. My heart pounded. Where was Peter?! We could hear his high-pitched screams. *Where is he? Where is he?!*

Mom knocked on the big blue box. "It's ok, Peter, we're coming," she tremored. *We are?!*

Dad then grabbed some clippers from a nearby toolbox. *But how can he cut through metal?!* I then noticed a twelve-inch strip of cardboard belting the cylinder two-third's of the way up the tower. Relentlessly Dad sawed and hacked until he had torn a huge hole in it. He grabbed a stepladder and reached down in the hole, with Mom murmuring sweet sounds all the while to the wailing baby within.

"I can't reach him," Dad barked. "Mike – get up here quick."

Before I knew what was happening, Dad had propelled Mike up the ladder, flipped him upside down into the opening, and dangled him inside by the ankles with only his feet showing. Little lightning streaks zapped all through my body.

"Don't drop me!" Mike shrieked.

"It's all right. I've got you," Dad called steadily. "Grab Peter's arms."

I closed my eyes and stared along with Mike down into the darkened hole. A tiny glowing face seemed tilted up at me, eyes wide and frantic. "It's ok, Peter," I quavered. With a long stretch I felt Mike swing his arms until they met up with his. *Did his hands grip around those tiny arms?* I opened my eyes. Dad slowly tugged them upward.

I gasped. "He's too heavy!"

"Hang on tight, Mike!" Dad commanded. With one swift jerk he yanked them up and over the edge to fresh air – and safety. Peter, plastered with a thick coating of fuzz, collapsed into a handful of bodies clamoring to sooth the sobbing infant. I crumpled in a heap behind them, shaking. Silent tears streamed down my cheeks.

"Peter…" I whispered to the shadows. *I'm so sorry, God.* Gradually I crawled into the fray…

…My pen poised now over the page, I sat up suddenly on my bed and attacked the diary with sure, bold strokes. "My…New…Baby…Brother," I wrote.

Peter had, at last, become a real boy.

The family at Heidi's Wedding Day, April 1961:
Daddy, Eric, Mommy, Peter, Heidi
Julie, Patrick, Timothy, Michael, Cathay

TreeHouse Blues

"Oh, Jo, this is a perfectly *splendid* spot for hiding out!"
I cooed. "Meg and Amy will never guess where we are!"
I turned to Carol in her black snood and long-ruffled
frock. On this Thanksgiving weekend we sat cross-
legged (under our 'old-fashioned' skirts) on the floor of
Mike and Pat's treehouse.

"It'll make a terrific place for spying on Laurie,"
nodded 'Jo.' "Don't you think so, Beth?"

I stared off between the branches, trying to imagine
what 'Laurie' looked like.

Just then a deep *rumble, rumble, screech!* broke through
the eucalyptus. I waited. Branches snapped; leaves
crumbled under heavy boots, now approaching.

"Well, hallo, my favorite little girls!" A long, craggy
face grinned up at us from below. Tom Merrill – our
family electrician and carpenter. "My, my!" His eyes
rolled sideways. "So today you're playing dress-up!"

I forced a smile and shrugged. I didn't want to
be mean. But we were *not* playing "dress-up!" That
sounded so – babyish. *We are real people! We really* are
the *"Little Women."* In a week I would turn eleven, and
I didn't want any suggestion that I was "only playing."
As much as I liked old Tom – I knew he just wouldn't
understand.

From behind his back he produced that tell-tale pink box.
Doughnuts! "Before I give these to your Mama, why don't
my pretty girls choose their favorite?" Guiltily, I plucked up
the glazed old fashioned and flashed a real smile.

"Thanks, Tom!"

"Yeah, thanks, Mr. Merrill!"

While I munched from my lofty perch, I watched his

retreating figure shrink smaller and smaller. At last it disappeared onto the porch.

"Okay, Carol – follow me!" With a grasp of our skirts, we scrambled down the rungs hammered into the trunk of the old eucalyptus tree. I eyed the back of our house, measuring that great gaping distance between it and us. No one else in sight.

"Go!" I cried. We took off. Adrenaline pumping, I shuffled my feet through the leaves and dirt, enjoying the *swish, swish* of the long skirt against my legs. At last we rounded the back corner of the house and sidled along the outside wall of the dugout basement. I could feel its cool roughness through the bodice of my dress. I breathed deeply and stared out at the endless ravine before us. Nothing else to see from there but that wild tangle – and no one to see *us. Good!*

"Okay," Carol said. "Now it's time to switch. You be Amy, and I'll be Meg."

"No! That's boring. Amy's selfish, and Meg is – is too grown-up." (Really, I wanted to be Jo. But Carol always claimed her.) "Besides. We have to plan our treehouse. *Our* treehouse. *Jo* would want a treehouse. *Not* Meg or Amy. And Beth, too." Beth would go anywhere for Jo.

"Oh, all right. Where?"

I motioned for Carol to follow me into the dugout. Our heads bent, we wormed our way through the cramped quarters. In the narrow space between two dirt walls lay my stash. I proudly pointed. Several rough boards peeked out, left over from the treehouse that cousins Jimmy and Billy built. Next to them lay a box of large nails I had snitched over time while Tom Merrill labored over the boys' built-in bunk beds.

I had the perfect plan. I could see it in my mind. A place where no one could find us. A place all our own.

"We'll build it tomorrow," I whispered. "In the ravine."

But the next day I waited in vain. When Carol did
not show up, I meandered up and down the rambling
garden through the nasturtiums and wild roses. Mike
and Pat had taken off down the hill to meet the mail
truck by the community row of mailboxes... without
me. I knew they would get a free ride from the driver all
over the mountain. I watched them wander off together,
a complete unit, shuffling through the underbrush and
chuckling. Abruptly I turned. Alone again, I fingered the
pink and purple fuchsia blossom that brushed against
my shoulder. *What a pretty ballerina you are!*

I stood perfectly still. The air hung heavy with tiny
sounds. A bird chirped, far away. An answering *caw,
caw* sliced through close by. I closed my eyes. Overhead
a propeller plane droned...quieter now, as it seemed to
slowly ease away. Somewhere a lone dog barked. Then
stopped. A sudden loud *buzz* assaulted my left ear. My
eyes flew open. A fat, furry bumblebee crawled inside
the wide-open rose beside me. I glared at it, and moved
on. *Where IS Carol, anyway?!*

Back inside the house, I closed the glass door to the
den behind me, then picked up the telephone on Dad's
desk and dialed. "Where ARE you?!" I grumbled into
the receiver.

"Oh," crackled Carol's voice. "I can't come over
today. We're going to my grandmother's."

"But...what about our *plans?*"

"Well, we can do it some other time, I guess."

I sighed. Carol had been less and less available lately.

Shoulders slouched, I shambled out into the living
room. I could hear Julie and Timmy playing house
outside. I tiptoed onto the porch and peeked over the
adobe wall.

"Mother, I'm home!" Timmy cried, lugging the old
plastic doctor's kit. Julie, wearing Mom's apron, sat on

the ground and stirred her pot with an old spoon. Just like I used to do.

Timmy sniffed. "What's for dinner?'

"Indian soup."

"Oh, good."

"So, go get one."

I ducked back inside and wandered downstairs. *I wonder where Quagie is…*

Quagie. I have no idea why Eric got that nickname. One day on the drive home from church, Pat popped his thumb out of his mouth and said, "His name is Quagie." Two-year old Eric grinned up at him. "Why Quagie?" I asked. "I dunno. It just is." And thus he became an overnight Quagie.

I reached the bottom landing.

"…And so tonight will be your first night in your new room!" Mom enthused. I peered around the corner into Heidi's old bedroom. There stood Mom, changing baby Peter on the bed, with Eric dutifully attending.

"Tonight?" I blurted. I knew Eric would eventually share a room with the new baby…some day. Heidi had gotten married and moved out. But I was unprepared for this. Mom wheeled around.

"Why, hello there! Yes. I think it's time. He's too big to still be in a crib in your room," she smiled. "Now that Timmy has a new built-in bunk bed with Mike and Pat, Julie should be back with you!"

"But I want Quagie!" I looked at Eric – *my* baby. Mom had hers. Quagie was *mine*. I changed his diapers (well, for bedtime now…) I got his jammies on. And I sang him his songs when he woke up at night…that is…when he *used* to…

"Quagie," I entreated. "Don't you want to stay with me…in OUR room?"

Eric grinned, then bolted past me into the hall. He

stopped long enough to glance back at me with a giggle, then scrambled out the side door into the yard.

"Wait!" I cried.

He slowed down at the cobbled path, turned and waited. Standing there in his plaid cowboy shirt and brown corduroy overalls, he didn't look so much like a baby. *Well, maybe he isn't! He's my special little brother!*

I caught up with him. "Hey, Quagie. Do you want to go for a walk with me?" He reached up and took my hand. I squeezed his fat fingers and led him up the steps to the road above. We scuffed our way along the edge through the damp debris from the eucalyptus trees.

"We can go down to that bend in the road," I told him. "I'll show you the funny white rocks you can see from there that are *very* far away." At that, he pulled back.

"No!" he pouted. "Don't want to go far away!"

"Oh! No, Quagie! I mean the *rocks* are far away. They're on another hill. But we can see them from here... that is, from just down the road there." I pulled ever so slightly. "Come on, Quagie. We can see through the trees! You'll like it!"

Mike, Pat and I had often stopped along the bend and squinted at the view, trying to guess just what those white shapes on that far-off hillside might be. But that was awhile ago. They had each other now. And Julie had Timmy. Mom had Peter. So Quagie was mine!

I crouched down before him and gazed into his elf-like face. He was not smiling now.

"We're buddies, Quagie! Let's have an adventure!" I stroked his arm. His face crumpled.

"No!" Eric lunged away from my grasp and clambered back up the hill towards the house.

"Wait, Quagie, wait!" I stood rooted to the ground and felt him evaporating before my very eyes. *Who do I have now? Nobody. I'm ALONE.*

I trudged back up the hill.

I stood a moment below the front porch as Eric disappeared inside. The trees rustled in the wind. My teeth hardened against each other. The breeze wrapped itself around me and tried to loosen my sweater. But I would not let it in. I was hard, hard as a telephone pole. Gently, then, it began whispering. *Now, now it's time... now it's time...* An electric current snuck up my spine and snaked its veins into my chest and arms. *YES!* I didn't need Carol! I didn't need Mike or Pat, Julie or Timmy to be my buddy – I didn't need Quagie! It was time to be ME.

I could keep still no longer. With sudden resolve, I pushed off and wheeled around the corner of the house to the dugout door.

Inside, I surveyed my stash. Grabbing up the three largest boards, I struggled till I could balance; then strode out the door and down the path with my load into the ravine.

It was harder than I had imagined. The boards kept sliding from one side to another, threatening to leap out of my arms altogether. Tangled weeds snared my feet and nearly tripped me up. I finally figured out how to lift each foot high enough to outwit those traps.

Now let's see...which way did I take before...?

I had to make sure I shunned the blackberry brambles. They snarled and snapped along side of me as I ventured deeper into the ravine. Without warning, a claw full of thorns ravaged my arm and sent the boards flying into the air. I stumbled backward; then threw myself sideways to the ground as the angry bush leered towards me. I sat there a moment, hands stinging as I eyed my fallen bounty. *This is NOT working!*

I grunted to my feet and gritted my teeth. One by one,

then, I dragged those boards through the underbrush till I finally found my special tree.

It was a beautiful tree. It swooped upward with easy curves high above for climbing. Two big branches splayed outward from the trunk in a horizontal 'V' – perfect for the floor of a treehouse.

Energized, I dropped the last board and pounded the earth through the brush, all the way back home for my final load.

Laden with one more board, several small strips of wood, Mom's hammer, and the box of nails, I plodded off again into the ravine.

This time I marched forward, sure I knew the way. I had a treehouse to build! No stupid brambles could stop me now! If they pulled at me, I yanked defiantly back. I felt nothing, but the task at hand. So close I could smell it! The air up high, the wood as it splintered with the drive of the nails…

I stopped short. Out of nowhere, where before I faced only trees, a vast canyon gaped before me, flanked by sheer reddened cliffs. Rays of sun bounced off those walls rising from the cavern. It was *huge!* An icy chill crept up my back. This didn't belong here! Where was I? *How did I get here? Is this the Twilight Zone?!*

I had seen my first ever episode when I spent the night at Dottie's house last year. Her family had six children – all running willy-nilly till we sat down together to watch "the scariest program ever." Now I was inside of one!

I felt a lump at the back of my throat, threatening to explode out the top of my head and send me shrieking in circles. *No! I can't do that. Maybe I'm lost – but it can't be the Twilight Zone! Don't think – don't think…* I averted my gaze. *Don't look at it. Turn around. Walk back; walk back… into the trees…* I retraced my steps, like Nancy Drew would do. *Try this way...now that way...* Each turn, I knew, would take me farther away from that monstrous cavity rising up to the sky.

At last I wended my way back through the eucalyptus, until I saw it – first my stash of dropped boards – then my big beautiful tree.

I knew just what to do. After all, I had watched big Jimmy and Billy swing the hammer for Mike and Pat.

First I pinched a nail on top of a strip of wood that I held against the tree trunk. After a few slips, I managed to hold it with one hand while I slung the hammer with the other. That hammer was heavy! But I couldn't stop now!

Many tears later, I stood back and gazed. Five steps marked their way up the trunk for my ladder. Yes! It was really happening! Faster now, I climbed those rungs and heaved each board across the big branches of the 'V.' The nails cooperated this time, as I aimed straight down toward the ground. At last they were in!

With a grunt I stood up on my new floor and tossed that old hammer through the leaves. I watched it sail silently in the air till it landed on the ground below with a resounding *thud*.

I did it! I did it!

I held on to the branch above and gazed from my celestial perch. The air did feel different up here – cool as it prickled my skin. It smelled greeeen and clear... The sound of the leaves whispering above my head surrounded me and lifted me up like the sea. I floated, weightless. Under my feet the floorboards quivered ever so slightly, as the branches swayed. That tremor shot right through me.

It's alive! It's alive! And the tree is ME! I am part of it!
We are free!
Up in the air! Where no one can find us!
And we are bigger than any other!
Because we fill...the...WHOLE...SKY!

Postscript
December 1961

Screeeech! The baby beige Fiat lurched to a halt in front of me. Abandoning the chattering students lined on the curb, I wrested the door open and climbed inside. Dad's dimpled face beamed over at me.

"Glad you could make it!"

I beamed back.

Last night Dad had casually mentioned, now that I was in the sixth grade, we needed to spend some extra time together – apart from the "younger gang." He and I would go on a "special date" after school – just the two of us. It would be a surprise.

Maybe we'll go to the movies! "Parent Trap" – with Hayley Mills as twins! I snuggled into the car seat, anticipating the huge Technicolor screen...

..."Oh, no-o...not a movie," Dad mused. He shoved the stick shift forward. "Let's go get a Coke."

Disappointed, I sighed, and stared out the window. Weaving his way up and down hills, in and out of traffic, at last Dad pulled up alongside a massive building with gleaming gold doors. A man dressed in a natty blue cap and uniform, laced with a double row of gold buttons, unlatched my door and offered his hand.

"Good afternoon, miss," he tipped his head, "Welcome to the Fairmont Hotel."

"Dad!" I whispered on the curb. "Why are we here?!"

"Wait and see."

Through the revolving glass doors we whirled. A lobby of deep reds and autumn browns rolled out across the marble before us. Rich mahogany tables with Tiffany glass lamps, brocade loveseats and wing-backed chairs spread sumptuously across the Oriental rugs. We sauntered right through this luxury and down the hall to the elevators. The double doors slid open. We stepped... into a glass cage! Without a sound the cool, airy capsule whisked up in the sky...

"Dad, we're *outside!*" I shrieked in a whisper.

"Yup," he grinned.

We peered out of the bubble as my stomach lurched downward. Bushes and cars slipped rapidly beneath us. People on the sidewalks shrank into puppets. Across the street loomed another tall, white building with lots of windows and flags on the roof.

"That's the Mark Hopkins Hotel," observed Dad. My head spun a bit as the rows of dark rectangles zoomed downward. Suddenly we gazed eye to eye with those fluttering flags...then they were gone!

"We're even higher!" I gasped.

"Yep. And here we are."

Ding! The elevator doors slid to the side. Soft music tinkled towards us. Stepping out, our feet sank into creamy white carpet beckoning onward.

"What is this place?" I murmured.

"A place for you and me to get a drink."

Directly ahead of us a mirrored bar curved around a band of white-coated men.

"It's a *bar!* I can't go in here – can I?"

"Sure you can – come over here…"

Once seated at the tiny table I turned and gaped out the wrap-around window. The sky seemed to reach out to me, unimpeded. I gazed slowly downward.

"Look! *Look!* The streets are black ribbons! The cars are like *toys!* …They move so slowly…"

Dad chuckled. "So how about a Coke?"

I perused the drink menu. "A Coke is *seventy-five cents?!* They're only supposed to be a dime!"

"Ah," nodded Dad. "Well, now. Look back out the window." I wheeled around, placed my hands on the glass and gazed. Something was not right…

"What happened to that hotel with the flags on it? It's not here any more!"

"Look way over to your left."

I squinted, my cheek brushing the window. "How'd it get over…*Oh!* Dad! We're MOVING!"

Dad's smile soaked into his words.

"You get what you pay for."

Dad raised his amber-colored drink towards me with a twinkle. I grasped my icy-cold glass and held it aloft, tiny water droplets slipping onto my fingers. The sunlight through the windowpane shimmered off the crystal. *So grown-up!* We clinked.

"You know, I was thinking," mused Dad. "How would you like to go Christmas shopping with me sometime?"

"Me?!"

"I could use a little help…"

❦

*Rumble, rumble...clackity-clack...vrooommm...honnkk!...
jingle, jingle... jingle, jingle...*A wash of downtown
sounds splashed over me. A tingle spread up my spine
and stayed there. Christmas shopping with Dad – *just
me, alone!* He and I had ventured into the heart of the Big
City to search out Mom's Christmas present.

Stopped at the crosswalk, I gazed into the crowd,
unseeing... Dad didn't know it, but I had brought my
own money to buy Mom a gift. *Thank goodness for my
allowance. Twenty-five cents a week.*

I *had* been saving for another Madame Alexander doll.
My first one I re-named "Nancy Drew." She had cost
me a whole three dollars. Lately I'd been saving to get a
"George." But now, I had better plans...

Cars puttered by, too many to zoom quickly. Tinsel
and lights glittered across storefronts. Hordes of
shoppers clogged up the huge sidewalks, halting our
progress. I hurried forward and touched Dad's arm.

"Where shall we go, Dad?"

"How about right here?"

I paused and stared up at the elegant white
colonnaded building. "CITY OF PARIS" the gilded
letters proclaimed. *Ooh! That sounds fancy!* Slipping
through the rounded glass entry, I stopped short. There
before us towered a gargantuan Christmas tree. It
seemed to stretch and grow before our very eyes – *just
like in the "Nutcracker"!*

"*Dad!*"

He pointed upward. "Check it out." The tip of the tree
seemed to graze the roof several stories above. Life-sized
dolls floated effortlessly among the shiny glass balls. A
red wagon somehow clung firmly to its branch...and
even a tricycle! As the colored lights glowed, the magical

tree slowly revolved.

Finally I lowered my gaze with a satisfied sigh. "Now where?"

"To the Men's Room."

"*What?!*" I gaped at him.

"Oh, ho," he chuckled. "Not *that* one. This is a special place to shop for beautiful things."

"Are you sure I'm allowed?"

"Come and see."

Up the escalator we skimmed. Squeezing tight to the rail, I thrilled at the moving stairs, with just a tickle of dread at the anticipated melting of the last one ...*Get ready...GO!* I leaped.

Ahead of us stretched racks of women's clothes and manikins with pursed lips and pointy figures. Dad wove our way amongst them till we rounded a corner filled with mirrors and plush chairs. A pretty blonde glided our way and smiled at Dad as if she expected us.

"How may I help you, sir?'

"I'm looking for something special for my wife."

"Would you care for a drink?"

"Oh, yes!" he beamed. "How about a Scotch?"

I curled my legs up under me on the loveseat and sipped my own Coke, while "Miss Susan" draped dresses of blacks and reds across her shoulder for Dad.

"No...no. How about a nice *hat?*" he queried. Moments later she reappeared wearing a jaunty jet-black fur beret. "It's black fox," she purred.

"*Ahh...*"

"And here's the crowning touch," cooed Miss Susan, "that will make her unique among women." The salesclerk whipped out of its box a matching fur cylinder.

I stared. "*What is it?*" I mouthed.

She smiled at me. "It's a muff. See?" Each of her

hands disappeared inside of it.

"*Oh!*"

"Would you like to try it?"

"Oh, yes!" I grasped the lush fur and inched my hands inside. So warm! *Why, it's just like Gretel's in "Hans Brinker!"*

And *so* grown up.

I studied myself in the mirror, lifting and lowering the muff against my red coat just *so*. Dad raised his eyebrows and grinned at me from behind. "So...do you think Mom would like it?"

"Oh, yes! Get it, Dad! Get it!"

He threw back his head and laughed. "I think she will, too – especially the hat."

Back on the escalator with the prized package, I tapped Dad's arm. "Now it's *my* turn!" I gazed over the rail as the next floor slid into view. "There!" I pointed. The jewelry counter.

So expensive! Disappointed, I idly fingered necklace after necklace. I only had two dollars... Suddenly my eyes riveted towards a round glass sphere, a yellow speck floating inside. Surrounded by a sliver of silver, it dangled from a silver chain. I peered at the tag. Only ONE dollar! The salesclerk lifted it out of the case and laid it on the counter.

"Mustard seed," she smiled. "Symbol of fertility."

"Fertility...that's like having lots of babies, isn't it?" I murmured with growing excitement.

"Ho, ho!" Dad chortled. "I think you've found the perfect gift!"

Yes! I found it! My feet curled inside my shoes as I watched the salesclerk swathe it in cotton gauze inside its own snug box. I couldn't *wait* for Mom to open it. I pictured her glow of pleasure and surprise as she unwrapped a present from *me!* A "real" gift from a jewelry store. I would tell her all about "the mustard seed" and its special meaning...

Outside among the bustling bodies on the street, I didn't mind the jostling this time. Dad and I swirled in a new, shimmering world of our own.

"Want to try a cable car ride?"

"*Yesss...*" I slid my arm into his.

At last we reached the head of the line. "Hop on!" he urged. I leaped up onto the platform and pulled Dad's arm towards the outside of the car.

"C'mon, c'mon!" I cried.

"You know the rule about ladies and cable cars, don't you?"

I shook my head, impatient to stake our spot.

"*NO* lady shall ride on the outside of a cable car," he winked, "unless she can: hold on to her hat, her skirt, her purse, *and* her packages, and hold onto the pole at the same time!"

I stuck my tongue out at him – then laughed. "Just *watch* me!"

Ding-ding!

WHEEEE!

Epilogue

As the sixth grade year progressed, Carol and I saw less and less of each other. I began spending more time with my school friends.

Mildred, Barbara, and I created the "Q's": Milk-Q, Barbie-Q, and Shrimp-Q (that would be me.) We grew adept at passing notes in school, decorated with symbols to denote each one of us. Somehow, 'three' was no longer a crowd with this new configuration, and we reveled in our own secret club.

Cindy and I eventually became friends again as we discovered something new we had in common: we each harbored a hidden desire to become a nun!

...Whispering furiously together one day in the Main Hall, we had staked a look-out point, and snagged an unsuspecting Mother Morris, the new Mistress General, passing by. But how to present our dilemma! We had not planned that little detail. To my horror, Cindy simply blurted, "Mother, do you think we would make good nuns?" Without a word, Mother snatched us up like a gift from God, and headed straight for her office.

"You must meditate, my child."

"I do," I said.

She bore down on me. "On what sort of things do you meditate?" Lordy! Did I have an answer?! I then snapped my lids shut, and in my mind immediately fell prey to the seductive powers of the warm wood of the chapel. The memory enveloped me. I visualized myself kneeling at the Stations of the Cross in the quiet shadows. Ritual, like a god itself, was everything. I looked up at Mother.

My words seemed to explode out of my mouth. "Well, you take the Passion," I boldly asserted in my new voice. "And you imagine yourself walking with Jesus. And suddenly it's like he's right there with you." Like magic!

Apparently, I passed the test, as, thereafter, Mother Morris held weekly tête-à-têtes with us.

Alas, that spring, the recently stabilized life in Mill Valley came to an end. With the completion of Dad's second residency, he began reviewing his prospects. An imminent move across country (again) reared its ugly head – a loss of friends, and new beginnings. And a new baby on the way.

But that's another story…

Afterword:
Meet the Parents

"How many children do you see us having, darling?"
Bonnie purrs dreamily. "I think four is a very nice
number...?"

"Ho, ho!" Walt rubs his hands with glee. "An even
dozen would suit us just fine! How 'bout it?"

I sit back now and try to visualize my (naïve)
young mother's reaction. To this day, she is one of the
rare innocents of the world, who sees only the good.
Eventually, they compromised with eight though whether
on purpose or simply happenstance, I'll never know.

Who Started This Family, Anyway?

The melody of movement mesmerized little Bonnie,
the second of four children, from the age of five. One
day her father Sam, a gymnast, brought her along for the
ride while he worked out his parallel bar routine at the

gym. Bonnie was dazzled, and begged him to teach her. She studied ballet and performed on stage at the age of nine in Green Bay, Wisconsin, where she combined ballet and acrobatics. After standing on her head on a paint can while still dancing to the music, then performing up the steps of a ladder to finish at the top with one leg swung over her shoulder, her teacher decided private lessons were in order.

At age 13 her family moved to Van Nuys, California, where she studied Spanish dance as well as ballet, and performed at the Wilshire Theatre in Hollywood.

Meanwhile, young Walt migrated from Pennsylvania farmland to California. He, younger brother Tom, and mother Mildred traipsed up and down the state between San Francisco and Hollywood, following Walter, senior's, footsteps. My grandfather was "Color" manager of the jockeys for the four California racetracks.

The Auspicious Meeting

At age 17 Bonnie met Walt, long after their families had become friends. Mildred dragged him with her one evening on one of her card-playing visits to the Moreaux household. Unaware of the uninvited guest, wearing a robe, her wet hair in curlers hastily wrapped in a towel, Bonnie leaped from the kitchen sink to answer the knock at the door. There he slouched in his Loyola letterman jacket, shuffling next to Mildred, his hands stuffed inside the back pockets of his too-tight jeans. Aware of her attire, Bonnie felt scandalized. "She was the most beautiful girl I had ever seen," Walt later confessed.

Walt then raced through his undergraduate studies at Stanford University, 400 miles away, in three years instead of four. Motivation: he lived in fear that he would lose his "dream girl" to one of the many Hollywood men who flocked around her.

Thus, three years later, after two refusals and three proposals, they were married.

When the momentous day of my birth arrived, 18 months later, Bonnie was now a model for a top Hollywood agency.

Being separated as a family was no longer an option. In the coming months, Mom and I journeyed up to Palo Alto, where we "lived in" while Mom cooked and cared for a woman and her young son with polio.

We soon "moved up in the world," when all three of us joined the Morton Salt family on their estate in Woodside, CA. Actually, we lived above the garage, with a stairway connecting us to the kitchen entry of the main house. This was Mom's domain. Mom cleaned the kitchen, five baths and upstairs parlor, as well as fed the two sons, ages 15 and 20. Once a week she served tea and cakes to Mrs. Morton's bridge club. "The baby" was not allowed in the kitchen, or any part of the main house, and thus, I cannot report "first-hand" on the doings there!

Dad looked after the grounds, and once a week polished the ballroom floor for the sons' dancing lessons.

The day the matron of the house eyed her immense silver collection and remarked it "needed polishing" was the day Mom and Dad planned their get-away.

With Dad now pursuing his medical school years at Stanford's hospital, located in San Francisco at the time, they set their sights on that fair city. Our name soon rose to the top of the list for the Sunnydale public housing project.

And here, my friends, is where my own memory kicked in.

Hope you enjoyed the ride.

Cathay and Grandmamma

Acknowledgments

I am extremely grateful for my beloved mother, Bonnie Moreaux, always positive, my biggest "fan," who read through my entire manuscript draft every time she visited me. She was also highly instrumental in clarifying minute details as they arose. The heart of our family, she loved to listen to my oral readings and enthusiastically cheered me on.

Thank you to my dad, Walt Gunn, my hero in life, who read my stories with a critical eye as they developed. He was quick in spotting grammatical errors and offered alternatives. Thankfully, he shed light on many a mysterious detail of those early years. He was my biggest supporter in giving me that frequent nudge to "publish that book!"

Thanks to all eight of my siblings: Mike, Patrick, Julia, Tim, Eric, Peter, and Jody, who, when all together, listened to me read my stories aloud many times; thus becoming my most raucous and challenging audience! I am deeply grateful that they have not complained about me putting a 'public face' to them!

In particular, I want to thank my brother Patrick and his wife Beth, who drove 200 miles to support me in my full-length show, TreeHouse Blues, on stage in San Francisco. (A special nod to 'Les' at the Bazaar Café for sponsoring me there!) Thanks to dear friends Terry Lai and Therese Devine for their fierce support at my many public readings.

Thank you to Raymond Hoche-Mong, fellow writer, who first agreed to 'beta-test' my manuscript, and provided a much appreciated copious critique.

I am very grateful for the Monday Night Playwrights' Group: in particular, Jeff Carter, for whom I participate as an actor. They have kindly allowed me to read my own work there, offering much needed constructive criticism.

Huge thanks to Erin Graffy at Kieran Publishing, who pushed and prodded me, beginning as a 'beta-tester,' to write the best possible story – long before she accepted my manuscript for publication. She has been tenacious in leading me through the process, wearing many hats. Thank you, Erin, for your incredible creativity, insight and support!

Anna Lafferty, graphic designer extraordinaire at Kieran Publishing, rose seemingly out of the woodwork to educate me in her mysterious world of design and layout, weaving her magic to create exactly what I wanted. She was completely in tune with my vision. Thank you, Anna!

A special thank you to my eldest daughter, Colette, also a writer, for her frequent scrutiny of my ongoing writing, with feedback. More often than I would care to admit… you were right!

And to all my children, Colette, Colin, Kyle, and Kirsten, thank you for supporting me at my various readings over the years. You bring me such great joy. Thanks also to Janan Yousif for attending – with or without Colette – and for his never flagging enthusiasm for my work. Special thanks, Kyle, for getting me out of many a computer snafu, understandable and patient to the end.

Last, but not least, thank you to my wonderful husband, Kurt Graffy, who believed in me, and taught me to believe in myself. You have lived through these many years of my frustration, doubts, and determination with great patience; supportive every step of the way. I love you very much.

TreeHouse Blues

Made in the USA
San Bernardino, CA
24 September 2017